Other Books by Norman N. Holland

The First Modern Comedies

The Shakespearean Imagination

Psychoanalysis and Shakespeare

The Dynamics of Literary Response

Poems in Persons

5 Readers Reading

Laughing

The I

The Brain of Robert Frost

Holland's Guide to Psychoanalytic Psychology and Literature-and-Psychology

The Critical I

Death in a Delphi Seminar

Poems in Persons (rev. ed.)

Meeting Movies

Know Thyself (with Murray Schwartz)

Literature and the Brain

Literature and the Brain

Norman N. Holland

The PsyArt Foundation
Gainesville, Florida

5000 S.W. 25th. Blvd., Suite 3117
Gainesville FL 32608-8931

Library of Congress Control Number: 2009929328

ISBN 978-0-578-01839-3 (hardcover)
ISBN 978-0-578-02512-4 (paperback)

To Jane,

with my deepest love and appreciation for

patience
help
knowledge
wit
love
editing
warmth
counsel
support
alertness
caring
advice
meals
laundry
companionship
savoir-faire
organization
sense of direction
love
phrasings
listening
sympathy
people skills
wisdom
competence
courage
interruptions
above all, love

And as for me, though that my wit be lite,
On bokes for to rede I me delyte,
And in myn herte have hem in reverence
And to hem yeve swich lust and swich credence,
That there is wel unethe game non
That fro my bokes maketh me to gon . . .

—Geoffrey Chaucer, *The Legend of Good Women.*

Contents

Literature and the Brain

Part I

The Questions

1 | About This Book

> I have a device to make all well. Write me a prologue . . .
>
> —Shakespeare, *Midsummer Night's Dream*, 3.1.

OUR BRAINS PLAY tricks on us when we respond to literature. We tense up when Poe's "Tell-Tale Heart" continues its deadly throbbing. We feel sad when Dickens' beloved Little Nell dies. We feel glad when Jane Austen's heroine gets her man—why? We know perfectly well that she is just a character in a book, no more than ink on a page.

The brain's tricks become even clearer at the movies (and I think film is a form of literature as much as plays). The cute blond starlet, looking for her missing friend, opens a creaking door. She walks down a dark hall. And we're thinking, Don't go there! Don't go there! And then the maniac in the hockey mask lunges out from a dark corner, brandishing a chain saw. You jump and I jump and all the people around us jump. Yet you and I and all of us know deep down that the blond and the maniac are just light flickering on a screen. We still jump—why?

I happened to see that fine old weeper *Love Story* in rural Florida. And there we were: the rednecks and the Ph.D., tears rolling down all our cheeks because Jenny Cavilleri, newly married Radcliffe girl, is dying of leukemia. Seeing *Casablanca* for the umpteenth time, we come to the final scene. Will Humphrey Bogart put Ingrid Bergman, the woman he loves, on the plane with her heroic but dull husband who needs her? Every time I wonder, though I know perfectly well he will.

Since Aristotle, people thinking about literature have encountered such psychological puzzles. But literary theorists from earlier times have faced the limitations of the psychology of those earlier times. Only in the last century have we had a "scientific" psychology. Only in the last few decades have we had a neurology with which we can observe actual brain systems.

Our brains on literature

When we are sitting in an armchair reading or in a theater seat watching, our brains are behaving oddly. We know that we ourselves cannot change the story, movie, play, or poem. Somehow that knowledge changes our brains. We go into a trance-like state. We become "absorbed." We no longer pay attention to our bodies or our environment, and that is not normal. We accept all kinds of improbabilities in science-fiction, fantasy, beast fables, Arthurian romances, epic poems, and so on, because we no longer test the reality of what we are reading or seeing, and that is not normal. Somehow, the mere fact that we are reading or hearing or seeing a sequence of words or images makes us believe in it—at least temporarily. We feel especially intense emotions toward the words that poets put before us. The language of literature, particularly poetic language, draws more on our right brain systems for processing language than normal, everyday languages does. Stories and plays appeal differently to the "what" and the "where" circuitry in our brains, and we are puzzled to find that we think about the characters in stories and plays as though they were real people. Perhaps the ultimate question is, Why have all human cultures at all times and in all places had some kind of literature? Why have humans, ever since we evolved into language-using animals, practiced this peculiar form of pretense, of lying, really? What does it do for us?

We humans are creatures of our biology. We can only do what our biology permits. We cannot jump a hundred feet in the air or hold our breath for six hours, but we can jump and we can hold our breath. Our biology both enables and limits us.

Our brains are part of that biology, and our brains enable us to create and re-create literature, but they also define how we can respond to or create literature. In this book, I shall try to say how our brains determine the processes of literature. This is *not*, then, a book of literary criticism that addresses particular works or types of literature. It is a book about thinking about literature. It is a book that poses questions.

Whys and hows

All my life I have wondered why people respond the way they do to jokes, movies, poems, stories, radio programs—all the fantasies that our society provides. As a boy, I would come to school, and my pals and I would compare notes about the radio shows we had heard the night before. Why did they prefer Fred Allen and I Jack Benny?

Why did that early form of literature puzzle me? Because part of me longs for certainties. I have always been uneasy about the way fantasy intersects with reality. Yet, too, I have always liked to imagine myself into a story, to lose myself in a movie or a play, or to savor the language of a poem. And the reason for that hovering between fantasy and certainty surely lies buried deep in my childhood in a small New York apartment

As you can see, I like asking questions. This book abounds in whys and hows. But I like finding ideas that answer my whys and hows even more. And I like to combine my love for ideas and answers to questions with my love for literature. I like to "theorize," as we professors of literature say.

Pursuing my wonderings about literature, I studied psychoanalysis. I wrote books offering psychodynamic accounts of the literary process, from creation to response.[1] I objected to current literary theories that seem to me to pay too little attention to the activity of the reader or audience member.[2] This book will address many of the same questions, but in what is for me a radically new way, through neuropsychoanalysis. Neuropsychoanalysis enables me to write about the actual brains of readers and writers in psychodynamic (that is, psychoanalytic) terms.

The most exciting ideas about literature that I've come across in recent years emanate from brain scientists and from a hardy band of my fellow literary theorists who use neuroscience or cognitive science to study literary phenomena.

Drawing on neuroscience, I think academic critics and professors will come up with persuasive answers to some of the wonderings we all have about literature. Even more, I think we will get a big bonus from this neuroscientific inquiry into literature. Understanding how and why we humans do literature asks us to understand ourselves as the biological creatures we are.

Chapter by chapter

With that hope in mind, I offer this book. Part I, the

opening chapters (1-3), sets out the general thinking and method: two ways of looking at mind/brain and the usefulness of neuropsychoanalysis. Incidentally, in an Appendix, I provide some basic information about the brain. Those who need or wish it should probably read the appendix early on.

Part II addresses what is to me the most puzzling thing about literature. Why do we lose ourselves in books and dramas? Why are we, in the psychologists' word, transported? Chapter 4 raises a preliminary question: Where is a text? We know that all we know of a literary work is what our senses tell us. Yet we *feel* as though a poem or a story or any text is something wholly separate from our senses, something "out there" beyond our skins. Why? Moreover, we assume that poems, plays or stories do something to us. How accurate is that assumption? The answer lies in some basic facts about the brain that apply to much else besides literature, to our relation to reality in general.

Chapters 5-11 deal with that trance-like state of mind we get into when we are "rapt" in a book, movie, play, or any work of art. Why don't we disbelieve the giants, ghosts, impossible science, talking asses (not the human kind), and all the other improbabilities literature offers us? We don't test reality when we lose ourselves in stories, plays, or films—why not? Why do we feel real emotions at things we know are fictional? Why do we imagine fictional people, who we know are just words or pictures or actors, into real people? We do so because our brains are functioning differently from the way they function in ordinary life. They are behaving differently because we are not going to act on the work of art. And we can sense that crucial difference when authors play metafictional tricks on us, calling our attention to the fact that what we are responding to is a fiction.

Parts I and II address our relationship to reality in general and to literature in general. Part III, chapters 12-21, looks at the process of enjoying, that is, responding to literature in particular: form, content, style, and meaning. First, though, when we pick up a book or buy a theater ticket, what do we want? How do we "set" our brains for literary effects? The short answer is, we expect pleasure, and we do not expect to do anything to the literary work to get it.

We meet a work of literature through its form, the fourteen lines of a sonnet or the successive chapters of a novel. Abstract things like rhyme or meter or cross-cutting or digression work in our brains to make our responses to what is being represented into pleasure.

Then, having allowed ourselves to be governed by the form, we make a text into a story or simply an intelligible sequence by a basic quasi-emotional brain process called SEEKING. Through SEEKING, we give narratives and poetic language coherence and significance. We also bring in our personal unconscious concerns. In general, we ourselves make "meaning" or "sense" from literary works, gratifying our wishes and fantasies in imagination.

Chapters 19-21 address the question, Why do we get pleasure from these purely imaginary gratifications? For example, we get pleasure from "literary" language, from jokes, and from clever metaphors. We do so because the brain makes them make sense by applying right-hemisphere language systems that, with ordinary language, are less used. We even enjoy ugly or fearsome things when they are represented in works of art. Enjoyment, however, difffers from person to person. There are styles of enjoyment and styles of interpretation. We enjoy the ugly and fearsome *if* we can fit them to our taste, ultimately our personal style of being.

Writers write and readers read and both enjoy in individual styles, and they can override those styles only with effort. Both reading and writing literature involve style, and Part IV goes on to apply the concept of style (from Part III) to the big questions of creation and evaluation. Writers need to evaluate what they produce, and readers finish a literary experience by deciding whether it is good or bad or even great.

The literary process begins with the writer's writing in that writer's style. To some extent the reader's brain in the act of reception mirrors the writer's act of creation. That is why no study of the brain's determination of literature would be complete without some account of creativity. What is it? Is it innate? Is it tied to madness? Depression? Addictions to drugs or alcohol? What is the difference between creating a work of literature and the work of creating an ordinary life? For me, creativity begins with the sense of compulsion writers, artists, and some readers feel. Creative people feel compelled to create in a certain medium because that medium has become part of a their personal style of being or identity embodied in their brains.

The compulsion can be painful, if unfulfilled, but creativity does not itself cause depression or an addictive self-medication for depression. The brain characteristics that give rise to the compulsion parallel those that give rise to depression.

Ultimately, however, we cannot fully understand creativity because it rests on a value judgment. When we say a literary work is good, we are predicting that it will please many and please long. We do not award the accolade "creative" unless we think the work has value, and that decision depends on what uncountable numbers of brains do now and in the future. The individual styles of readers play a role in evaluation and therefore in what we deem "creative."

The final two chapters (25 and 26) deal with ultimate questions. All human cultures have had some form of literature. Shall we conclude that we are innately programmed to do literature? Does literature confer an evolutionary advantage? Some literary theorists think so. I think not. Why do we do literature? My answer is simple and not evolutionary: we do literature because we enjoy it. We enjoy it because of the way our brains deal with it. Our brains on literature function differently from our brains in ordinary life, but in some ways the same. We seek satisfactions, and when we get them, that gives us pleasure.

This is *not*, in short, a book of literary criticism. It does *not* assess or interpret individual literary works. This is a book of questions about literature and its many forms and an effort to answer those questions. *The point of this book is not to change what we do and feel about literature, but to change how we think about what we do and feel.*

2 | The Alp of Mind

> O the mind, mind has mountains; cliffs of fall
> Frightful, sheer, no-man-fathomed.
> —Gerard Manley Hopkins, "No worst."

SOMETHING PROFOUND IS happening to what the French call *les sciences de l'homme*, the "human sciences." I think that we who study literature or art or philosophy or history no longer study just the texts or the techniques of our disciplines. I think we are now, as Mark Turner wisely says, studying how the human mind works when we are "doing" literature or art or philosophy or history.[1]

What is literature? also asks, What is mind?, because literature is a human process. For there to be literature, human beings must create it, and human beings must re-create it. Our eyes and ears make literature and take it in. Then we may, if we wish, interpret it or create theories about it, as I and my academic colleagues do. But before all that, guiding and using our eyes and ears are our brains. No brain, no literature. No brain, no writing, no reading, no making or watching plays or movies, no meanings, no forms, no structures, no theories. Meaning and the rest are things we *do*. A poem lies inert, like Sleeping Beauty, until we love it into life.

What you or I say about literature involves us inevitably, then, in thinking about our own minds and our own brains. We are saying psychological things. We have entered the domain I have long worked in, "psychological approaches to literature" or, as I usually say, "lit-and-psych." When we raise psycholiterary questions—why do we enjoy? how do we empathize?—then we humanists put ourselves in much the same position as the neuroscientists. For them, even more than for the humanists, the ultimate goal is the discovery of mind. What is it? How does it work? How did we get it?

The Alp of mind

I think of neuroscience and the human sciences as like two very small miners energetically tunnelling in from opposite sides of an immense Alp. Although the neuroscientists on their side of the Alp do not listen much to sounds of digging from the humanists on the other side, some humanists, those concerned with the brain's role in the arts, listen very closely to what the neuroscientists on the other side are saying. We draw hopefully on a great many researchers (in a great many notes at the back of this book). We hope for answers from them to the questions that bother us. The neuroscientists and we of the human sciences, even if we are divided into two groups, share the same hope. Although dwarfed by the mountain, we hope our diggings will meet in the middle of that huge Alp, and there we will discover this mysterious, magical treasure, Mind. We hope.

From the human science side, Noam Chomsky and his group in the 1970s set out the basic reasoning when they began talking about Universal Grammar.[2] If all human lan-

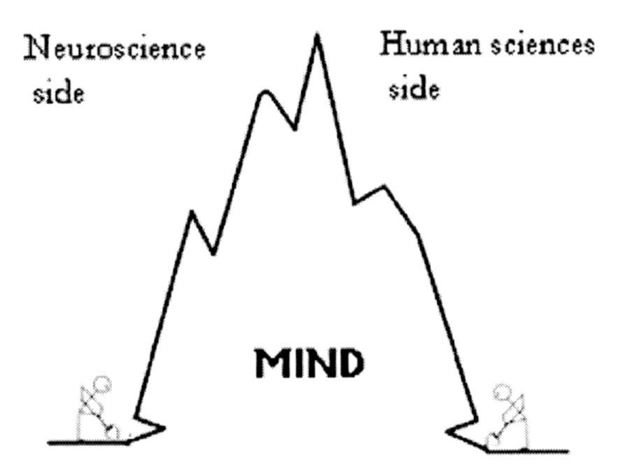

Figure 2-1. The Alp of Mind.

guages in all times and places share certain common grammatical practices, then that common or universal grammar (UG) must somehow be built into our brains. If all normal humans can make sentences using nested phrases, then we must be able to infer something about the brain from that remarkable ability. The potential, at least, for doing grammar must be innate in our brains as much as a four-chambered heart and a five-fingered hand are innate in our bodies. In general, then, *in the human sciences, such as linguistics, people infer things about brain and mind from universals, things that all human beings do.*

In a way, Freud anticipated Chomsky's reasoning when he wrote the "Project for a Scientific Psychology" in 1895. Like Chomsky, he was trying to reason backward from universal human behaviors like dreams and inhibitions and oedipus complexes to innate, inherited structures in the brain. Unfortunately, working in the 1890s, the neurology did not exist with which he could address these complex behaviors. At the time of the "Project," even the neuron was still a hypothesis. Freud accepted it, to be sure, but many of his colleagues still did not. Even the way that neurons communicate with one another would not be discovered for another quarter-century.

Because Freud could not find a neurological basis for the complicated symptoms that he was finding in his psychiatric practice, he never published the "Project." Instead, he turned to psychology. In his later writings, he lacked the electronic knowledge which would have given him good models for his theories that might have led him back to neurons. Instead, he had to resort to hydraulics, a clumsy and unappealing analogy. Nevertheless, he never gave up hoping that someday biology and neurology would confirm his ideas by finding structures in the brain that underlie the psychological phenomena he discovered.

In an opinion widely shared on the neuroscience side of the Alp, neuropsychologists Kenneth Heilman and Edward Valenstein have criticized this approach from universals as a "black box" method. It is "limited because the brain itself is not studied."[3] By contrast, the neuroscientific tunnelers are digging directly into our gray matter. Instead of inferring from all humans, they work from specialized populations, left-handed people or victims of autism. Or they give ordinary people special tasks, to name objects in pictures or to bisect a line or to pretend they are using a screwdriver. To explore the consequences of the specialness, the neuroscientists create special experimental situations that do not correspond to ordinary life—"non-ecological" situations as the psychologists say. That is, after all, how you do experiments: with controlled conditions. The neuroscientists then explore what parts of the brain are involved in the experimental actions by the experimental population. If the subjects in the experiments have brain lesions, visible *post mortem*, the damage suggests what parts of the brain are involved in their particular deficiency. Nowadays, the neuroscientist can watch in a brain imaging device (fMRI, PET, MEG, or DTI) the parts of the living brain that "light up" when normals do this or that task.

Within that general framework, explanations get very knotty indeed. Some rely simply on neuroanatomy, parts of the brain, as when the neurologists say that the right side of the brain tends to be the side that reasons holistically, while the left side deals with sequential processes.

Neuropsychologists would go further. Their work often takes the form of modeling a behavioral process, like speech, in carefully orchestrated experimental situations. Then they use the behavior of people with lesions in certain areas to try to combine anatomical features into systems that connect, typically, higher brain functions in the neocortex or outer limbic system to regions in the midbrain or pons. It is the neuropsychologists' work that most applies to literary studies.

As so often in psychological research, though, it is hard to draw general conclusions from highly specific experimental procedures. As a result, the neuroscientific literature consists of very precise experiments and techniques with very tentative suggestions of larger implications. Life is easier, if less reliable, on the humanists' side of the Alp, with linguists and anthropologists and theorists of literature. We are all too ready to jump to sweeping generalizations, expanding the neuroscientists' carefully circumscribed work to span the universals in human behavior.

Why all the neurology?

One of my readers fired that question at me, a poet exasperated at reading Greek and Latin anatomical terms like "ventromesial prefrontal cortex." The terms happen to be in Greek and Latin (and therefore incomprehensible to my twenty-first century reader), because study of the brain has gone on since antiquity, and much of the brain's anatomy was established in Early Modern times. Until the last century or so, Latin and Greek were the language of medical and scientific learning (and didn't Molière have fun with that in *Le malade imaginaire!*).

I impose some medical terms and a few anatomical diagrams on you to show that I am drawing on solid neurological facts to understand what you and I do in our brains when we do literature. In this effort, as in my psychoanalytic writings in previous decades, I believe that the more you know about the science and the more you face up to the complexity of the discipline, the stronger will be your conclusions.

Even so, I know that reading scientific language can tax the humanist beyond endurance. Mindful of some of my colleagues' wariness toward science, I have bracketed my more neurological sentences with modifiers like, "Technically," "In biological terms," "As for the specific brain systems," and the like. Even if you skip these scientific statements, what remains will still make sense. And I have provided in the Appendix an introduction to the brain that will make these phrasings comprehensible.

Why psychoanalysis?

When I use psychology for literary purposes, I now draw on cognitive science and neuropsychology, but for decades I have drawn on psychoanalytic psychology. And in this book, I will continue to use psychoanalysis' theory of mind. As Nobelist Eric Kandel has famously written, "[P]sychoanalysis still represents the most coherent and intellectually satisfying view of the mind."[4]

Psychoanalysis' heyday came in the mid-twentieth century. Alas, in the twenty-first, one has to justify using it at all, because of the many attacks on its scientific standing. Those attacks focus primarily on its value as a therapy, but that is not my concern here. I am interested in what Kandel finds valuable, psychoanalysis as a theory of the mind.

The "Freud wars" have spread a number of myths about psychoanalysis as a theory. One of them is that psychoanalysis has no scientific standing, first, because its ideas have not been tested experimentally and, second, because, by their very nature, they cannot be tested or (to use the more accurate term) falsified.

I take these questions about psychoanalysis' validity seriously enough to have added my own essay to this much-vexed topic in a "debate" with one well-known critic of psychoanalysis, Frederick Crews.[5] My essay makes two points. First, there is in fact a good deal of *experimental* evidence about psychoanalytic theory. Sometimes it does not confirm Freud's ideas, but oftener it does. Second, the critics have failed to appreciate that psychoanalysis relies, not on experiment, but on participant-observer method and holistic reasoning. Psychoanalysis shares this approach with social sciences like anthropology and archaeology, with qualitative research within psychology, and with hard sciences like paleontology, geology, astronomy, and even some aspects of chemistry and physics where experimentation is not possible. To be sure, psychoanalysis as a science presents other difficulties, notably the bias inherent in clinical evidence and the fact that clinical evidence cannot be made public. Nevertheless, a good deal of psychoanalytic psychology can fairly claim the status of "science." In this book, I have confined myself to those psychoanalytic ideas that have received experimental confirmation.

Further, within the last decade or so, a movement has grown up to revive Freud's original hopes for a neurological grounding of psychoanalysis' insights. To me, it is the most exciting development in psychology that I have encountered in decades.

3 | Neuropsychoanalysis

The brain is the only organ that studies itself.
—Neurological saying

INSIDE OUR SKULLS, two things are going on: brain processes and mind functions. Mind and brain, however, seem two completely different kinds of thing. "Brain" consists of many, many cells doing the kinds of things cells do. "Mind" has to do with our thoughts, feelings, and actions, the things that human beings do. While we might all agree nowadays with the neuroscientists' saying, that "mind is what brain does," therein lies a mystery. How? How can a three-and-a-half pound mass of gray and white cells become our panicky fear at a snake? Our sense of the red of a tomato? Of love? Of Hamlet? Neuroscientists call this "the hard problem"—with good reason.

Dual-aspect monism

Sensations and thoughts and feelings and consciousness seem completely different from the cellular matter that gives rise to them, so much so that Descartes invented and bequeathed us the "dualism" of the mind, the "mind-body dichotomy." Mind and brain, he famously concluded, are two entirely different kinds of stuff. The opposite position, monism, says there is only one kind of stuff, brain; sensations like the red of a tomato simply display a pattern of activation of certain brain cells. "Mind is what brain does."

Philosophers have come up with a third way of thinking about mind and brain: "dual-aspect monism." That is, we are made of one kind of stuff (cells) but we *perceive* this stuff in two different ways.

One is the neuroscientists' "objective" way. They dissect the brain with scalpel. They scan it and then trace neurochemical pathways. The neuroscientists observe "mind" from *outside*, that is, by means of the neurological examination: questionnaires, the Boston Naming or Wisconsin Sorting tests, acting out how you use a screwdriver, and a variety of other tricks in the neurologist's doctor bag. They can compare what the neurological examination shows with the associated changes in the brain, either *post mortem* or by means of modern imaging technology.

Then there is the layman's (or Descartes') way. We can observe "subjectively," from *inside* a mind, how we feel and what we think. Freud refined this kind of observation into free association, the most powerful technique we have for perceiving complex mental functions that simple introspection will not reveal. We can discover mind's *unconscious* functioning.

Dual-aspect monism offers an escape from the mind-brain dilemma, the "hard problem" of reconciling consciousness with our biological being. It shifts the question from what mind and brain are to how we can know about them. *Mind and brain are one, but we have two ways of findng out about the unity which is their combination.*

Neuropsychoanalysis

The new discipline of "neuropsychoanalysis" looks at

brain systems that might correspond to traditional psychoanalytic ideas like id, ego, and superego, repression, regression, impulsivity, and compulsivity as well as psychiatric disorders like depression or schizophrenia. In an increasing number of articles and books, this group is tracing the ways brain systems correspond (approximately!) to long-applied and, sometimes, well-demonstrated psychoanalytic concepts. Neuropsychoanalysis' over-arching theory combines the free associative talk that psychoanalysts interpret with the neurons and neurotransmission that neurology examines.

For example, two leading neuropsychoanalytic researchers, Mark Solms and Oliver Turnbull, following Freud, posit that "mind" is just one thing.[1] It is hidden from our view like other basic things in science, the subatomic particles, the Big Bang, or the extinction of the dinosaurs. We *infer* mind, and we infer it in two different ways. One is the "objective" science of the neurologist and neuropsychologist. The other is psychoanalysis, sometimes described as the "science of subjectivity." Combining the two creates neuropsychoanalysis, an application of the philosophers' "dual-aspect monism."

Neuropsychoanalysis makes much use of the traditional "clinico-anatomical" method of neuropsychology. The investigator compares two things. First, the neuropsychologist locates damage to the patient's brain or the brain of an experimental animal. In the old days, with humans, researchers had to wait for an autopsy. Nowadays they can use the dazzling techniques of modern brain imaging. (One needs to remember, though, that these magnificent machines that produce such colorful pictures have serious problems. They lack spatial or temporal precision. Their human subjects have no clear zero state. The process itself influences the subject's mental processes, etc.[2]) Second, the neuropsychologist looks for differences in behavior that one might fairly attribute to the differences observed in the brain. To find the differences in behavior, researchers use various tasks devised in the tradition of academic psychology: clicking a clicker as images appear on a computer screen, questionnaires, taps on one's kneecap or Achillles' tendon, and so on. These will show whether the patient can hear words, can repeat words, can call up vocabulary, can shift easily from one thought pattern to another, can move a limb here or there, or can see in all quadrants of the visual field. In short, these experiments can reveal what the systems in the brain are doing.

But! As Oliver Sacks has written: "Neuropsychology, like classical neurology, aims to be entirely objective, and its great power, its advances, come from just this. But a living creature, and especially a human being is first and last . . . a subject, not an object. It is precisely the subject, the living 'I,' which is excluded from neurology."[3] It is this lack that the neuropsychoanalytic movement addresses.

Neuropsychoanalysts use the first part of the neuropsychologist's objective toolkit, the location and study of elements in the brain. They point out, however, that the second, the neuropsychologists' questionnaires and other psychological tests, look only at the patient's *conscious* activities. For the unconscious processes, they turn to psychoanalysis.

Psychoanalytic method

A good deal of needless mystification surrounds psychoanalytic method. It is simplicity itself, as Freud pointed out. An "analysand" simply says whatever comes into his or her mind without regard for propriety or purpose. Eventually, in this rambling discourse, the individual will say something that is, one, surprising and, two, not entirely welcome. That happens because, underneath the conscious choice of words, *un*conscious desires and fears, things we would rather not be aware of, color and drive the conscious choice. Eventually, the psychoanalyst and perhaps the patient will be able to observe those unconscious issues as recurring themes in the words. Such issues will come as a surprise, because they had been unconscious. They will not be welcome, for ideas and feelings become unconscious because they are painful.

The psychoanalyst's (and the patient's) interpretation of themes resembles what literary critics sometimes do. That is the reason I have found psychoanalysis so congenial and (I say it with postmodern hesitation) true. Whether psychoanalytic insight leads to a therapeutic result is, of course, another question altogether.

Neuropsychoanalysts try to live up to both halves of their name. They want to observe neurological symptoms but also to listen to what the symptoms *mean* to the patient. They want to find the pattern underlying the isolated bits of conscious behavior tested by the psychological exams. Is this stroke an assault on the patient's masculinity? Does this woman look on the hospital staff as imperfect mothers?

Solms and Turnbull sum up their and their colleagues' method this way: "People who suffer brain tumors, strokes, and so forth . . . . can be studied psychoanalytically just like anyone else. In this way, basic clinico-anatomical correlations can be drawn, directly linking psychoanalytic variables with neurological ones and thereby integrating them with each other on a valid empirical (rather than theoretical) basis."[4] By relating psychoanalytic inferences about unconscious processes to neurological inferences about the brain, neuropsychoanalysts are beginning to show that various psychoanalytic entities (like libido, repression, word-representation, or superego) function as brain systems.

To be sure, any such program has just begun and has a

long, long way to go. There are, however, groups of analysts and neuroscientists in the U.S. and around the world taking on this new approach to neuropsychology (as reported, notably, in the journal *Neuropsychoanalysis*).

Neuropsychoanalysis and literature

I am writing in the spirit of this neuropsychoanalytic project. I think I can ground traditional ideas about literature, traditional in both literary and psychoanalytic thinking about literature, ideas like "character," "meaning," "distance," or "form," in brain science. That is what I have tried, in the various chapters of this book, to do, to explore how the brain both enables and limits us in creating and responding to literature.

Cognitive science and literature

What I am trying to do differs from some of the promising work that other literary scholars have been doing under the rubric "cognitive science and literature." They draw on familiar terms from psychology like "identification," "imagination," "empathy," "plans," or "goals," that is, "functional descriptions" or terms that refer to mental functions and activities.

Functional descriptions may or may not, as the neuroscientists say, "cut nature at the joints." That is, they may or may not coincide with any physiological system in the brain. Also, these "functional descriptions" tend to be indeed "cognitive." They tend not to address emotional systems or systems that are unconscious in a psychoanalytic sense.

I hope to address both of these problems by referring directly to brain systems alongside traditional, familiar ideas and experiences of literature. For example, we know that, experiencing literature, we get into a peculiar trance-like state of mind where we accept remarkably unreal things in science-fiction, beast fables, fairy stories, or jokes. We feel real emotions toward fictional people or the sequence of words in a poem. We experience literary works in some ways the same—for example, we would all agree that a sonnet has fourteen lines—and in other ways quite differently. While these and other literary facts usually cannot claim experimental proof, they form part of the literary experiences we are all familiar with.

Modern neurology and, in particular, neuropsychology have established certain things about the brain. We have several different memory systems in our brains, for example. We process perceptions through two different paths, a "what" path and a "how" path. We process language differently in our two hemispheres. Humans probably have certain fixed emotional patterns. There are, as we shall see, a good many of these well-established principles available from neurology for thinking about literature.

Literature and the Brain puts these widely accepted propositions from the two different areas, neurology and literature, side by side.[5] I believe that we can explain by means of neuropsychology and neuropsychoanalysis at least some literary facts by facts about the brain. And that is what I propose to do in the chapters that follow.

Part II

Being Transported

4 | Where is a Text?

> If Perceptive Organs vary: Objects of Perception seem to vary:
> If the Perceptive Organs close: their Objects seem to close also.
>
> —William Blake, *Jerusalem*, 2.55-56.

WHERE INDEED IS a text, a story, a poem, a play? We base just about everything we think about literature or art or media on the answer to that question. But the answer is perfectly easy and obvious, isn't it? A story is in my hand when I am reading a book or a manuscript. It's on a computer screen, if that's the way I'm reading a poem. It's in the theater, spoken by the actors as I watch a play or a movie. But is that so obvious? Not to philosophers who debate whether "the" poem equals its printing in this or that edition, the poet's original manucript, the poet's reading it aloud, a reader's experience of it, and so on. One can raise the same ontological issue about a novel, a song, a play, and even a movie (because different projections vary so).

Scratch my back and . . .

I was preparing for a seminar on "the brain and literature" by reading my students' textbook, M. Deric Bownds' valuable *The Biology of Mind.* One particular passage stopped me short.[1] Bownds was describing "the brain's ability to generate perception distinct from sensation," that is, the brain's sense of a whole thing as opposed to the mere sensations of color, edge, texture, and so on, out of which that sense of a whole thing is composed. He recounted an experiment involving blind people. It began with

> attaching to their backs a patch driven by a video camera that the subject controls, a camera whose output to the patch causes the stimulation of multiple points on the skin. Each point represents one small area of the image captured by the camera. Within hours, some subjects can learn to recognize common objects such as cups and telephones, to point accurately in space, to judge distance, and finally to use perspective and parallax to perceive external objects in a stable three-dimensional world. . . . After a few hours, the person no longer interprets the skin sensations as being of the body but projects them into the space being explored by the body-directed "gaze" of the video camera. What develops is not necessarily understanding but a strategy for responding appropriately. Test subjects do not locate objects as lying up against their skin—any more than those of us with vision locate objects as lying up against the retina of our eyes. Instead, they perceive objects as being out there in space. Thus a tactile sensation of "what is happening to me" is converted into a vision-like perception of "what is happening out there."[2]

Now that result is surprising for the blind subjects, but it is surely true that, all the time, we sighted people experience objects as quite separate from our bodies. We don't think of the things we see (like books or plays) as lying up against our retinas.

Yet so far as our minds and brains are concerned, all we know of those objects does in fact lie on our retinas, our eardrums, or our skins. All we know of the world beyond our own bodies is sensations. Neurologist Todd Feinberg states the evolution of this adaptation:

> [M]illions of years of evolution have established that the neural states caused by outside objects will *automatically* cause the animals to respond in a fashion appropriate to where the stimuli are in the world, not where the neural states *really* are which is in the brain. This is not some sort of mental magic. The brain has found a way to produce neural states that capture features of the world. But the brain of course does not literally "capture" the world. We should not be deceived into thinking that the brain actually "absorbs" these features of the environment. We can artificially stimulate the brain with an electrode, in the absence of such stimuli, and create the same sensory effects.[3]

And cognitive linguist Gilles Fauconnier sums up the way we translate that adaptation in our brains into our everyday thinking about reality: "In the case of perception, the folk theory, an extremely useful one for us as living organisms, is that everything we perceive is indeed directly the very essence of the object perceived, out there in the world and independent of us."[4]

Why do we feel the world as "out there," in a "not-me" domain, when it is obvious that the only way it happens to us is as electrochemical pulses, action potentials, in our nervous systems?

Seeing a world "out there"

One can easily supply, as Fauconnier notes, an evolutionary answer. Sensing objects as "out there" in a not-me world is useful, even essential, for survival. I have to know that somewhere beyond my skin is a mountain lion, a banana split, or Marilyn Monroe, depending on which basic need I am trying to satisfy at the moment. It is not much use sensing any of them as *in* my brain or sensory organs. Rather, I need that depth or "distal" information to carry on activities essential to all but the simplest animals. We humans need that information for the four Fs of the medical students' old joke: feeding, fighting, fleeing, and sexual reproduction. And our constructed world must be "ecological." That is, it must be enough like the unknowable real world "out there," beyond our sense organs so that we can survive and reproduce. And that must be true for any organism that moves. The roots of this, our unconscious, unavoidable, irreversible translation of inner sensations onto a not-me world must go very far back in our evolutionary history.

Unfortunately, though, what served us well in paleolithic times does not help at all in the world of today's literary theory. That projection outward leads to confusion for a modern, philosophical, and inquiring human, especially if that *homo sapiens sapiens* happens to be thinking about a story or a poem or a movie. We now have considerable evidence, though, from neuroscience not only that this folk theory misleads us, but also why we so firmly believe it.

Our projection of our sensory data onto the world "out there" takes place relatively late in a very elaborate mental processing. Consider just vision. We can skip over the complex path from our retinas at the front of our

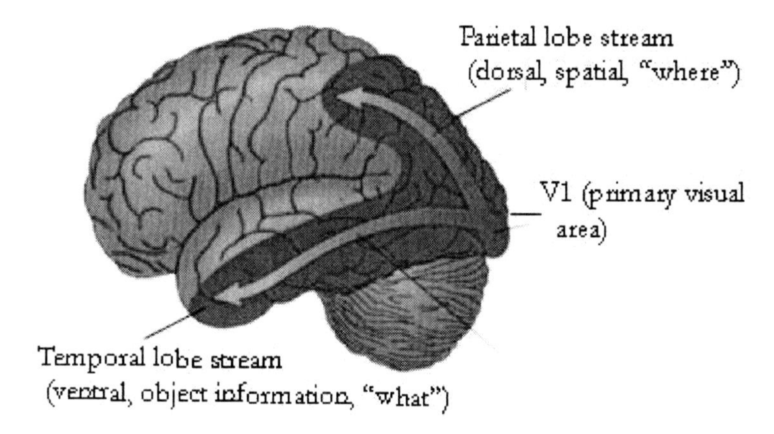

Figure 4-1.The "what" and "where" visual systems.

brains to the areas for visual processing at the back of the head in the occipital cortex. But we should note, in passing, that considerable processing of the visual information takes place even within the retina. In one of the brain's dual systems, magnocellular (M) cells specialize for changes in a light stimulus (size, contour, motion), while parvocellular (P) cells respond strongly to perceptions of object features such as color and high contrast, information useful when we recognize what an object is. As neurons carry information from the eyes themselves to the visual areas at the back of the brain, this same combination of M- and P-cells functions to differentiate information about features from information about location. Our brains begin to separate "what" from "where."[5]

Information from our two eyes begins to combine so that we can see the world three-dimensionally. This information from the retina, beginning now to be binocular, traverses optic pathways back to the primary visual cortex in the occipital lobes at the back of the head.

There, a complexity of layers and different cell types further segregate the M- and P-cell information. One can think of these visual processing areas (beginning with the primary area V1, then V2, V5, etc.) as filters that selectively amplify color, line, edge, contour, shape, and motion. Probably, all these areas act simultaneously to process these attributes separately and among them, most intriguing for our purposes, depth. Somehow, perhaps through synchronous firing of neurons, these separate pieces of information come together. This stage of visual processing also deals with binocular signals from the eyes.

This process of perception, however, has probably not yet yielded a unified sight of which we can be conscious. The nerve impulses themselves bear no resemblance to the object that we will consciously "see," although as a group they may form a limited map of that object. The information from the visual cortices now feeds forward toward the frontal areas of the brain. Information (for example, about depth) travels from neuron to neuron forward from the visual centers at the back of the head. As shown in Figure 4-1, the information travels in two parallel, but interconnected, streams. A lower ("ventral") stream leads downward into the temporal lobe, where some language processing takes place. An upper (or "dorsal") stream passes under the dome of the skull into the parietal lobe and projects to the motor regions of the frontal lobe.

To some extent these two streams talk to each other, and both carry the same kinds of information. Each is specialized, however. The lower stream, usually called the "what" pathway, the inheritor of the P-cells, specializes in recognizing objects. The upper or dorsal pattern is a "where" pathway. It draws on information from the M-cells and specializes in spatial awareness and the guidance of rapid spatial actions, like dodging a truck, catching a softball, or reading a page.

The two streams function differently. "Where" is crude; there is, for example, no perception of color in the "where" path. "Where" operates rapidly and uncritically and enables us to run around obstacles and catch softballs and dodge cars bearing down on us. Having this fast "where" path considerably improves our chances of survival. "What" operates more judiciously—it does have color, obviously—and this ventral pathway allows us to correlate (probably in the inferior temporal lobe) our immediate sensory data with what we already know. We can identify objects and, most important, people.

Neuroscientists increasingly think of the "where" pathway as a "how" pathway because the dorsal or upper path is specialized for setting up motor actions in response to perception. This dorsal stream contains a comparatively extensive representation of the outer edges of the visual field, and it is specialized for detecting and analyzing moving visual information. This upper stream also projects ultimately to the regions in the frontal cortex that program actions,[6] and, in the process, the brain filters out information that has no relevance to moving its body.

The "where" or "how" system is, as neurologists say, "quick and dirty," useful for rapid, life-preserving actions. The "what" system is more thoughtful (so to speak). If we think evolutionarily, we can see how important it is for the "what" path to identify objects "out there" as chickens or lions, things that are likely to aid or end survival. Similarly, it is crucially important for the "where" or "how" pathway to be able rapidly to locate the lion or the chicken as something in a specific place in the not-me world, not just sensations in the within-me world. And our brains do that, successively and very functionally, translating the perceptual information through a succession of eye-centered, head-hand-centered, body-centered, and object-centered frames of reference in a series of brain systems.

Picking up a book or watching a stage play involves this dual "where-how" system. Understanding what one reads or views, however, involves just the "what" system. It is a special form of object recognition in which the objects are letters, graphemes, margins, words, meanings, or actors on a screen or stage, all identified as "out there" in a certain region of space.

Hearing an outer world

Neuroscientists have not learned as much about our ways of locating objects in auditory space as they have in visual space. "Hearing where" differs from "seeing where." For example, auditory spatializing works differently for near objects and far.[7] To make matters still more intricate, the brain calculates the horizontal angle for a sound (azimuth) differently from the vertical angle (elevation). The auditory system specializes hemispherically to some extent. The left hemisphere does more with information about "what" and the right with information about "where," although both hemispheres do both. The brain calculates from sounds information about "what" and "where-how," in the parietal lobes, specifically, the inferior parietal lobules. "Higher" processing centers in the prefrontal cortex then reach back for this information and feed it forward to the appropriate motor systems.

Auditory "where-how" and "what" go to upper and lower areas, respectively, in the prefrontal cortex, quite near the endings of the localizing process for the eyes.[8] That proximity, therefore, raises the possibility of further processing that combines auditory and visual localizings. In the term neuroscientists like, further processing "binds" them. That is how, when playing softball, we sense the crack of the bat and the flight of the ball as a single event. And we sense it as an event "out there," separate from us.

A world constructed

This excursion into brain functions tells us something basic and profound. Our eyes and ears (and likewise touch and smell) plus their associated systems in the brain translate sensory processes inside us into perceptions of objects in a world outside us that seems "not-me." Our brains do this quite involuntarily, willy-nilly, and quite outside our consciousness of the processes. We have innate, "hard-wired" circuits that make this conversion. So far as location is concerned, the brain's interpretation must be accurate, or else we could not survive. As for the content—what *is* at that location?—that we can never know in any absolute sense (as Freud pointed out).

"Reality will always remain 'unknowable,'" he wrote near the end of his life. "We have no hope of being able to reach [the real state of affairs], since it is evident thst everything new that we have inferred must nevertheless be translated back into the language of our perceptions, from which it is simply impossible to free ourselves."[9]

That was in 1938. In 2002, neuropsychoanalysts Mark Solms and Oliver Turnbull summed up this, the standard position of neuropsychology, this way:

> We adults *project* our expectations (the products of our previous experience) onto the world all the time, and in this way we largely *construct* rather than perceive (in any simple sense) the world around us. The world of our everyday experience is doubly removed from the "reality itself" that philosophers speak of . . . first by the interposition of our perceptual apparatus (which is designed to *sample* and *represent* certain selected features of the world), but also by our memory (which, on the basis of past experience, organizes and transforms those selected

features into recognizable *objects*).[10]

Francis Crick and Christof Koch, well-known for their work on consciousness, state that fact this way: "We are not directly aware of the outer world of sensory events. Instead, we are conscious of the results of some of the computations performed by the nervous system on the various neural representations of this sensory world."[11] Neuroscientist Walter Freeman says the same thing: "A stimulus excites the sensory receptors, so that they send a message to the brain. That input triggers a reaction in the brain, by which the brain constructs a pattern of neural activity. The sensory activity that triggered the construction is then washed away, leaving only the construct."[12] In 1998, in a summarizing article, neuropsychologist M-Marsel Mesulam described in detail how what we perceive as a world around us (or a book or a drama within it) is, in his concluding phrase, "a highly edited subjective version of the world."[13] In general, brain scientists have no trouble with this understanding of our relation to the outer world, although it troubles philosophers and literary theorists.

We cannot know the world as such, because we know it only through our own senses (or mechanical extensions of those senses) with all their various biases and peculiarities. Yet our brains make us believe that electrochemical impulses in our neurons *equal*, say, a book or a movie with such-and-such properties and so-and-so location in the world out there, in the "not-me." The brain does this quite automatically. Once the process starts, we have no control over it at all. Hence we get the folk theory that what we see simply is what is.

All this seems obvious to neuroscientists, but many literary theorists write about "the" story or poem as though they had access to it free from the activities of their brains and sense organs. They write as though their knowledge of the language of a literary work were absolute. "The" text, as it were, goes round our senses simply to "be" in our brains.

This belief had its heyday with the "new critics" who insisted on treating literary works as having a single, determinate meaning. But the belief persists into postmodern literary theory. As I pointed out in *The Critical I* (1992), many literary critics of today (formalists, structuralists, deconstructionists, cultural critics, new historicists, and so on) write as though they had some impersonal access to "the" text and its action on its audience. The folk theory, *that what we see simply is*, is alive and well in literary academia.

But what we perceive as the pages of a book or the spoken words of an actor is a construct. It is not the very page or actor, some *ding an sich*, the thing-in-itself. It is not something that directly imprints itself on our minds. It is what results from our sense organs' neurochemistry plus a good deal of cognitive massaging. We readers and hearers and spectators may process words automatically, willy-nilly, but we are not inactive as the linguist Ferdinand de Saussure thought or as the many contemporary theorists who adopt his linguistics think. Rather, we begin by constructing the physical text, and we go on to construct meaning and emotions in our individual brains from what we read or hear or watch. As neuroscientist Walter Freeman writes of our sensory activity, "That pattern does not 'represent' the stimulus. It constitutes the meaning of the stimulus for the person perceiving it."[14]

So far as philosophy is concerned, this position harks back to Hume and Kant. It is sometimes called "noncontroversial relativism," meaning that one can hardly argue with the statement that *what we take to be the world is what we sense of the world.* What we take to be "the" physical literary text (the book, the sight and sound of play or film or reading) is what we sense of the literary text. But there is a complication.

The great end of life

"The great end of life is not knowledge, but action," said that energetic Victorian, Thomas Huxley. And much earlier, "Knowlege must come though action," said Sophocles. Huxley was acknowledging an evolutionary truth: to survive and reproduce, we must act. Action or *the knowledge that we can act on what we perceive affects perception.* At this point, I need to introduce a sentence I omitted from the passage I quoted from Bownds' book.

Bownds described an experiment in which blind people sensed video-driven buzzes and tickles on their backs as objects seen "out there" in a stable three-dimensional world just as we sighted people do with micro-electrical sensations inside our eyes. "The patterns projected onto the skin," however, Bownds wrote, "develop no such 'visual' content *unless the individual is behaviorally active*, directing the video camera via head, hand, or body movements" (italics mine). But if the blind person does direct the video camera, after a few hours the prickles on the back seem to be beyond the back, "out there," in the space explored by the camera, just as what our sensory organs deliver to our brains seems "out there."

This result fits very neatly the brain scientists' identification of systems developing a sequence of frames of reference geared to action. Our visual sensations go through, successively, eye-centered, head-hand-centered, body-centered, and object-centered frames of reference. In effect, *intentions to act* draw forward the information needed for the action from the visual processing areas at the back of the head into first, the parietal cortex, then the frontal cortex. In the process, the data become more and more associated with movement. The same thing happens wth hearing.[15]

We don't need actually to touch the object, though. For the blind subjects, it was enough to direct the video camera. Out of our mere moving to see objects, we get the sensation of an object-centered world. Thus, when we read, our eyes' scanning the page of a book further guarantees that we will experience the page as "out there," in the world of not-me. When we are in a theater, our very acts of focusing on and listening to live actors or scenes in a movie will reinforce the feeling that all this is independent of our own senses and bodies.

Constructing literary works

The feeling that a book or a stage or a television or movie screen simply is, quite separate from us, *corresponds to our experience.* That's what reading a book or watching a play or a movie *feels* like! The translation into "out there" is automatic. It is almost impossible to reverse. It is necessary for our survival.

Evolution has so constructed our brains that they make us believe that what we take to be a book or a play or a movie is not just our sense organs' output. We think it *is* that book, play, or movie. Our brains' acts of projection are sturdy and useful and deeply rooted and incorrigible. So much so are they that, if I refer our experiences with a literary work back to where we really know, if we think about it, that they are taking place—in our sense organs and our brains—I am perceived as denying the reality of the object "out there." "You're saying the text doesn't exist!" People object so vehemently, you would think a psychotherapist was undoing their repressions and denials.

Actually, I have not claimed and *could not claim* anything about a reality "out there," because all I or you or anybody knows for sure of it is perceptions "in here." *Saying that sensations take place in our brains says nothing at all about the thing that the sensations are sensations of.*

A literary work exists, so far as we will ever know, in a system. That system consists of something "out there" (a physical "text" that we know only through this same system) plus the neuronal entities that bridge inner and outer worlds. A poem, a story, a play, or a movie occurs somehow *between* us and the world around us. It is in both, because it is our construct. What we perceive is that physical book or page or screen or stage elaborately processed by our sense organs and the primary and association areas of the sensory pathways of our brains. Our perceptions plus our physical action, such as going to a theater or just looking at a book, establishes the physical work of literature that we then encounter as "out there," beyond our skin and other sensory organs. To be sure, what we perceive must correspond in some way to the "real" physical world "out there," because we humans can cope with that world. In particular, we can do science.

Obviously, though, I am caught in an epistemological contradiction. It is only by this very same system that we know about those sense organs and brain processes, of which I speak with confidence. Are brains somehow realer than books?

No. This framing of our knowledge of literary works also holds true for neuroscience. This is "non-controversial relativism." Scientists are well aware that what they perceive depends on the systems, usually extensions of the senses like microscopes or MRI scanners, that they use to perceive those systems. Neuroscientists accept that, as Freud put it, "everything new that we have inferred must nevertheless be translated back into the language of our perceptions, from which it is simply impossible to free ourselves."[16]

Physical books and stages and screens, of course, are no more or less real than the brains that scientists study. I rarely read literary critics or theorists, however, who acknowledge that "the text" that they are writing about consists of their perceptions of it. The folk belief that our perceptions simply equal whatever is "out there," be it text or brain, is alive and well in literary circles.

Perhaps this is necessarily so. We need that belief for our survival. The hunter-gatherer going after a mango or a mammoth needs this seeming, and so does the literary critic or theorist. The folk belief sustains us in all our actions on the world, even neuroscientific expesperiments. To be sure, it is a picture of the world that sometimes deceives us, as with mirages, hallucinations, optical illusions, or dreams. Mostly, however, it serves us well, but not, I think, when we are trying to think systematically about literature.

As we shall see in succeeding chapters, this first translation of our brain's activity into a world beyond our sense organs provides the foundation for our "poetic faith" in what we perceive, our emotional response, and our interpretations of meaning. And, just as the unavoidable belief in a world separate from our perceptions confuses us about the physical nature of books, plays, or movies, it confuses us when we come to think about the beliefs, meanings, and feelings we derive from literature.

5 | Four Brain Changes

> I go back to the reading room, where I sink down in the sofa and into the world of *The Arabian Nights*. Slowly, like a movie fadeout, the real world evaporates. I'm alone, inside the world of the story. My favorite feeling in the world.
>
> —Haruki Murakami, *Kafka on the Shore.*

MURAKAMI DESCRIBES THE experience most of us have when we are "lost" in a book, "rapt" (in its literal sense, seized), "entranced," or, in the psychologists' term, "transported." We go into a trance-like state that has four aspects. We cease to be aware of our surroundings or our bodies. We tend not to judge the reality of whatever fabulous story or film or play or poem we are "lost in." And we feel real emotions toward fictional people and events.

Something special is happening in our brains. We know we cannot possibly act to change what we are paying attention to. By contrast, in ordinary life, we know or believe that, if we choose to, we can act or try to act to change the stimuli around us. In Murakami's example of *The Arabian Nights*, however, our brains go into a peculiar state because, even as improbable as those stories are, we know we cannot change anything in them.

There is an interesting exception: literature in which we do have to act on the work. With the advent of computers came hypertext, in which the reader must continually choose a path through a narrative or poem. Because the reader constantly acts on the work, the experience of being transported becomes impossible.[1] The world cannot evaporate, nor can we feel transported into the world of the story. Instead, we are busy at the computer. I suspect this is why hypertext has never caught on with the reading public. We want that trance-like experience.

Being Transported

How do you feel when you are thoroughly "into" a movie or reading something very enjoyable and not very challenging, a detective story or a science-fiction novel? I have often asked people to describe the experience of being "transported" by a literary work. One recent group, for example, said things like: "I lose track of time." "I am feeling engrossed." "I feel as if I am in the story." "I feel as if I am inside the book." "[M]y mind would be completely captivated." "I get so engrossed that I feel a bit dazed when I stop reading." "If I didn't know better, I would have thought I was a fly on the wall of each scene." "I'm easily taken in. Not in the sense that I feel a part of whatever world it is that I am watching or reading, but more like I don't exist or at least I am out of the equation for the moment, and the only thing there really is, is whatever there is in the movie." "'Taken over' is what comes to mind when I think about how I feel once I snap out of it. The 'it' being something along the lines of a spell or a trance, like I've lost sense of place and self." "[M]y mind disregards the external environment . . . . My mind temporarily forgets its own sense of self." "I can forget everything in the real world while I am within the fantasy world." "I'm completely absorbed, intently focused . . . . I tend to ignore external or interfering stimuli, and find myself feeling personally invested in the outcome." "I was entranced by [*Phantom of the Opera*]. I was so engrossed by the cinematic wonder, that when my mother reached over to hand me a Hershey's bar, I jumped. I had forgotten that she was there. More importantly I had forgotten that *I* was there."

A psychoanalytic critic listens for recurring themes in people's choice of words, and I hear at least three in these responses. One is a sense of merger, being one with the movie, absorbed into it. Two others are the loss of a sense of one's own body ("self") and of one's environment (time and place).

The two-way experience

When we "lose ourselves" in a work of literature or art, we experience a double merger. That is, the boundary between us and the work of art disintegrates in two ways: from us to work of art; from work of art to us.

We project the work *outward* from ourselves when our brains automatically translate sensations within our bodies outward into a three-dimensional text independent of our bodies (ch 4). We also project *into* that literary work "out there." We flesh out the people, events, and language. We fill in gaps in a story. We infer the inner thoughts of characters or the parts of an environment that we cannot see because of the limits of a stage or screen. Indeed, German theorists of *Rezeptionsäthetik* (notably Wolfgang Iser) have treated this as *the* central phenomenon of reading.[2]

We also merge in the other direction, however. We introject. We take in what we take to be the text's portrayals, so that what is "out there" in the literary work feels as though it were happening "in here," in your mind or mine.

Regression

In psychoanalytic thought, this two-way merger has a name: regression, that is, returning to an earlier way of thought or an earlier experience. As adults, we come to literature having experienced a long history of developmental stages. At an adult level we bring memories of recent pleasures like those the writer describes in words. From a somewhat earlier level, we bring the memory of the intense fantasies and reading of latency. Still earlier, we may recall being read to by our parents, perhaps being held on a lap and cuddled and read to all at the same time. Still earlier, at a time prior to conscious memory, we had our first experience of pleasure, being held by a nurturing mother and being fed.

In that first stage of life, we did not act on the world, except indirectly, by gurgling or crying. At that stage, we could only imagine satisfactions. As adults, at night, when we sleep, we no longer act; we dream; we imagine. When we enjoy movies, books, plays, or poems, we do not act, and we consciously know that we cannot change the work. We imagine; and we let literature and other media help our imagining.

Orality

Our infantile pleasure was oral. Specifically, we took something into our mouths that quieted our hunger. Curiously, or perhaps not so curiously, even as adults we associate reading with eating, as when we call a man who "devours books" a "voracious" reader. We "take in" a movie. A novel may be a "treat" or a parody "delicious." One of Shakespeare's pedants says of a dullard: "[H]e hath never fed of the dainties that are bred in a book. He hath not eat paper, as it were; he hath not drunk ink. His intellect is not replenished."[3] "Some books are to be tasted," said Bacon, "others to be swallowed, and some few to be chewed and digested." The Book of Common Prayer enjoins us, "Read, mark, learn, and inwardly digest." Psychologist Victor Nell, in his fine study of being "lost in a book," devotes a whole chapter to "Reading as Eating" with many examples of this oddly appropriate metaphor.[4]

Also, with literature and the other media, we are almost always *looking*, either at a person, a printed page, a stage, or a screen. Years ago, psychoanalyst Otto Fenichel pointed out, "In the unconscious, to look at an object may mean various things, the most noteworthy of which are as follows: to devour the object looked at, to grow like it (be forced to imitate it), or, conversely, to force it to grow like oneself."[5] A leading psychological observer of babies, Colwyn Trevarthen, has described (and quantified) how a mother's baby-talk, as she leans cooingly over her infant, eye to eye, evokes the infant's responsive movements of arms and limbs in time to her phrasings. It is a "dance" in which the two partners are perfectly attuned to one another.[6] The oneness of that "dance" we sometimes recapture when we become "absorbed" in works of art. If we are fully experiencing, we are not only taking in the thing we sense; we are making our minds like it or it like our minds.

A psychoanalytic concept of "orality" describes the open-mouthed wonder with which we "absorb" a theatrical performance through our eyes and ears. Suspense, too, has an oral quality. Reading authors like Dickens or Scott or P. D. James creates a problem in us and what amounts to a hunger for its resolution, a hunger so great that we can scarcely wait for the next episode. As we say, "I could not put the book down." Nor is it surprising that we feel a peculiarly sharp frustration, even a sense of rage and betrayal, when "Network Trouble" flashes on the screen or when a movie film breaks or when we find the last pages of a detective story torn out. Our sense of frustration and anger becomes particularly sharp if what disrupts our visual feast is a person; we go through a miniature and adult version of the overwhelming rage of a child at someone who interrupts a feeding. Thus, too, we can guess the reason virtually all cultures mix eating with drama and literature: the symbolic eating of the slain hero in ancient Attic drama, the beer and oranges of the seventeenth-century playhouses, the wine bar in a modern theater, or popcorn at the movies. *We use literature and the other media to create a hunger in ourselves and then to gratify that hunger.*

The psychoanalytic description of orality tells us why people have that sense of losing themselves, but the phenomenon of being "transported" by a literary work is more specific than "regression." Being transported with literature has four specific aspects. My daughter, when she was eight years old, described her feeling when she was lost in Tolkien's *The Hobbit*. "When I read a book, I sort of feel like I'm invisible and walking around unseen with the things or people in the book (a Hobbit is just a thing). When I read it, just word by word, then it's just like reading a book. But when I get into a stage of reading, sort of, then it feels like a dream." In effect, she listed the four things that need to be explained if we are to understand our rapt state and the brain's processing of literature and other media.

What needs to be explained

First, being invisible. We lose the experience of our own bodies. We become unaware that we are sitting in an armchair with the light coming over our left shoulder. Or we become unaware that we are sitting in a movie theater, the popcorn redolent around us. In the same way, we don't notice that we are turning the pages to read the book or sitting up straight to see better in a theater.

Second, walking around with the things and people: that's the indeterminate space that replaces a clearly bounded "inside my skin" and "outside my skin." We also forget that we are perceiving the book or play as an object "out there" in a space separate from our own bodies. We think of it as happening neither "in here" nor "out there," but somehow "in the world of the story" (as in the epigraph).

Third, the book "feels like a dream." One does not disbelieve; one accepts the reality of Hobbits. (We'll come back to her feeling of reading word by word when it is "just" reading a book, that is, somewhat difficult.) We stop troubling ourselves as to the probability of the events we are watching or reading about. We accept in *The Arabian Nights* genies with magical powers popping out of bottles and in *Harry Potter* an airborne field hockey game.

Finally, fourth, the most perplexing thing of all: just as in some dreams, we feel fear or sadness or anger toward the people and events of a literary work as if it were not "just a story." We believe, at least so far as our emotions are concerned.[7] In the chapters that follow, I will explore these four changes in our relation to the world—body; environment; reality-testing; emotion—one by one.

6 | Losing Self, Losing the World

> Drawing nearer, he saw Poimenos sitting very close to the Singer, a little behind him. The boy was motionless, listening with head tilted upward in an exact replica of the Singer's pose. He was lost in the story, spellbound, as sightless in his way as his new master.
>
> —Barry Unsworth, *The Songs of the Kings.*

OUR BRAINS BEHAVE oddly when we are transported by a literary experience. We cease being aware of our bodies and even our environment, like the boy in the epigraph. We escape. We also do not doubt impossible things, and we also feel real emotions toward imaginary objects. But of these four, what is easiest to understand is losing track of our own bodies and their relation to the world around them, because we do that all the time.

We do it when we concentrate on some task, a phenomenon called "flow." We do it when we become habituated to some stimulus (like our shoes). We do it when (or if) we meditate. But, most importantly, we lose track of self and world in responding to works of art because we know we will not try to change them. That cognition has important consequences within our brains and, surprisingly, all the way down to our spinal cords. We inhibit impulses to do something to the aesthetic or literary object, and that inhibition changes what we believe.

Attention

We humans have a finite amount of attention or "psychic energy." Attention is a way of focusing that limited energy on what matters. If we concentrate on one thing, an important thing, we pay less attention to other things. Those other things become unconscious (or, more accurately, "preconscious" in Freud's term).[1] If we use more energy and excitation in one prefrontal function, following the play or story, we have less energy available for other prefrontal functions, like paying attention to our bodies or to the world around that play or story.

Evolution made the brain an economical organ. It conserves its energy, paying attention to what needs paying attention to, namely, any new stimulus. Something new in the environment could be a danger, an opportunity for food, or a chance at sex. Our bias toward new stimuli is one of two large ways that we focus attention: top-down and bottom-up.

In bottom-up mode, new things in the environment grab our attention. We become "stimulus-driven." A sudden noise, a flash of light, anything new, and we immediately focus on it. Typically, though, when we are reading or watching a literary work, the world outside the work is quiet: the theater or the library or the den in which we read. The only new perceptions we have are coming from the play, movie, or book. We focus on those to the exclusion of the quiet stuff. Neuropsychologists contrast "floodlight" with "spotlight" attention.

In top-down mode, higher processes instruct lower ones. As we say, we deliberately, voluntarily "direct" our attention to something. Reading or watching a literary work, it is that work that we have decided is important. Within the brain, the thalamus, located a little bit above the brain stem, is the gateway through which sensory information passes from eyes, ears, and body to sensory regions in the occipital, temporal, and parietal lobes and thence to the frontal lobes to become percepts of whole objects or scenes. In top-down attention, the prefrontal cortex in effect tells the thalamic gateway nestled in the middle of the brain, "This literary work is important. The rest isn't. Forget sensory information that doesn't pertain to this poem or story or drama."[2]

The neuropsychologists have something further to offer someone thinking particularly about the way we perceive literature, plays and movies: the "ventriloquism" effect. Certain cells in the midbrain (the superior colliculi) put together a crude but coherent three-dimensional picture of the world for the body's most rapid reactions to its surroundings. Multisensory neurons in these regions respond to combinations of, say, sight and sound, so as to unite them: the movements of the dummy's mouth and the ventriloquist's voice become one. If two stimuli originate from the same event, such stimuli multiply the response of these multisensory neurons. Evidently, then, if you are watching events on a stage or screen, your brain will strongly associate the sights and sounds coming from that source.[3] You will only weakly sense other, separated sights and sounds like the rustlings of the audience or the hum of the air conditioner.

Focusing of attention can explain our inattention to self or world when we respond to a literary work. I think, though, there are additional factors even more pertinent.

Habituation

I put on my shoes in the morning. I may feel them in place for a second or two, and then, for the rest of the day, I am unaware of them. If, on the other hand, I get a pebble in my shoe or my feet begin to hurt, then my shoes step right back into consciousness.

Neuroscientists explain this phenomenon as "habituation." The neurons that tell me about my feet fire furiously when first I put my shoes on. They are shouting to me, "Something is happening down here." But I choose not to do anyth.ing about that foreign object, and eventually those neurons, in effect, get tired. They settle into their resting rate of fire, the way they are when nothing novel is going on.[4]

The same thing happens when I am sitting in a theater watching a movie or a play. If I am wholly focused on the stage or screen, I stop feeling my back and legs in the seat. So too, sitting in an armchair reading, I don't feel my body. If book, movie, or play becomes boring, then I begin to get restless. I move my body, becoming aware of it. And, if I have to act, if I need to get up for another glass of wine or for some other reason, then I pay attention to my body and the effort to move it.

Absorbed in a literary work, I also lose track of my environment. In the theater, I become habituated to the others around me, the exit sign, or the seat itself. Reading in my armchair, I lose track of the room around me. I am not aware of things outside a literary work unless I stop to think about them, interrupting my focus on the play, film, or book. If I do stop paying total attention to the play or film, "restless," literally, I become unable to "rest" in place without concerning myself with my body position, my seat, the person next to me, and so on. I have undone the normal habituation that blanks out body and world.

Flow

Habituation can explain part of our loss of awareness while experiencing literature. But surely our concentration on or absorption in what we are reading or watching has as much or more to do with our loss of awareness. We also lose awareness of body or environment when we are intensely concentrating on some task, like working a chess problem or writing a chapter like this. Mihalyi Csikszentmihalyi has studied this phenomenon closely in many experiments and calls these moments when we are so absorbed in some effort, "flow."

We have a "flow" experience when we achieve an optimum balance of effort and satisfaction. If we are "rapt" or "absorbed" in a literary work, we are experiencing "flow." We make neither too little effort, and so become bored, nor too much, and become fatigued. "The aesthetic experience," write Cszikszentmihalyi and Robinson, "is related to other forms of enjoyable flow experiences, relying as it does on the use of skills to match situational challenges within a field of action delimited by clear goals and constant feedback. Like other flow experiences, it provides a sense of transcending everyday reality, a deep involvement with a more ordered and intense world."[5]

More simply, as my eight-year-old daughter put it: "When I read it, just word by word, then it's just like reading a book," too much effort. "But when I get into a stage of reading, sort of"—she was describing "flow," I think—"then it feels like a dream." She was describing the right balance between effort and satisfaction.

Neuroscientists can tell us a certain amount about "flow" and our becoming unaware of the physical world around one's reading or watching. There is also a related phenomenon to which they have paid a good deal of attention: meditation as practiced in various religions.

The Zen of it

James Austin, studying Zen meditation, found a key area within the thalamus that could be responsible for experiences like "flow." The thalamus, we have seen, serves as a gateway for transmitting sensory information from the sensory posterior brain to the motor-directed frontal lobes. Austin points to the "posterior thalamus" as the key area, "the smallest volume of nervous tissue where sight, hearing, vestibular [i.e., balance] input, and other vital proprioceptive sensations from the head and body *can all be disconnected at one time*."[6] That and other thalamic nuclei can shut down transmission of information about the body and the environment to the frontal lobes. Another blockade comes from even more ancient parts of the brain, the reticular formation in the midbrain. It too can inhibit the thalamus' transmission of sensory information to the frontal cortex.[7]

As a result of these shifts in particular activations, the brain as a whole can be very excited—hyperattentive to what it is focused on—yet relatively unaware of, and unresponsive to, the body and its environment. This is the meditator's situation, and also, I think, that of someone intensely absorbed in some intellectual activity. And I think it is the situation of a reader or theater- or moviegoer intent upon a literary work. The literary work feels really, really real to us.

Perhaps, though, we do not need to delve into such esoteric matters as Zen meditation to understand why, in being intensely involved with media or literature, we forget our physical bodies or the world around us. Sitting in an armchair engrossed in a book or sitting in a theater watching a play or a movie differs from the "flow" we experience in solving a crossword or composing a chapter or meditating on a *koan*. To be sure, in all five of these situations we can lose track of body and environment, but a literary experience has a difference and one with important brain consequences. Victor Nell, in his psychological study of our reading for pleasure, draws a helpful distinction between "absorption" (like Csikszentmihalyi's "flow") and "entrancement." Entrancement is special for literary and artistic experience.[8] Something special happens because we are dealing with art.

What is art?

Theorist Northrop Frye answered that hardy perennial in a way that I find satisfying: "The question of whether a thing 'is' a work of art or not is one which cannot be settled by appealing to something in the nature of the thing itself . . . . It may have been originally made for use rather than pleasure . . . but if it now exists for our pleasure it is what we call art."[9] A Tlingit totem pole may have had profound religious and family significance for that tribe. To me, it is sculpture, and that is why Frye's answer satisfies me. *It is our agreement to treat a thing as art that makes it art.* It is what we bring to a work of art, not "literality" or "fictionality" or "textuality" or any other construct supposedly "in" the work.

Throughout the history of aesthetics, philosophers have generally agreed that what we bring to art is a special way of attending to works of art, an "aesthetic attitude." They have offered many ways of describing it: aesthetic contemplation, being not personally involved, being disinterested, concentrating only on the aesthetic object, being "distanced," viewing in a non-practical way, paying attention only to the perceived characteristics, detachment, and so on. "We are detached [from *Oedipus Rex*] only in the sense in which we know that it is a drama and not real life . . . and that what is on the other side of the footlights is a different world, to which we are not supposed to respond as we do to the practical world around us."[10]

Better than "detachment" or "distance," what makes art art is that *we agree not to be practical.* We will not act or plan to act in order to cope with what is in the work of art while we are enjoying it. We may cry or laugh in response to what we are reading or watching, we may turn pages or look through our opera glasses, but we don't plan to do anything to the work of art itself. I watch Othello strangling Desdomona, and I do not rush to the stage to stop him. I do not even feel an impulse to do so. Many theorists have observed this phenomenon, but it was Kant who enlarged the idea and established "disinterestedness" as a cardinal criterion for our appropriate response to artistic works.

Kant's idea has become a commonplace among theorists of the arts. Thus, the *Encyclopedia Britannica:* "Can we then single out a faculty, an attitude, a mode of judgment, or a form of experience that is distinctively aesthetic?" "Taking their cue from Kant, many philosophers have defended the idea of an aesthetic attitude as one divorced from practical concerns, a kind of 'distancing,' or standing back, as it were, from ordinary involvement." Were we involved, we would try to save Desdemona. Kant enlarged the idea, though, beyond immediate impulses to act. "Kant . . . . described the recipient of aesthetic experience not as distanced but as disinterested, meaning that the recipient does not treat the object of enjoyment either as a vehicle for curiosity or as a means to an end. He contemplates the object as it is in itself and 'apart from all interest.'"[11] Richard Gerrig has closely studied this mental stance, which he calls "side-participation," the state of mind of someone overhearing a conversation.[12]

Kant's word was *interesselosigkeit*, lack of interest. "Interest" in this context means having an aim or purpose, like having a business "interest" in what is happening or an investment in one's critical opinion. (*Dis*interested, one must sometimes remind students, does not equal *un*interested.) Experiencing aesthetically, we do not try to save Desdemona. Neither do we desire to possess the work of art or to take up any particular attitude or purpose toward it. We are not studying it or planning a critical article or observing our own admiration. Our "delight," in Kant's words "is not based on any inclination of the subject (or any other deliberate interest)." We feel "completely free in respect to the liking which [we accord] to the object." As Victor Nell notes, on the basis of his experiments, "Indeed, the moment evaluative demands intrude, as in the case of an absorbed reader suddenly told that he or she is to produce a critical review of the book, ludic reading [reading for pleasure] . . . at once becomes work reading: the response demand triggers a perceived effortfulness."[13] This is not to say that the act of developing a critical viewpoint or even imagining a critical article as you read a novel does not give pleasure. It does. I should know. But that pleasure differs from simply enjoying a work of art for its own sake.

According to Kant, we enjoy the free play of imagination and understanding in relation to the object, and the harmony between these usually conflicting faculties leads to our pleasure.[14] *Kant thus grounds aesthetic pleasure, not in the work of art as such, but in the observer's mental state, namely, our not acting or planning to act on it.*

When we are disinterestedly enjoying a work of art, we inhibit actions on it. The inhibition is a process like other brain processes of which we remain unaware. The inhibition is "unconscious" in a cognitive sense rather than Freud's. I may have an impulse to save Desdemona, but I will be aware of neither the impulse nor its inhibition.

Neurologist Joaquin Fuster locates the key region for such inhibition of action in the orbital prefrontal cortex—that would be the regions just above and behind your eyebrows (Brodmann areas 10, 11, 13, and 47). Patients with lesions in these areas suffer from an inability to exclude stimuli to action. "The orbital patient is unusually distractible, unable to inhibit interference from external stimuli that are extraneous to present context and not part of the action currently under way. . . . the patient shows hyperactivity, unable to inhibit spontaneous actions to react to the extraneous stimuli."[15]

I was talking to a neuroscientist about this losing of oneself in art, and he offered some anecdotal evidence. He has a relative with frontal lobe damage. When he goes to the movies with this person, the man can't sit still. He squirms around. He talks to the screen. He jumps up and down. In short, he lacks the inhibitory control necessary for an aesthetic response. Such patients are showing "utilization behavior." Confronted with even simple outside stimuli like a pencil or comb, they cannot help picking it up and using it. *This is exactly the opposite of our behavior when we "lose ourselves" in a literary work.*[16] We become unaware of outside stimuli, we resist distraction, and we do not act, spontaneously or otherwise, on the work of art..

Giacomo Rizzolatti and his associates, the group famous for their discovery of "mirror neurons," note that "the parieto-frontal circuits that control action are, in normal individuals, tonically inhibited by frontal lobe 'centres.' . . . [I]t has been shown that during action observation, in parallel with motor cortex excitation, there is an inhibition of motor neurons in the spinal cord."[17] Thus, when we merely watch another's action, an impulse to do the same occurs but simultaneously an inhibition of that impulse. We are as unconscious of this inhibition when we watch a play or read a narrative, as we are when we do not pick up and use a pencil or comb we happen to see. The process takes place deep in our brains.

"Disinterestedness" and play

Disinterestedness, not acting purposefully on the material work of art, leads naturally to the idea of art as "play," to be constrasted with "reality." The play theory of art came to be adopted by many theorists, particularly psychoanalytic theorists: Freud, Erikson, Winnicott, and many another (like me). Kant came to his conclusion from introspection, the observation of others, faculty psychology, and his general belief that freedom and lawfulness could be reconciled. But later psychologists, psychoanalysts, and neuropsychologists would confirm his view. As Robert Storey notes in applying neuroscience to narrative, we "can have the pleasure of the emotions that accompany loss or injury while remaining certain that [we] will suffer the real effects of neither."[18]

Usually we know whether we are dealing with literature and whether we are not to act, because literary works come to us marked off from the rest of our experiences. Poems and cartoons are printed in such a way that we immediately recognize them as different and separate from news stories. A sentence or two usually tips us off that we are dealing with a short story or a novel, fiction not fact.

Obviously, though, some kinds of literature (broadly defined) demand action from us: propaganda or advertising or political polemics. But typically, we are to act later. We are not expected to jump up in the middle of Leni Riefenstahl's propaganda film, *Triumph of the Will* and rush off to join the Nazi party. Nor does the advertiser of the Lexus or Expedition think we will turn off our televison program and race off to the car dealer's. Indeed, one MacDonald's commercial makes fun of just this uncalled-for response: hubby sees the ad, gets up, and abandons wife and children as he rushes out for a Big Mac.

Literature is only pretend. It is play. We are disinterested. To be sure, some kinds of literature may give us data relevant to action. Even so, the reading of non-fiction, such as biography, history, essays, and criticism often yields a literary experience. Some literary experiences, like those, we are meant to believe. Others we are not, like science fiction, fairy tales, or beast fables. Yet, to some extent, we believe those as well, at least in a temporary way. As we shall see, what we believe and what we don't believe in a literary experience has more to do with our state of mind than with the words or genre of the writing.

Both absorption (or "flow") and "transport" (or "entrancement") come from our customary task-oriented focusing of attention. Both lead to loss of one's sense of self and surround. "Entrancement" or "transport," however, are different. They come from the disinterestedness special to art, the unconscious inhibition of impulses to do something to the aesthetic or literary object. As we shall see, when absorption becomes transport or entrancement, we change what we believe. As Victor Nell puts it, "Attention holds me, but trance fills me, to varying degrees, with the wonder and flavor of alternative worlds."[19] We not only cease to be aware of self and environment, we begin to believe, to feel as real, the imaginary worlds of literature.

7 | Why Don't We Doubt?

> You may not believe that I am right,
> But how can you believe that I am wrong!
> —Bai-Xiangshan (Bai-Juyi, 772-846)

LOST IN A LITERARY work, we do not doubt that the Three Bears can talk, that Superman can jump over tall buildings, or that Sherlock Holmes can tell all about people from the mud on their boots. For those moments when we are really "into" a poem, story, movie, play, or even a comic book, we simply don't bother about likelihood and lifelikeness. We believe the fiction, at least for the moment. We have what one reader in my questionnaires described as "escapism, a feeling of joyful unreality, lack of any worry."

Escapism does in fact play the key role. Our brains have no intention of acting to change what we are paying attention to and believing. In life, we ordinarily act or at least contemplate acting on the basis of what we believe. But not with fictions (Kant's "disinterestedness"). We believe, but we do not plan to act. Therefore the brain ceases to test the reality of what the literary work portrays in the way that the brain ordinarily tests the reality of the things in our environment with which we have to cope.

In most of life, simply to survive, we need to be able to tell what is real (or probable) from the information our senses give us. I need to know whether that is really a Hummer bearing down on me or just a car chase on a movie screen. I need to know whether what I am seeing is a dream or reality. Were I the hunter-gatherer beloved of evolutionary psychologists, I would need to know whether I am really hearing a lion's roar or just some fellow-hunter's skillful imitation of one. The ability to decide these things would confer an evolutionary advantage, to say the least. Indeed, the *in*ability to decide them would doom the organism. Hence this ability to judge probability or realism must be present very far down the evolutionary bush. It must involve the deepest of the systems for our emotions, particularly fear.

Yet, somehow, when we watch Superman jump over a building or read a fairy tale or science-fiction, we put this primeval ability aside. That is why our not doubting puzzles me so much. Babies begin to understand probability and realism as early as six months.[1] Even an infant could tell that something is odd when Spider-Man starts swinging through a cityful of skyscrapers on his webs. Yet in adult everyday life, we give up realism all the time for various kinds of media experiences. When I am fully concentrated on something, even something as prosaic as a television commercial, I stop testing reality for the moment, and I take unquestioning pleasure in seeing a Chevrolet soar over Monument Valley. I enjoy "the art of the thing." Why?

The "willing suspension of disbelief"

Coleridge invented the term we use to describe the credulous aspect in our trance-like state of mind when we are transported by a literary work. He was justifying his writing about "persons and characters supernatural, or at least "romantic" (in the older sense of the word, extravagant or fantastic): "Kubla Khan," "Rime of the Ancient Mariner," or "Christabel."[2] He therefore asked that his readers grant him "*that willing suspension of disbelief for the moment that constitutes poetic faith.*" He asked us *not to disbelieve, at least momentarily, for brief periods,* the improbabilities that he had written and that we were about to read. That stance, he said, constitutes a kind of imaginative or empathic belief, which he called "poetic faith."

Coleridge's phrase, "willing suspension of disbelief,"[3] has lasted more than two centuries, probably because it describes very well what we *feel* is happening in a lot of situations that Coleridge could never have imagined, like a menaced starlet in a chain saw movie. When we read that some "rough beast, its hour come round at last, / Slouches towards Bethlehem to be born," we don't disbelieve; we don't doubt. We have "poetic faith" in what we are reading or seeing.

Psychologist Richard Gerrig, however, has convincingly rewritten Coleridge's "willing suspension of disbelief." He notes that we take away only some information from a fiction. That is, if I am reading Sherlock Holmes stories, I will take away information about hansom cabs and gazogenes as part of my permanent knowledge. But I will not believe that there was a Sherlock Holmes or a Dr. Watson or a Mrs. Hudson. One can explain this phenomenon, Gerrig claims, by saying that we believe all and then we disbelieve some.

To justify this position, Gerrig introduces an idea from philosophy. Spinoza believed that, in order to comprehend what we perceive, we must at first believe it true. Only then, if necessary, do we disbelieve it. Following Daniel T. Gilbert and Spinoza, Gerrig asserts that *simply comprehending something automatically includes belief.* Gilbert defines belief in this context as "propensity to behave."[4] In his view, people automatically accept what they perceive, get ready to act on it, and only on second thought, with a little extra effort, "unaccept" it. Gilbert cites research showing that "people are particularly poor at ignoring, forgetting, rejecting or otherwise failing to believe that which they have comprehended."[5] Science writer Natalie Angier summarizes this line of research:

> In more than 100 studies, researchers have asked participants questions like, Is the person on the videotape lying or telling the truth? Subjects guess correctly about 54 percent of the time, which is barely better than they'd do by flipping a coin. Our lie blindness suggests to some researchers a human desire to be deceived, a preference for the stylishly accoutred fable over the naked truth.[6]

That "truth effect" or "lie blindness" makes sense evolutionarily. Your basic hominin gets away faster from something that looks like a snake—and suffers fewer fatal snakebites—if she believes right away that what she has seen is a snake and immediately jumps back without checking. We would have lower odds of surviving if we went though the full two-step process of first perceiving, then assessing.

Following this theory, Gerrig asserts that, when we read a fiction, we presume that all the information that comes our way is true until we deliberately "unaccept" some. We process fiction (and plays and movies), he claims, by two different systems. One is "unsystematic." It simply perceives and *believes what it perceives.* The other system is, in Gerrig and Gilbert's term, "systematic," and it assesses the reality of what we are sensing.

This second, reality-testing system is turned off for moments or minutes by our knowledge that what we are watching is in fact "only a story," "only a play," or "only a movie." We cannot change it. "Fictional information is persuasive because it is processed via some nonsystematic route." "Belief in fiction [that is, in the factual representations in a fiction—nnh] is determined not by a critical analysis . . . but instead by the absence of motivation or ability to perform such an analysis."[7] Thus readers, he claims, will have to "expend explicit effort to understand [fictions] as fictional."[8]

A review of the psychological literature in this field suggests that this second system (involving memory via the hippocampus) weighs the reliability of the source of the information and the compatibility of the new information with already stored data.[9] It would be some such second system that concludes, "It's only a story" and disbelieves, while the first system suspends disbelief for the duration of the "transport."

Narratives trump reason

Gerrig has experimented with readers' responses for a number of years. He and his associates have repeatedly demonstrated a fascinating phenomenon they call "anomalous suspense."[10] Gerrig had his subjects read a short-short narrative about George Washington. It created suspense by telling of obstacles to his becoming the first president of the United States (Washington's fatigue after the war, his reluctance, and a rise in John Adams' acceptability). After reading the story, subjects were significantly slower in marking as true or false the statement, "George Washington was elected first president of the United States." Gerrig concluded that, while reading the narrative and when suspense was introduced, subjects did not check what they were reading against their real-world knowledge of American history.

Every parent has seen the phenomenon. When I was a

child, one of my favorite stories was *The Little Engine That Could.* I can distinctly remember heightening excitement and suspense as the engine neared the top of the mountain. Yet I knew all the time that this was the little engine that "could" *and did.* Another instance: a friend tells me about her nearly having a fatal auto accident. I know perfectly well the accident did not happen, for my friend is standing there before me. Yet I will feel fear and worry and suspense about the fatal possibility. Such suspense is indeed "anomalous." It doesn't make sense in the light of what we really know. But I grant what Coleridge called "poetic faith" to the story. And notice that anomalous suspense happens equally for fiction and non-fiction (as with the George Washington story). I credit biographies as I do novels.

Gerrig therefore disagrees with Coleridge's "willing suspension of disbelief"

> This phrase is widely cited to stand for some cluster of special processes that readers are supposed to undertake when they know themselves to be experiencing fiction. If we contrast fiction and non-fiction, the implication is that there is a toggling back and forth between suspension and nonsuspension of disbelief.[11]

Gerrig rejects this toggling. We have a set, he says, to believe all stories unless we make an effort to disbelieve. He speaks repeatedly of the "construction of disbelief."

Evidently, the problem is Coleridge's word "willing." Some people understand that as a deliberate, conscious decision during reading. I think, in this context, though, "willing" means no more than that I am willing to pick up the book or read the poem or buy the theater ticket. I do not think it means a conscious invoking of either belief or disbelief or suspension of disbelief.

Similarly, I think the toggling is real enough provided,

again, that we do not think it is deliberately "willing." Often, something distracts us from a narrative. The telephone rings when I am reading a novel. The person next to me in at the theater makes too much noise unwrapping a cough drop, and I am taken "out" of the play. I lose the feeling of being "rapt," and I have to make an effort to focus on the novel or play and get that state back. In that sense, I have to "will" myself back "into" it. But that is not deliberately deciding to suspend disbelief.

The neuropsychology of it

I think Coleridge's other phrasing, "for the moment . . . poetic faith," better describes what Gerrig called "anomalous suspense." And I think Gerrig (and Gilbert) introduce a helpful distinction: systematic and unsystematic systems. They write of prior, memory-based knowledge being outweighed by what Gerrig calls "participatory" responses, that is, one's current involvement in the narrative, be it fiction or non-fiction. Their findings make neuropsychological sense.

As we have seen (in ch. 6), the prefrontal knowledge, the "set," that we know we cannot possibly change what we are sensing, reduces incoming information about the body and environment. We go into a kind of trance. We are "transported" or "absorbed" or "rapt." The turning off of systems for planning actions on the literary work (a systematic system, in Gerrig's terms) also turns off our systems for testing reality and for disbelieving. Without movement or the impulse to move or some plan to move, we need not check the reality of what we might move toward, *and we don't.* If we know that we can't act on something, it doesn't matter whether it's real or not real. And that is what we mean by a fiction, that it doesn't matter whether it is real or not.

That is why, then, we are not concerned with whether

things are true or false when we are transported by a literary work. We believe because we do not reality-test, and we do not reality-test because action on the stimulus is ontologically impossible. Once we do plan to act, once the experimenters ask the subjects to say whether Washington was the first president of the U.S. or not, then they and we take a few extra milliseconds to return to our prior, systematic, and relevant-to-action knowledge (in semantic or episodic memory).

Evolutionary psychologists John Tooby and Leda Cosmides have also studied the way we humans do literature. They note, "Although fiction often embeds real facts, places, events, and people, they are not necessarily or even usually marked off from the nonexistent 'facts' . . . . Within a fictional narrative, everything (whether true in reality or not) has the same undiscriminated and largely indiscriminable standing."[12] And, say I, we need no such marking off, because we know that, by the very nature of a literary work, we will not change what we are focused on. Therefore, we need not and do not reality-test.

In the words of the poet and painter Bai-Xiangshan that began this chapter, "You may not believe that I am right, / But how can you believe that I am wrong!" Absorbed in poetry and fiction, transported with a play or a movie, we may not "really and truly" think that what we are seeing is real, true, or "right," but we cannot not-believe it. We cannot believe it is "wrong" unless we break our absorption and begin reality-testing. The end result is the behavior Gerrig observed. We believe unless and until we remind ourselves, "This is only a story," "just a movie," the way I can laugh at myself for flinching at the movies when the chain saw killer jumps out at the blond starlet. So long as we are transported, we have "poetic faith," because we have no "disposition to act" and hence no mechanism for testing reality. But we don't lose touch altogether.

The limits of the fantastic

In an ingenious paper, Michael Kelly and Frank Keil, psychologists, studied the transformations in Ovid's *Metamorphoses* and the Grimms' fairy tales.[13] In these stories, nymphs turn into trees and straw turns into gold and scullery maids turn into princesses. There are, in short, all kinds of totally unreal, improbable transformations.

What Kelly and Keil found was that these transformations could not just be any old transformation. They stayed within certain limits. You could, for example, write a story in which milk turns red; you couldn't write a story in which an idea turns red. (At least, Ovid and the peasants who retold these stories to the Grimms didn't. What a modern cyberpunk writer might do—who knows?)

Philosophers speak of "predicability." That is, certain predicates can go with certain subjects and other predicates cannot. Milk, being a concrete thing, can be red. An idea cannot (as in Chomsky's famous grammatical but meaningless sentence, "Colorless green ideas sleep furiously"). One can go on, Kelly and Keil show, to set up a "predicability tree." Such a diagram arranges predicates to sort out which can go with which. A predicate such as "is nearby" is above a term if it can be predicated of that term, as "is nearby" can be predicated of a man or a rose or a refrigerator or milk or a kiss. It would be above those. But "is nearby" cannot be predicated of love or fear or an idea or "literature." It would be below those.

Kelly and Keil sorted out the transformations in *Metamorphoses* and the Grimms' tales and found that conscious beings could be transformed into other conscious beings, animals, plants, inanimate objects, liquids, or even events, but in all the stories no conscious being was transformed into an abstraction.

With respect to our "poetic faith," I find it interesting that Terminator 2 could turn into a pool of liquid metal but not into "Thou shalt not commit adultery." That is, "is a liquid" could be predicated of a Terminator, but not "is one of the Ten Commandments."

Possibly these categories and the limits they propose are built into our brains. Children can distinguish animate from inanimate things at a very early age. These "predicability trees" may correspond to the well-established fact in neurology that there is a certain area in the brain (the inferior temporal cortex, part of the "what" system for visual perception) that is essential to naming and processing information about objects in specific categories, such as tools, animals, or edible materials. We know this because of the lesions of some patients. Some patients or some experimental subjects in whom particular areas of the inferior temporal cortex have been taken out of commission, lose certain quite specific abilities, to name a tool or an animal or an edible material or a verb. (These categories may relate to basic human activities like grasping or eating.) Could it be that a "predicability tree" is wired in us? Or is it simply learned?

Either way, within the limits of predicability, we abandon considerations of probability and realism when we are completely engrossed in a movie, play, or story. Why? And how?

"It feels like a dream"

The primary business of any brain is to move its body. From the neurological point of view, we begin to test reality when we act or plan to act in response to a stimulus.[14] "Perception,"sserts Andy Clark, "is itself tangled up with specific possibilities of action—so tangled up, in fact, that the job of central cognition often ceases to exist."[15] Another neuroscientist, Rodolfo Llinás, writes, "What I must stress here is that the brain's understanding of anything, whether factual or abstract, arises from our manipulations of the external world, by our moving within the world and thus from our sensory-derived experience of it."[16] And two specialists in frontal lobe function, Robert T. Knight and Marcia Grabowecky, say, "Reality checking involves a continual assessment of the relation between behavior and the environment."[17] Without movement or the impulse to move or some plan to act, we need not check the reality of what we perceive, *and we don't.*

Why does absence of action lead to absence of reality-testing? Our brains seek our survival and reproduction through goals that we must imagine ahead of time. To plan actions, therefore, we imagine situations. That is, if I want to push the chair in front of me aside, I have to imagine where I want the chair to be in order to tell my arms and legs to make the necessary moves. I have to imagine something that is not actually the case. Neuroscientists call this a "counterfactual." I feed forward to my systems for planning motions the future position of the chair, which is not what "is." Conversely, having moved the chair I feed back its present position to the position I desired and, if it matches, I stop moving the chair. If it doesn't match, I continue to move it. Again, I have to imagine things that are not the case, the former and future positions of the chair, in order to move it. *To act effectively on my environment, I have to have an idea of what is and is not physically real.*[18]

In general, we humans simulate in order to arrive at the best, the most appropriate physical actions. We imagine counterfactuals in order to set out alternatives. Then we select the one that *feels* best to us. *Ultimately, emotions guide our choices.* We act out what feels good and right. We obey Freud's "pleasure principle," and we avoid unpleasure. To do so, we must be able to imagine unrealities and know that they are in fact not physically real.

If we lose the ability to imagine unrealities, to create narratives, we cease to judge reality.[19] Some brain-damaged patients have trouble generating both appropriate actions and alternative versions of reality. Because they are impaired in their ability to generate and evaluate counterfactual alternatives, they become bound to whatever stimulus comes their way. In the phrasing of Joaquin Fuster, they suffer from "dysexecutive syndrome," "a defect in motor preparation set." "The patient cannot formulate plans of future action that deviate from ordinary routine. His [or her] capacity to create new speech or behavior is severely restricted."[20]

These patients suffer from lesions in a particular region of the most anterior part of the brain, the prefrontal cortex. This is the region above and to the side from your eyebrows, the dorsolateral surface of the prefrontal cortex (Brodmann areas 9 and 46). This region is apparently essential to simulating internal models for actions.[21]

Kay Young, a professor of English, and Jeffrey Saver, a neurologist, have compared narrative, or at least the creation of narrative, to fundamental cognitive operations of our brains.[22] They studied cases of "dysnarrativia," patients who had trouble making up counterfactuals—fictions—things that never really happened. In some brain-damaged people, injury to the frontal lobes of the brain, where advanced thinking takes place, shuts down these monitoring abilities. Young and Saver suggest a regionally distributed network for the creation of narrative: episodic and autobiographical memories, generated in the amygdalo-hippocampal system; the formulation of narrative language (left perisylvian region); and the organizing of persons and things into real and fictional temporal narrative frames in the frontal cortices and their sub-cortical connections to the "feeling" parts of the brain, the limbic system. Although Young and Saver are discussing the ability to *create* narrative, the "dysnarrative" inability to tell what is fact and what is fiction seems to me very like the suspension of reality-testing and Coleridge's "poetic faith."

Young and Saver compare their cases of "dysnarrativia" to those patients the neurologists term "confabulators." Confabulators make up stories to explain things that are happening to them that they don't understand, things that result from brain damage or hypnosis or psychologists' experiments. Confabulators misremember or misperceive but produce explanations and rationalizations for their errors. While the victims of dysnarrativia have trouble generating narratives at all, confabulators generate narratives inappropriately. Clinically, the neurologists again find frontal lobe damage, perhaps coupled with damage to related systems, notably the basal forebrain in the limbic system.[23]

So far we have looked at confabulators, the victims of dysnarrativia, the patients with dysexecutive function who cannot plan, and ourselves, when "transported" as we respond to works of literature. All share a disturbance in the normal ability to generate counterfactuals appropriately. In particular, the three with brain damage all suffer from some form of frontal lobe deficiency. It seems reasonable to me to conclude that the fourth, the person transported by media or a literary work, has also shut down or by-passed those same frontal lobe systems for generating counterfactuals preparatory to acting.

Mixing memory and desire

A team of Swiss researchers has made an intriguing suggestion regarding "spontaneous" confabulations. By that, they mean confabulations not provoked by any stimulus, not, for example, the kind of hasty explanation any of us might produce to compensate for forgetting an acquaintance's name. They suggest that spontaneous confabulators have a problem in processing information in the immediate present, the "now." Instead, they mix up the time sequence of events and bring into the "now" traces of events from hours, weeks, or even years past.[24] The patients' brain lesions impaired, the researchers said, the anterior limbic system (technically, the medial orbitofrontal cortex, basal forebrain, amygdala, and perirhinal cortex or medial hypothalamus). That is, not only had these patients' lesions damaged the thinking part of their brains but also parts specifically associated with memory.[25]

Interestingly, this confusion of the past with the here and now corresponds to a part of our response to literature described in 1957 by a psychoanalytic critic. Simon O. Lesser introduced the idea of "analogizing."[26] We bring to bear on what we now see or read, some feeling or experience from our own past. I see Othello enraged at Desdemona, and I bring to bear (probably preconsciously) my own feelings of jealousy from some painful occasion decades earlier. And my bringing my own past to bear on the here and now of the tragedy makes me feel it all the more strongly. Richard Gerrig includes this in what he calls "participatory response," and he notes how it can enrich and intensify one's emotional experience.[27]

Finally, then, I think we have arrived at a description of what our brains are doing in the third aspect of being transported (after ignoring body and environment). A brain serves one basic purpose, moving a body in the real world toward survival and reproduction. Intending to move in the real world involves imagining counterfactuals, and therefore testing reality and judging probabilities. If we know that, by its very nature, we cannot affect what we are paying attention to, as is the case with literary and artistic works, we inhibit motor impulses from our frontal lobes. *We may then disregard whether what we are perceiving is true or not. We may shut down our judgments of realism or probability.* If we do, we have granted "poetic faith" in Coleridge's sense.

Thought of this way, *fictions and media in general resemble confabulations, but somebody else is making up the story.* And if and when that becomes ambiguous—whether someone is making up a story or not—strange things happen to our responses.

Breaking "poetic faith"

Our "poetic faith" can last for minutes or even hours, but it often lasts only a moment, or a few moments here and there as we read or watch. Whatever from my environment brings into play my systems for assessing and acting on the real world will end my "poetic faith" in what I am reading or watching.

Readers or audience members can also break the dyadic tie to the work if mental discomfort becomes too severe. For example, if I find the book I am reading very hard going (late Henry James, for example, or Proust), I probably do not get "lost" in the experience. Some of the people who described being transported (ch. 6) contrasted their alert, active mental puzzling when the book or film gets difficult. "The continuum goes from totally absorbed (cinema) to fairly distanced, self-conscious hunting for something (non-fiction). Fiction can go either way (rarely a blend though)." "Varies but usually I'm completely absorbed—even by crude stuff—in fact, apt to be more critical, aware and less absorbed by 'high art.'" My daughter (at age eight) contrasted reading that transports and reading that takes effort: "When I read it, just word by word, then it's just like reading a book."

Conversely, I may find a book or a film trite and predictable. In those situations, I do not grant poetic faith—I feel my boredom. In short, I need to feel just the right amount of effort to maintain, in Mihalyi Czikszentmihalyi's concept, "flow."[28] Too much effort and we become aware that we are working at it, and Kant's "disinterestedness" ends. Too little effort, and we cease to pay attention or we become bored.

If we act, as when we try to "solve" a puzzling text, we break "poetic faith." The work can break it, too. And when it does, it gives us a nice test of this explanation of our credulity when we are transported.

8 | Metafictions

> There is even, in the last section of the book, a harsh mock review of the book itself, intended, I imagine, to disarm criticism. Well, it fails entirely. Many is the book reviewer, I suspect, who, like myself, will see in it his own distaste articulated. In fact, I am now quoting word for word from the same mock review.
>
> —Charles Simmons, *Powdered Eggs*

TINKERING WITH OUR "poetic faith" leads to some of the more dizzying effects possible in literature and media. I am thinking of those novels, like *Tristram Shandy* or *Les Faux-Monnayeurs*, which are novels about writing the novel which is the novel. In Doris Lessing's *The Golden Notebook*, for example, one of the notebooks tells about a novelist trying to write a novel. A friend asks her to give him the first sentence, and the novelist rattles off the first sentence of *The Golden Notebook* itself. Somehow the story has stopped being a fiction and become a fact. The writing of the memoir narrated in *Tristram Shandy* seems as real as the physical copy of *Tristram Shandy* I am holding in my hand.

But surely the genial grandfather who sired all these metafictional effects is that first and perhaps greatest of novels, 400-year-old *Don Quixote*. Part 1 has its uncertainties. We are never sure where Don Quixote comes from or what his name is or who is writing the book. But the book turns fully metafictional when Part I (published in 1604) becomes a cause of events in Part II (published in 1614). In Part II (II.iv), a roguish scholar, toying with Don Quixote's fancies, tells us that the author of Part I, the Moor Cide Hamete Benengeli (or perhaps Berenjena) is an Arab whose narrations therefore cannot be trusted. (But he swears like a Christian they are true, although he is an Arab.) This fictional author, says the scholar, will produce a Part II, which, of course, we are holding in our hands as we read this announcement. The fictional characters of Part II go on to discuss errors and distortions and even the sales figures of Part I. Don Quixote finds, as he proceeds through Part II, that everybody knows about him and his goofy knight-errantry because so many have read Part I. *The physical existence of Part I causes events in Part II.*

There's more. Part II tells us that, trying to capitalize on Cervantes' success, one Avallaneda has written a sequel to Part I (there was in fact such a book). In the genuine Part II, Don Quixote makes a point of discrediting the other text: its Quixote and Sancho are not like the "real" Quixote and Sancho. The "real" author of the novel (Benengeli? Cervantes?) then has a reader of the fake *Don Quixote* swear an oath before a notary that the "real" Quixote and Sancho are not at all like the ones in the plagiarist's novel (II.lxxii). In short, Cervantes' metafiction tells us about something that never happened, *on which, therefore, I cannot act,* but that story includes the physically real book I am holding in my hands at that moment *and on which I can act.*

Drama gets this effect in the metatheatrical tradition of Pirandello and the absurdists like Genet or Ionesco or Weiss. For example, in Pirandello's *Six Characters in Search of an Author*, the six characters wander about the stage looking for an author to write the play which is, of course, the play we are watching.

Dozens of movies develop the same effect: Buster Keaton's *Sherlock Junior*, Ingmar Bergman's *Persona*, Woody Allen's *Purple Rose of Cairo*, and many another. The shortest example I know is Groucho Marx's turn to the camera—us—in *Horse Feathers*: "I've gotta stay here, but there's no reason you folks shouldn't go out in the lobby till this thing blows over."

One can even create such an exotic effect with criticism, as in the epigraph. Charles Simmons's comical book includes a supposed review of itself which quotes itself—some kind of infinite regress.

I find such effects peculiarly unsettling, and I am not alone. The film *Adaptation* (2002) shows us Charlie Kaufman (a real-life screenwriter) suffering from writer's block as he tries to write a movie based on a non-fiction book (that really exists), Susan Orlean's *The Orchid Thief*.[1] Real-life Charlie is outdone as a screenwriter by his devil-may-care twin brother Donald, fictitious, but played by the same actor, Nicolas Cage, who plays Charlie. Both real-life Charlie and fictitious Donald appear in the credits for the film. And, to top the joke, in 2003, both Charlie and Donald were nominated for the Oscar for the best "adaptation" screenplay. In the course of the film, the writer who wrote the article comes to see the real-life orchid thief. The two screenwriters intervene, and the thief and the article writer nearly kill them.

In effect, the (real) writers of the film have become characters in the (fictional) film that they are writing and I am watching. The events in the film have somehow become real, that is, actable on. *Adaptation*, writes a reviewer, A. O. Scott, "is, most obviously, a movie about itself, as gleefully self-referential an exercise in auto-deconstruction as you could wish. But it is also, more deeply, a movie about its own nonexistence . . . . Common sense suggests that there could never be such a movie." Interestingly, Scott describes his reaction in terms like "panic," "frantic anxiety," or "paranoid."[2] Like Scott, I too feel dizzy and uncertain—and delighted—at this playing with levels of reality.

In such works, I get that strange feeling Freud called "The Uncanny." It is the feeling we get from reading stories about doubles, ghosts, or the undead. It is the vertigo we get when something familiar seems suddenly strange and unfamiliar. Is the supposed fiction I am reading something I can act on (the physical literary work) or not (the "content" of the work)?

This is not just an intellectual puzzle. *Shifting the physicality of the story shifts systems in my brain.* A system (involving the dorsolateral prefrontal cortex) had been using the total literary situation to know that I could not act to change *Don Quixote*. On that basis, it had shut off my planning. I was not thinking about my body or my environment. I was not imagining counterfactuals. I was not testing reality or probability. But now that system has been fooled, and it "knows" it has been fooled. I *can* act on this thing. The ventral striatum, where I had been monitoring the reliability of those predictions, now becomes activated by the sudden, unexpected change in context, with resulting changes (probably) in emotions and feelings toward potential actions.[3] I start wondering about the status in reality of what I have been reading.

At first it was clear. I could act on the book I was

holding or the theater I was in. I could not, however, act to change the events represented. But then the narrative takes a metafictional turn. The events represented are the same kind of thing as the book I am holding or the theater I am in. Can I, then, act on the events represented? Do I need to test them for reality, probability, and truth? Do I need to bring those frontal systems into play? My brain has to figure out this new situation. My attention is drawn away from the events represented to the conflicting signals I am getting, and my being transported, my "poetic faith," comes to an end. Furthermore, I feel anxious at the uncertainty.

Suspending disbelief three ways

In short, in that special, trance-like state of being transported with literary or other works of art, we shut down, one, our awareness of our bodies, two, our awareness of our environment (except for the work itself), and three, our monitoring the reality and probability of what we are seeing, hearing, or imagining. But there is a fourth system we do not shut down—if anything, we amplify it. And that is, to me, the most puzzling phenomenon of all. Why do we feel real emotions toward the unreal things represented in fictions and dramas and poems?

9 | About Emotions

> We think by feeling. What is there to know?
> I hear my being dance from ear to ear.
> Theodore Roethke, "The Waking."

SO FAR, WE have explored three aspects of our being transported by a narrative. We know we cannot act so as to change the work of art. We are to be purposeless, passive, or, in Kant's term, disinterested. As a result, we lose track of our bodies, we lose track of our surroundings, and we believe all manner of impossible things at least for the time we are transported.

We come then to the fourth, and, to me, the most puzzling, aspect of what Coleridge called "poetic faith." We feel real emotions toward people and situations that we know perfectly well are fictitous. I am sad to the point of tears at Frank O'Hara's beautiful elegy for Billie Holliday or when Lear carries in the body of the dead Cordelia. Yet these are merely verbal, imaginary happenings. To explain this oddity, we need to consider some basic things about brains. We need to understand the separation between our cognitive knowledge that we cannot change the work of art and a deeper system that gives rise to emotions.

What is an emotion?

Emotion has evolved into one of the most difficult and contested areas of today's neuropsychology. Theories abound and compete. Even the terminology is tangled. I think most brain scientists would agree that an emotion happens when something stimulates a sensory system which in turn gives rise to a percept or cognition, something sensed or known. We can distinguish four things that might accompany that cognition to make up what we call an "emotion."

First, we *feel* fear or disgust or anger. We have a *feeling* in our minds. The neuroscientists call that "affect." Sometimes, when speaking specifically of a good or bad feeling, brain scientists will introduce the term "valence," which can be positive or negative.

Second, usually but not always, when we feel an affect, *we are consciously aware that we are feeling* it. I know that I am afraid or angry or disgusted. Sometimes psychologists term this aspect of an emotion "cognitive appraisal," and presumably the "cognitive" is supposed to contrast with simply "feeling." As we shall see, emotions are what decide us on actions. We do what *feels* best to us, and to decide rationally what to do, we ought to be aware of what we are feeling. But, as a century of psychoanalysis has shown, we can also have the feeling without the awareness. Literary theorist Keith Oatley and psychologist Philip Johnson-Laird put appraisal more precisely. Emotions rank order ("hierarchize") the various impulses and directives we are feeling at any given moment.[1] One can think of this appraisal, then, as a form of communication between different systems (modules, perhaps) in the brain and also as messages to the body.

Third, we experience *bodily changes* through the sympathetic and parasympathic branches of our autonomic nervous system. We have the sweaty palm, the cold chill, the faster heartbeat, the rapid breathing, or the warm, fuzzy feeling. The sympathetic nervous system prepares the body for the brief, intense, vigorous responses that we call "fight or flight." Books or movies or plays can stimulate this system with car chases and shoot 'em ups and searching out clues in dark houses. Situations more romantic or amusing might energize the parasympathetic nervous system, which increases other, more relaxing processes associated with conservation of energy and preparation for later action.[2]

Fourth, we also feel an *impulse to act.* An emotion is a "call to action"[3] or a "disposition to act."[4] "It is hard to imagine someone ever feeling really truly angry," one neuroscientist writes, "despite the person's face turning red, and feeling lots of sympathetic arousal, if there was no internal impetus to verbally or physically strike out."[5] These impulses would be musculoskeletal responses as opposed to autonomic. Because this kind of bodily response is visible to others, it *communicates.* As Darwin pointed out in 1890 in his classic *The Expression of the Emotions in Man and Animals*, our emotion-driven bodily movements signal to other humans around us.[6] If we are afraid or disgusted, those nearby may have reason to feel afraid or disgusted. If we show anger, they may feel fear or mobilize a "fight or flight" reaction. They may feel as we do (emotional "contagion") or they may react against our feeling. The impulse may even become unconscious. But emotions do communicate.

Still more knotty is the relation among these four aspects. Common sense and some theorists say that we see something, we feel about it, and that conscious feeling leads to the "gut" feelings and impulses to act. From this point of view, feelings are a kind of information in working memory that leads to a body state. Other theorists say that stimuli produce autonomic changes in our bodies, and those, when sensed, are what cause feelings. But, other theorists point out, our emotions are faster than that. Another theory claims that the impulses to action establish types of resonances in the neuro-symbolic representation of the body in the brain stem, that is, in deep and ancient areas of the brain. Yet another theory holds that the stimulus only excites us in a general way. What we sense or know at the moment determines the specific way we will feel mentally and react physically.[7] And there are many other theories of emotion, none so widely accepted as to be "the" theory.[8] All have their plusses and minuses.

Emotions pose still other puzzles for the neuroscientist. Emotions are asymmetical in the brain, be they short-lived emotions ("states") or longer-lasting ("affective styles" or "traits" or "moods"). The anterior right hemisphere becomes active with negative emotions, while the anterior left hemisphere "lights up" with positive and assertive emotions.[9] We know that emotions are worldwide and universal, but are they innate in the brain or are they constructed by common human social experiences? Most neuroscientists agree that there are certain basic or "prototypical" emotions, but disagree as to how many or how to classify them.[10]

Then, more complicated emotions form from combinations of the basic ones. Some neuroscientists think of emotions on a two- or three-dimensional continuum: pleasure vs. unpleasure; arousal vs. calming; and approach vs. avoidance. Even within a given emotion there are complications. Consider pleasure. How can we distinguish the pleasure from eating a chocolate bar, the pleasure at watching *Hamlet*, and the pleasure of an orgasm?

Someone, like me, trying to use neuroscientific knowledge about the emotions to think about literature faces these and other persistent puzzles. Nevertheless, feelings play so central a part in our response to literature that I would like to posit at least a provisional idea of what goes on in our brains when we feel emotions while reading or viewing literary works.

Basic emotions

Many neuroscientists agree that there are certain basic, discrete emotions. Prominent among them is Paul Ekman. Following Darwin's claims, Ekman and his team have shown that there are discrete emotions that give rise to discrete facial expressions that can be measured and simulated. They have also shown, most tellingly, that people in cultures all over the world recognize and give these facial expressions the same meaning.[11] Moreover, Scandinavian researchers have shown that we mirror in our own facial muscles the happiness or anger in the facial expressions of others. We do so even if the others' facial expressions are presented subliminally so that the facial expressions are not consciousnly known. We do so, remarkably, within 3-4 milliseconds after perceiving the other's face. That speed suggests biologically controlled fast operating "affect programs,"[12] presumably innate and evolutionarily ancient. We need not debate, therefore, whether we are born with emotional systems in our brains or whether our emotions are "socially constructed." Presumably, our genome gives us a set of underlying start-up processes for emotions on which culture and individual development then build.[13]

This universality argues that our emotional systems are innate, built genetically into our physiology. To the extent that we humans feel emotion though a vocabulary of fixed emotions (rage, disgust, fear, joy, anger, and so on), many people will share the same emotional response to a given work of literature. Patrick Colm Hogan has made the sensible suggestion that the world's cultures have developed prototypical narratives (boy-gets-girl; hero-defeats-villains) to evoke these prototypical emotions.[14]

What are these prototypical emotions, then? There is considerable agreement about fear, anger, disgust, sadness, and joy. Ekman himself has added these: amusement, contempt, contentment, embarrassment, excitement, guilt, pride in achievement, relief, satisfaction, sensory pleasure and shame[15] As for how basic emotions are manifested in brain systems, I have found Jaak Panksepp's work the most convincing (see the Appendix). Because one cannot stimulate humans to emotional activity and then study their brains, Panksepp has worked primarily with animals' brains. One sees, after all, cats and dogs expressing fear, anger, joy, sadness, and other emotions (and all mammalian brains have the same basic structures). He can therefore look inside animals' brains for emotional systems in ways that would be unethical in humans. What animals *feel* is, of course, debatable. What counts is that our brains have the same basic structure, and we, at least, do feel emotions.

In his major statement, *Affective Neuroscience* (1998), Panksepp develops in detail the brain systems involved in his set of basic emotions (limited to those he can find specific neurochemical pathways for). They are: SEEKING, RAGE, FEAR, PANIC (separation distress), PLAY (joy), and CARING (nurturance). There may, of course, be others. Panksepp uses capital letters for his basic emotions to distinguish a specific scientific meaning, associated with the brain systems and neurochemicals he describes. But he clearly intends the layperson's meaning as well.

RAGE and the rest we have all felt at one time or another. What is probably less familiar is SEEKING, but it is the most important for our literary purposes. Long before

Panksepp, Keats described it vividly: "I go among the Feilds and catch a glimpse of a stoat or a fieldmouse peeping out of the withered grass—the creature hath a purpose and its eyes are bright with it—I go amongst the buildings of a city and I see a Man hurrying along—to what? The Creature has a purpose and his eyes are bright with it."[16] The SEEKING system is the basis in the brain for the bright-eyed purpose of both the fieldmouse and its fellow mammal, the man.[17]

"The mammalian brain," writes Panksepp, "contains a 'foraging/exploration/investigation/curiosity/interest/expectancy/SEEKING' system that leads organisms to eagerly pursue the fruits of their environment—from nuts to knowledge, so to speak." It controls "appetitive activation—the search, foraging, and investigatory activities—that all animals must exhibit *before* they are in a position to emit consummatory behaviors."[18] That is, you have to find the desire-satisfying object before you can actually enjoy it and reduce the desire or need. The SEEKING system is "wanting" as opposed to "liking."[19] And it has a distinct feeling tone, Panksepp continues, "a psychic energization that is difficult to describe but is akin to that invigorated feeling of anticipation we experience when we actively seek thrills and other rewards." "The affective state does not resemble the pleasurable feelings we normally experience when we indulge in various consummatory behaviors. Instead, it resembles the energization organisms apparently feel when they are anticipating rewards." Like Keats' bright-eyed fieldmouse.

Pretty clearly, in Panksepp's view, when we turn to literature we are SEEKING. Although at first without cognitive content, SEEKING translates correlations in environmental events into perceptions of causality. It is perhaps the source of "confirmation bias," because it gives us our drive to seek evidence for our hypotheses and to perceive the world as confirming our hypotheses. In writing this book, I am SEEKING. And, when we enjoy literature, it is SEEKING that makes us go on reading or watching. *It is SEEKING that drives us to interpret the metaphors and symbols of poetry and to make sense of the plots and characters of dramas and narratives.*

Panksepp's account tells us three things about emotions that are widely accepted by other neuroscientists. First, while overall theories may differ, we do know a good deal about the brain systems that give rise to particular emotions. We do not need to rely on impressionistic or introspective ideas about emotion. Second, emotions derive from the mammalian brain.

Paul MacLean introduced in 1973 a highly influential idea: the triune brain. On evolutionary and physiological grounds, he suggested that our brains had evolved outward from a core that we share with reptiles, a brain stem that controls such basic functions as heart rate and blood pressure. When animals evolved from egg-laying reptiles to mammals that bore their young alive, they therefore had to nurture the young. They needed emotions, and evolution developed a mammalian brain surrounding and enlarging the reptilian brain that brought emotions into the scheme of things. As mammals continued to evolve, the primate order (monkeys and apes) arose with a greatly developed outer cortex and frontal lobe. Among the primates, man's brain is the largest. I weigh about as much as an orang-utan, but I have five times the amount of prefrontal cortex. This is the part of our brain just above and behind our eyebrows projecting up and behind our foreheads. This is where we plan and initiate actions. I think we can contain our human vanity, if we remind ourselves that our large prefrontal cortex is just one more of nature's specialized developments like the bat's hearing or the elephant's trunk. But, oh the consequences!

According to neuroscientists generally, the key factors in human as well as animal emotion come from a widely distributed architecture with key components in MacLean's mammalian brain, that is, below the level of the outer cortex. In technical terms, the emotion systems that Panksepp and others describe run from evolutionarily early periaqueductal gray in the brain stem to hypothalamus to basal forebrain to cortex. Different neurotransmitters are involved: the neuropeptides seem to relate more to specific emotions than the more familiar amines like norepinephrine or dopamine.[20] What we should note for thinking about literature is that the thinking and emotional parts of our brains interact. They are linked structurally. When we are reading Browning's "My Last Duchess," we are not only cognizing the speaker; we are also responding emotionally, using parts of the brain we share with cats and dogs.

We can glean a third bit of information from Panksepp's account. The systems he describes all derive from or react onto the periaqueductal gray or PAG. This is a region in the midbrain in the upper part of the brain stem, that is, in the most ancient and fundamental reptilian core of our brains. This is a region that is much involved in attention and in defensive behaviors. Together with its role in emotion, I have come to believe that this region plays an important part in shaping what kind of person we are and therefore the way we experience literature, what we like, and how we evaluate what we encounter, in short, our taste. I think we can hypothesize that systems radiating to and from the PAG determine our taste and our style, both in creating literature and enjoying it.

10 | Why Do We Care?

> Many readers judge of the power of a book by the shock it gives their feelings—as some savage tribes determine the power of muskets by their recoil; that being considered best which fairly prostrates the purchaser.
>
> —Henry Wadsworth Longfellow, *Kavanagh: A Tale*, ch. xiii.

STORIES CERTAINLY CAN prostrate us emotionally. I remember the 1970 film *Love Story*. It was an emotional blockbuster. All over America, tears ran down cheeks as we watched Jenny Cavalleri, the working-class Radcliffe girl who has just married the rich Harvard boy, bravely die of leukemia. Why? Why did any of us care about Jenny Cavalleri, fictional college girl?

Arousing emotions

Enjoying a poem, a story, a movie, or a play is a cognitive activity. It draws on verbal skills. It uses knowledge of the world (declarative memory) and personal experince (episodic memory). These all rely on cortical systems, mostly in the frontal and temporal lobes. Emotions, however, are sub-cortical. The cortical, cognitive enjoyment of literature taps into these subscortical systems.

We can distinguish three kinds of arousals from literature and other media: direct emotional stimulation; emotional memories; and emotional situations. The three work somewhat differently.

Simplest is direct emotional stimulation as illustrated by a story Darwin told on himself:

> I put my face close to the thick glass-plate in front of a puff adder in the Zoological Gardens, with the firm determination of not starting back if the snake struck at me; but, as soon as the blow was struck, my resolution went for nothing, and I jumped a yard or two backwards with astonishing rapidity. My will and reason were powerless against the imagination of a danger which had never been experienced.[1]

Darwin jumped back, just as I did when, at the horror movie, the chain saw murderer jumped out at the cute blond starlet. I jumped, even though it was "only a movie."

Darwin explained his reaction by nineteenth-century faculty psychology: "imagination" can override "reason." In today's terms, perceptions going to and from the amygdala immediately arouse feelings of fear. The amygdala (Joseph LeDoux has shown[2]) has two kinds of output. One process creates a rapid response. It projects directly to the hypothalamus (to reset the body's autonomic responses) and then on to the brain stem and spinal cord to move the body. In the dim light of dawn, I see a snake on the closet floor, and I jump back. A fraction of a second later, I realize my heart is pounding. Another fraction of a second later I realize that what I am seeing is a belt that has fallen off a pair of trousers. The second, later process is more cognitive. The signal has gone more slowly from the amygdala to the frontal lobes, which evaluate the stimulus and the reaction. One can easily see the evolutionary advantage in having a self-preservative system that reacts very, very fast and only evaluates the threat later. It is better that I should jump back and it not be a snake than that I wait to decide if it is a snake and get bitten. Literature uses the slow response, obviously, but also the fast one. Shown a movie of a chain saw killer suddenly appearing, we will fear (as Hollywood well knows).[3]

Given that we respond to direct emotional stimulation, generations of psychological experimenters have been able to use mere representations to stimulate emotions on demand. Big shapes looming up in front of us, sudden darkness, flashing lights, or loud noises all stimulate our emotions directly. Many neuroscientists believe that other emotions besides fear use this kind of this dual system. Porn pictures arouse desire. Seeing a picture of recent dog droppings, we will manifest disgust. Direct emotional stimulation makes us feel emotions willy-nilly, like reflexes. We cannot consciously control or prevent them.

Literature draws on a second kind of emotional arousal. We bring to a literary work our own memorized emotional associations. In the movie *A Clockwork Orange* (1971), the actor Malcolm McDowell played a character Alex, whose actions terrified and revolted me. I have never forgotten. Ever since, whenever I encounter poor Mr. McDowell on-screen, no matter how kind and benevolent the character he is playing, I can feel in my gut that same fear and disgust, skewing my response. Patrick Hogan has identified this process with what neuropsychologists call "emotional memory," not something that can be put into words, but something that calls up our own emotional response to what we are perceiving.[4] Psychoanalytic critic

Simon Lesser, we have seen, called this "analogizing,"[5] bringing personal experience to bear on represented experience.

Antonio and Hanna Damasio, Antoine Bechara, and others in their group have long experimented with what they term emotional markers. Working with rigged decks of cards in the Iowa Gambling Task, they have shown that bettors become aware emotionally which decks have the better and worse payoffs without their being able to articulate a winning strategy consciously. In effect, choices become emotionally marked. Creating or responding to literature, we bring such emotional markings and memories to bear, and, like direct emotional stimulation, they operate outside of conscious intellection, Darwin's "reason."

Finally, literature uses a third kind of arousal. We respond emotionally to emotional situations in narratives or dramas. Psychiatrist Leslie Brothers, who has specialized in studying primate social cognition, writes, "When we see facial displays, we register them in evolutionarily old brain networks that include structures such as the amygdala. . . . these networks are set to trigger behavioral dispositions appropriate to the social situations in which primates have commonly found themselves throughout their history."[6] We need, she writes, to think of our brains not as though they were isolated inside each one of us but rather as interconnected with the person we are relating to. In effect, our brains are porous to that other person's feelings.

The eighteenth-century philosopher, Adam Smith, noticed himself and others doing just what Brothers describes.

> Upon some occasions sympathy may seem to arise merely from the view of a certain emotion in another person. The passions, upon some occasions, may seem to be transfused from one man to

> another, instantaneously and antecedent to any knowledge of what excited them in the person principally concerned. Grief and joy, for example, strongly expressed in the look and gestures of any one, at once affect the spectator with some degree of a like painful or agreeable emotion. A smiling face is, to every body that sees it, a cheerful object; as a sorrowful countenance, on the other hand, is a melancholy one.[7]

Leslie Brothers' and Adam Smith's accounts suggest why we engender strong feelings from literary works. We can feel real fear as we read about a hero hanging from a cliff or real grief as we watch a heroine like Jenny Cavalleri dying. Then we are feeling sympathetically or empathically "with" a character or "for" a character.

In most narrative works, however, the characters' goals conflict. In the film *His Girl Friday*, for example, Cary Grant and Ralph Bellamy are competing for Rosalind Russell. We may want to see Russell end up with Grant, but that is surely not Bellamy's goal. Our goal coincides with Grant's, not Bellamy's. Something somehow decided us.

A number of film and literature theorists have tried to explain that kind of emotional response based on appraisal theory, originally put forward by Nico Frijda. These writers derive emotions from cognitive appraisals of situations in relation to goals. Will my goal be frustrated? If so, I feel anger. Will my goal be achieved? If so, pleasure. Patrick Hogan, following film theorist Ed Tan, argues that we form goals in the narrative *for ourselves*.[8] It is not so much that we want Cary Grant to win Rosalind Russell. *We want to see* Cary Grant win Rosalind Russell. Why? Because energetic Cary Grant suits her better than limp Ralph Bellamy. Hogan goes on to develop a general theory of emotional responses to literature based on prototypical results for our goals.

While I think this theory may explain our emotions in a situation like that in *His Girl Friday*, the very limited goal of a wished-for boy-gets-girl outcome to a movie does not account for the depth of emotion one feels at the death of, say, Jenny Cavalleri. I think one should question a theory of emotions in literary response based solely on goals. What are the goals associated with, say, disgust or play? Such a theory does not capture the dual responses of fear, one fast, one an appraisal, as described by LeDoux. I find it hard to relate appraisal theory to what the brain scientists are telling us about the relation between cognition and emotion.

Leslie Brothers and Adam Smith observed that we echo or mirror in ourselves the emotions natural to humans (or, indeed, primates) in situations that we are merely watching. We feel grief, for example, at Jenny Cavalleri's love and death. In general, at mere representations of human (or primate) situations, we feel the emotions we would feel if we were actually in the situations and the situations were real. Recent research may provide an explanation.

"Mirror" neurons

Giacomo Rizzolatti, Vittorio Gallese, and others on their team based at the University of Parma may have found the key to this empathy in "mirror" neurons.[9] This group recorded individual neurons from the ventral pre-activity area in the frontal lobes of macaques. They found that specific motor neurons fire when a monkey performs one particular action with its hand. Different neurons fire in response to different actions: pulling, pushing, tugging, grasping, or picking up and putting a peanut in the mouth.

One might be tempted to think that these motor neurons simply make muscles do certain specific things. In fact, however, these neural assemblies also include "mirror" neurons. Any given mirror neuron will *also* fire when the subject monkey watches another monkey (or even the experimenter!) perform an action like grasping a peanut. This group also believes it has located the brain region in which the observed action and the copy of the action are compared (the superior temporal sulcus).[10] Another experiment suggests that mirror neurons enable subjects to infer goals. That is, subjects watched a hand's movements in the context of a full or emptied tea setting. The subjects' mirror neurons lit up as they inferred the intention, either to drink tea or to clean up.[11] Two Harvard psychologists offer evidence that when we think about the future actions of another person, we project ourelves into that person's situation.[12] Still more remarkably, *listening to action-related sentences modulates the motor system* through mirror neurons, particularly those in Broca's area, specialized for speech movements.[13] These experiments imply that, in a literary setting, while watching or reading about actions, the motor regions of the brain experience an impulse to imitate the action (mirror response) *but then the brain inhibits at lower levels that musculoskeletal expression* (an "inverted mirror response").[14] In effect, these experiments link Kant's high-level, cognitive disinterestedness to a low-level, unconscious motor inhibition of action.

Generally, when we watch someone else doing something, our mirror neurons fire as if we ourselves were doing the same thing. Because we are acting (in imagination) like the other person, we will feel the same emotions as the person in the situation we are watching. In an emotional sense, now, we are empathic. We identify. We bring our personal associations to bear. We analogize, in Lesser's term. Our brains are porous as Leslie Brother claims.

Thus, watching a movie in which a character hurtles through space, we will feel in our own bodies that sensation and the emotions that go with it. My students write of such a situation: "I can almost feel the sensation of hurling [sic] through space—my stomach may lurch." "I react as if I am hurtling through space alongside the movie character." "I would most likely cover my eyes in fear." "I find myself suspending my natural breathing patterns until that character lands safely." Indeed, a recent experiment confirms that one's brain responds to fearful body expressions, a person recoiling, say, with fearful feelings and impulses to move one's own body, perhaps to flee.[15]

Could it be that the *sight* of faces and bodies is why most people find movies and plays more arousing than written texts? The right, visuospatial hemisphere, the perceiver of emotion, is at work when we watch a scene, and the left, verbal hemisphere when we read a page. At any rate, seeing an actor act aggressively in a movie or television show activates (unconsciously, at least) the audience's own pattern of aggression, although we in the audience will not, presumably, jump up and start hitting people during the performance.[16]

In general, as Adam Smith and Darwin noted, we humans respond to the emotional expressions of others with similar emotions in ourselves, and this makes evolutionary sense. Feeling and so knowing what others are feeling confers advantages in survival and reproduction for a very social animal. We humans (and other primates) have a long childhood of dependency on others, and all our lives we depend on other people—unless we are hermits or castaways. And even castaways need others, like Robinson Crusoe's Friday or "Wilson," Tom Hanks' volleyball companion in the 2000 film *Cast Away*. Audiences report that the saddest moment in that film is when "Wilson" floats away. Emotion toward a fictional volleyball! It should be no surprise, then, that our evolutionarily earlier emotional system mirrors the emotions of others. For all our elaborate frontal reasoning, we humans need emotional intelligence in order to survive.[17]

Mirror neuron research may therefore explain, as literary theorist Suzanne Keen has suggested, what literary critics call "empathy" or "identification" in our experience of literature.[18] At a cognitive, that is, cortical level, perception of emotional situations triggers at a sub-cortical level our own mirroring emotions (including feelings, physiological reaction, and impulse to act). Yet, since it is a mirroring, not one's own action, the impulse to act is inhibited. We have the feeling but no impetus to do anything about it.

To return to *His Girl Friday,* Cary Grant drives the plot in this comedy, while Ralph Bellamy is, as I say, limp. We respond to Grant's energetic scheming by similar impulses in ourselves because we mirror his actions in ourselves. We too want to win back Rosalind Russell and get the front page story for the newspaper. When I say, then, that we *want to see* Grant win Russell back, I am saying that we neuronically mirror both his actions *and their motivations.* It is in this way that a combination of Panksepp's SEEKING and the Italian team's mirror neuron assemblies explains what literary critics have traditionally called "identification" or what the cognitive critics have called "goals for ourselves" in literary works.

Mirroring and metaphor

Mirror neurons may also bear on our emotional response to poetic language. That is what recent work by metaphor theorist George Lakoff and Vittorio Gallese (a member of the mirror neuron group) suggests.

Lakoff, Mark Johnson, Mark Turner, Gilles Fauconnier, and others have developed a particular way of thinking about metaphor. In their theory, metaphor involves mapping some concept that is difficult and only partly understood (the "target") onto some other concept that is more easily understood (the "source"). Thus, in order to say something about a complicated moment in a love affair, you might say, "We're spinning our wheels." You have mapped the complicated love affair onto something familiar, an automobile stuck in sand or snow. The mapping follows a general schema of mapping one general concept onto another general concept: LOVE IS A JOURNEY. "We're coming to a crossroads." "Our relationship is going forward." "We've had a bumpy time of it," and on and on. There are hundreds, maybe thousands, of such metaphorical schemas, each giving rise to dozens or hundreds of metaphors. Some occur in all cultures, like ANGER IS HEAT with particular mappings like: "I was boiling mad," "She got steamed up," or "He got hot under the collar." Others are specific to a few cultures, like MIND IS A COMPUTER: "I'm not programmed for this," or "Cognition involves digital computation, emotions involve analog computation."[19] Some are "conventional" or "dead" metaphors—clichés, like "I'm beat." Others are new and fresh, and they can become poetry.

Lakoff and Gallese have some evidence that the mirror neuron theory applies to metaphor. When we use a metaphor (like "grasping" an idea) that involves doing something with our bodies, they claim, the same neurons light up as if we were in fact performing that act.[20] Also, some recent evidence about language processing suggests that the brain processes fresh, poetic metaphors differently from dead metaphors like "grasping" an idea.[21] In general, poetic language involves a great deal of brain activity.

Consider some famous lines:

> April is the cruelest month, breeding
> Lilacs out of the dead land, mixing
> Memory and desire, stirring

Dull roots with spring rain.

or,

Thou still unravish'd bride of quietness,
Thou foster-child of silence and slow time . . .

Such language involves, obviously, intense intellection as one explores the connotations and implications of "unravish'd" or "memory and desire." The brain draws on right hemisphere language functions to get those extra meanings (ch. 16). But so far as emotion is concerned, consider just the individual words of these excerpts: "unravish'd," bride," "quietness," "foster-child," "silence," "slow time," or "April," "cruelest," "breeding," "Lilacs," "dead," "land," "mixing," "memory," "desire," "stirring," "Dull," "roots," "spring," "rain." If we break down the lines that way, we can see how poetry presents us with a rich language in which virtually every "open-class" word, that is, almost every word other than function words like "and" or "is," evokes some action or situation with a probable emotional or motor response. These responses may come from Adam Smith's or Leslie Brothers' contagion or from the the mirroring of actions, but the very richness and density of one's responses to the words evokes in a committed reader a deep and vigorous emotional response.

Poetry also involves, of course, the motor activity of our own mouths as we say or imagine saying the long *i*s of Keats' lines or the *l*s and *r*s of Eliot's. Over the centuries critics have debated whether or how the "sound mirrors the sense," but what we can say with some confidence is that the sound involves us in motor activity as we say or imagine ourselves saying the poet's carefully chosen vowels and consonants. That motor activity may or may not fit the situation represented in the words, but it may very well evoke some emotional response appropriate to itself like our feelings at sucking, growling, or tasting.

Emotion and cognition

Direct emotional stimulation, emotional memory, and emotional situations, including the richness of poetic language—all three play a part in our emotional response to literature. And when we are transported by a story or a drama, we feel emotions although we know consciously that "this is only a story," "only a movie," "only a play." We cannot help feeling those emotions. The sub-cortical processes by which stimulus leads to feeling and emotion go on despite our cortical knowledge that that these literary works cannot affect us physically.[22] And brain scans show activity in the appropriate brain areas.[23] But we inhibit the motor actions seemingly called for.

Frontal lobe specialist Joaquin Fuster locates that inhibitory control of motor action in the prefrontal cortex. It is in the prefrontal cortex that we do our most complex planning, and *planning entails waiting, not acting on impulse.*[24] Importantly for literature and other media, it is there that we start the cognitive inhibition of action, as when we sit in a theater or read a book. (Specifically, Fuster assigns this inhibiting to the part of your brain just above your eyebrows, the orbital prefrontal cortex, and extending back toward the brain stem at the base of your skull. He diagrams Brodmann areas 10, 11, 13, and 47.) It may be that the right hemisphere plays more of a role in this inhibition than the left.[25] The right hemisphere tends to be the one that determines the socially appropriate behavior for a given occasion.

Giacomo Iacoboni suggests that "super mirror neurons" monitor and inhibit, if necessary, the impulses to imitate coming from ordinary mirror neurons. He also locates this inhibitory control in the orbitofrontal cortex but adds the anterior cingulate cortex and the presupplementary motor area.[26]

Our emotions, however, arise in the limbic system. It lies beneath the outer cortex. It consists of a half-dozen (or, in some accounts, more) structures, clustered around the deep, ancient brain stem.[27] Our emotional systems are richly connected back and forth from the homeostatic systems that govern blood pressure, heart rate, and the like, giving rise to the physical signs of emotion and to the cognitive systems in the front brain that make us consciously aware of "feeling" an emotion. Thus, the limbic system modulates cortical thinking (through its fiber projections to the frontal lobe).[28] As a result, emotions affect our "purely" intellectual understanding of the world, and we cannot prevent that.

Zoltán Kövecses has pointed out that all our metaphors for emotion rest on one superordinate schema, EMOTION IS FORCE.[29] "Anger drove me to it." "Sadness got me down." FORCE is the easily understood source domain, EMOTION the more mysterious target. This schema expresses our experience that *emotions persistently "force" us in our bodies toward this or that feeling and action.* The mapping reflects our knowledge (and our feeling) that we cannot control our emotions with our rational mind. Reading a poem or story or understanding a movie or play—these are verbal, cognitive activities. Nevertheless, they "prostrate" us as Longfellow suggests in the epigraph, because our emotions force themselves on our cognitive selves.

The feelings and emotions come willy-nilly. That is the key point that concerns literature and the other media. You cannot block your feelings. You can control what you do about them. You can control whether you show them or not, for example. You can even repress them, rendering yourself unaware of them. But you can't stop the subcortical brain activity associated with emotions.

Emotions interrupt, as it were, our previous cognitive activity, demanding to be heard and dealt with. They can override thinking. They can override what you know perfectly well, as with Darwin and the puff adder. They can produce intellectual biases that we cannot control (or at least can only control by strenuous self-discipline as scientists and journalists try to do). To be "objective" is not easy, nor does our self-discipline always succeed. And some, like me, would say it can never fully succeed. Our own personalities, and therefore our emotions, always have a residual effect on what we believe and think and even what we can perceive.[30]

What we are finding with literary works and other media is that, because the reality-testing systems of the frontal lobe are weakened, the emotional systems that the reality-testing systems normally manage become relatively stronger. We respond emotionally more to literature and to media, perhaps even more than when we are paying attention to realities.

Emotions affect cognitive decisions, and cognitive decisions affect emotions, and that provides an evolutionary advantage. We can know what really matters to us, because we can feel its importance emotionally.[31] Our genome "sets" us to feel pleasure at some things, at least, that will ensure our survival and reproduction (food, sex, winning a fight, or being liked by other humans) and displeasure at some of what is bad for us. Then, with our cognitive abilities, we set about achieving these good things. In effect, evolution uses our systems to combine emotion and cognition to detect pleasure and unpleasure (Freud's "pleasure principle") so as to act to ensure the survival of our species.

Involved in literature, however, we separate action from emotion. Because we know that we cannot possibly change the represented situation we are perceiving, we cognitively inhibit the action the emotion would normally prompt. We do so at high, frontal levels (Fuster, super mirror neurons) and at low motor levels (inverted mirror response). From the perspective of evolutionary psychology, "Fictional worlds," write John Tooby and Leda Cosmides "engage emotion systems while disengaging action systems,"[32] and, I would add, poetic worlds do so as well. Knowing that I cannot change that poem or story or drama, I can have my feelings free from any check from reality. I can feel sad, even horrified, when Othello smothers Desdemona, but I know—cognitively—both that the situation is a fiction and that I cannot change it. Desdemona will curtsy for her curtain call even after Othello has smothered her. This result is a paradox. *It is precisely the cognition that I cannot change what is represented in the literary work, that it is not part of my real world, that leads me to feel uncritically and intensely the emotions that I would feel if it were real.*

We do this because mental feelings occur in a different system from cognition. Literary theorist Patrick Hogan puts it neatly: "[E]xistence judgments [judgments of fictionality] are cortical. They have relatively little to do with our emotional response to anything."[33] Jaak Panksepp states the neuropsychology: "[A]ffective feelings are, to a substantial degree, distinct neurobiological processes in terms of anatomical, neurochemical, and various functional criteria, including peripheral bodily interactions." Slow-firing, evolutionarily ancient analog processes constitute the core of our emotional systems, responsive to inner body states. By contrast, cognitive systems fire rapidly in response to information from our senses about the outer world.[34] We cannot deliberately turn off emotions (short of putting down the book or leaving the theater) because emotions and cognitions are generated by different brain systems.

Once again, then, our knowledge, in literary and artistic settings, that we are not able to change what is represented turns out to be crucial. There are no choices to be made. We indulge emotions for their own sake, not as guides to conduct. We enjoy—and seek!—even unpleasant emotions.

Henry goes to the movies

Before we pick up the book or go into the theater, *we know ahead of time that we will feel real emotions* toward the fictional reality. My grandson Henry gave a nice illustration of this phenomenon when my wife and I took him, then aged five, to the movies. We saw a feature-length animated cartoon, *Monsters, Inc.* (When you are a grandparent, you get to see movies you might not otherwise see.) Because it was an animated cartoon, *Monsters, Inc.* was already quite unreal. Yet we all became quite "transported."

The movie tells the story of some monsters who hide under beds and in closets to get energy for a giant corporation from the screaming of children whom the monsters frighten. But then an unfrightened little girl named Boo teams up with some good-hearted monsters to reform this cruel system. Naturally, there are some bad monsters who menace Boo and the good monsters. At those points, Henry would clamber onto my lap (thereby acting on the real world, breaking "poetic faith" or the suspension of disbelief). He would hide his eyes, saying, "I don't want to watch this."

Notice his phrasing. People sometimes say that children have trouble telling fantasy from reality or that they do not yet know the convention that art is not "real." That is false. Children Henry's age, experiments have shown, not only distinguish fantasy from reality, but they understand different fantasy worlds: they know that a fantasy about, say, Batman will not include SpongeBob.[35] Henry knew perfectly well that he was watching something—he said so—and he knew that my lap was there, hardly consistent with the world of this animated cartoon. But he also knew (at age five!) that, *if* he watched, he would of necessity get absorbed and *he would have to feel*, he could not prevent, emotions—fears—that he did not want to feel.

A well-known nineteenth-century episode with grown-ups duplicated Henry's response. As the serial publication of *The Old Curiosity Shop* progressed, Dickens' readers would in desperation write to him. "Don't let Little Nell die," they would beg, "Please don't let Little Nell die." We can spell out the oddity that was going on. "Were I to read of (fictional) Little Nell's (fictional) death, I would feel emotions that would give me pain. I do not want to feel them. I know Little Nell is a fiction and you, Mr. Dickens, control her fate. That's why I'm writing you." The knowledge that one would feel painful grief at her death co-existed quite comfortably with the knowledge that she was a fiction.

Seeking unpleasant emotions

If they did not want to grieve for Little Nell, why were they reading the book? They knew, as Henry knew, that the literary experience would bring emotions they would probably find painful. Yet they read the novel, and Henry asked to be taken to the movie. *We turn to literature in order to have our emotions stimulated, even in unpleasurable ways.* Why? The question is as old as Aristotle.

Why do we enjoy still lifes with ugly things in them?, he asked. Why do we enjoy tragedy? His answer was purely cognitive. We learn even from ugly or painful things, and we enjoy learning, that is, "gathering the meaning of things."[36] I think the answer has more to do with emotion. I think we enjoy having our emotions aroused by some desire (say, winning Rosalind Russell), because then we are SEEKING. SEEKING itself entails pleasurable emotions: Panksepp's "invigorated feeling of anticipation." Then, when we feel even unpleasurable emotions, we don't have to do anything about them. We need not in fact try to defeat Ralph Bellamy, to rescue Desdemona, to flee the Terminator, or to bury Little Nell or Jenny Cavalleri. Yet again, Kant's "disinterestedness" provides the key. The unpleasant emotions subside harmlessly, unlike unpleasant emotions in life.

Emotion: a summary

We have seen that there are four components of emotion: feeling, awareness of feeling, visceral (sympathetic, parasympathetic) "gut" response, and a communicative, musculoskeletal response. We have seen three literary triggers for an emotional response: direct emotional stimulation, emotional memories, and emotional situations, including rich, dense poetic language; all evoke emotional mirroring. We feel real emotions in response to fictional situations, because emotions are sub-cortical while our knowledge that we cannot change the literary representation is cortical.

To the extent that we humans feel emotion though a vocabulary of fixed emotions (rage, disgust, fear, joy, anger, and so on), our emotional responses to a given work of literature will be similar. Writers over the millennia have developed prototypical stories to tap into these prototypical emotions. Yet what we enjoy differs widely from person to person. What we enjoy depends on personal style (ch. 17).

We know that the literary representation is imaginary. We therefore know that no action by us can change what is represented (except for hypertext [ch. 5]). We therefore freely feel real emotions in response to fictional situations. We also know ahead of time that we will experience these emotions. We want to experience them, provided we do not have to act in response and there are no consequences. We therefore turn to literature—we engage in SEEKING—

because we enjoy SEEKING without actually having to act.

From this preliminary understanding, we can proceed into further mysteries: what we expect from literature and media, how form works, how we construct content and meaning, and why we enjoy, in different and individual ways, those special mental experiences.

But before going on to those questions (in Part III), I want to linger on one more aspect of what Coleridge called "poetic faith." I know, the instant that I think about it, that Little Nell is a figment of Charles Dickens' fertile imagination. Yet in some ways I regard her as a real person. And even sophisticated literary critics treat fictional characters like real people.

11 | Characters and People

> The ingenuity of the first novelist lay in his understanding that . . . the suppression, pure and simple, of "real" people would be a decided improvement.
>
> —Marcel Proust, *Swann's Way: Combray*.

WE HAVE ARRIVED, in the last seven chapters, at a neuropsychoanalytic picture of what Coleridge called "poetic faith." That includes feeling real emotions toward fictional situations and feeling literary characters as real at the same time that we know perfectly well they are not. It is even more puzzling that we think cognitively about those characters, some of us, as though they were real. The answer to the puzzle lies in the "where" and "what" systems in our brains. People draw on both, but literary and dramatic characters evoke only one at a time, and that produces the anomaly.

Hamlet's big toe

Does Hamlet have a big toe?" When I was teaching Shakespeare, if discussion flagged, I used to ask my students that. They would look at me oddly for a few seconds—what is he up to now?—but then they would burst into a passionate discussion of the paradoxical nature of literary characters. "Of course he has a big toe! He's human, isn't he? Humans have big toes. If he's human, he has a big toe. It's simple logic." Maybe someone would quote Shylock's famous line about human inclusiveness, "If you prick us, do we not bleed? If you tickle us, do we not laugh?"

Then other, perhaps cannier, students would chime in, "How can Hamlet have a big toe? He's not real. He's just a lot of poetry on a page." "Shylock bleed? How can a tissue of words bleed?"

Then would come the most damning comment of all. "The text never mentions his big toe." To be sure, toes are mentioned twice in *Hamlet*, but not, as it happens, Hamlet's big toe. (The big toe is, however, mentioned in *Coriolanus*.) And, of course, what is not mentioned in the text cannot be, as we critics say, "in" the play. If not "in" the play, then it is something we supply, and we are guilty of "reading in." And that, some think, is a mortal sin.

Critics' disagreement

Now, obviously, my students do not think Hamlet is a "real human being." When they claim that he is "human," they are uisng that phrase to say that they feel toward him and think about him *as if* he were human and "real." Obviously, too, his big toe is not the issue. Rather, watching *Hamlet*, it feels to us as though the prince is making his own decisions about putting on a play-within-the-play or out-maneuvering Claudius' plot to have him killed. But, of course, he isn't. It is Shakespeare who has made all these decisions. It only seems as though Hamlet does.

My students' debate, however, reflects a critical controversy about literary characters among Shakespeareans (and others) that has gone on for two centuries now.

Marisa Bortolussi and Peter Dixon sum up: ". . . work in literary theory on characters . . . has been dominated by the tension between treating characters as real people versus treating them as a collection of textual signs."[1] We could call the two sides the realists and the formalists.

If we look just at writers about Shakespeare, the realist idea that one could consider imaginary characters as real people began in the late eighteenth century with Maurice Morgann's influential essay of 1777, which purported to prove that Falstaff was not a coward. Morgann proceeded by assuming Falstaff was a real person. That is, he assumed that it was "fit to consider [literary characters] rather as Historical than Dramatic beings; and, when occasion requires, to account for their conduct from the whole of character, from general principles, from latent motives, and from policies not avowed."[2]

Morgann adopted—or created, really—the principle that literary character determines literary actions rather than literary actions defining literary character. As writers like to say, "The character took on a life of his own." "The character himself decided what he was going to do." Morgann thus inaugurated a long period of character criticism based on that principle, culminating in the elaborate analyses of character by A. C. Bradley at the beginning of the twentieth century.[3] In general, nineteenth-century readers and critics tended to look *through* narratives, whether poetry, fiction, or drama, toward a supposed historical reality they purported to represent, and they would go on to infer things about that supposed reality. Producers gave Shakespeare elaborate stagings based on this idea: a famous production of *Midsummer-Night's Dream* had real rabbits on real grass.

Psychoanalytic critics adopted this realist position with enthusiasm. Ernest Jones insisted in his early study of *Hamlet*, "No dramatic criticism of the personae in a play is possible except under the pretence that they are living people." "In so far and in the same sense as a character in a play is taken as being a living person, to that extent must he have had a life before the action in the play began, since no one starts life as an adult."[4] Hence Jones claimed that he and Freud stood on sound ground intellectually when they wrote about Hamlet's childhood and therefore his oedipus complex. They could talk about Hamlet's motives for "his" decisions. And psychoanalytic critics have carried on this tradition ever since.[5] Thus, psychological critic Bernard Paris writes in 2008:

> I think that a major source of Shakespeare's universal appeal is his genius in the portrayal of characters and relationships. This aspect of Shakespeare was much appreciated in the late eighteenth, nineteenth, and early twentieth centuries; but . . . . [f]or the past eighty years, most critics have argued that it is inappropriate to try to understand Shakespeare's characters in the same way that we do real human beings and have insisted on seeing them mainly in terms of their formal and thematic functions."[6]

As Paris says, beginning in the 1930s in Europe and somewhat later in the United States with the "New Critics," writers about Shakespeare's characters took the "formalist" position.[7] What Shakespeare creates are words. We should pay attention to his language. We should read his plays as long poems. We should not turn to some fancied reality behind the words. This view continued among the French structuralists, post-structuralists, postmodernists, and their followers: all treat language as autonomous, a reality in and of itself.[8] Hence literary characters are merely collections of textual signs. They do not make decisions or have motives or oedipus complexes or big toes.

Writers in particular have argued for the formalist position. Thus Edgar Allan Poe complained of the "radical error" of trying to account for Shakespeare's characters' actions, "not as if they were the coinage of a human brain, but as if they had been actual existences on earth."[9] E. M. Forster had fun distinguishing Homo Sapiens from Homo Fictus. Homo Fictus rarely sleeps, he pointed out, only eats food for social purposes, and is much given to dying or getting married at the end of novels. As for Homo Sapiens, in real life, Forster notes, "We cannot understand each other, except in a rough and ready way." "In the novel we can know people perfectly . . . . "[10] Proust praised (in the epigraph) that first novelist who decided to suppress "real" people, yet he could also call literary characters, "[t]hose beings to whom one had given more of one's attention and tenderness than to people in real life."[11]

In the realm of fine art, the painter Matisse answered a lady who was visiting his studio and complained, "Surely, the arm of this woman is too long." "Madame," replied Matisse, "you are mistaken. That is not a woman, that is a picture."[12]

The artists are claiming a creativity that goes beyond merely representing physical or historical reality. Art has a form that artists create. They do not simply copy some supposed reality. You don't talk blank verse, and I don't talk blank verse, but Hamlet talks blank verse. Therefore, one should not think of Hamlet or other literary characters as real human beings.

The bullying triangle

The psychologists have long had something to say to us about the realist and formalist positions and our oddly mixing up poems and paintings with real people. In 1944, Fritz Heider and Marianne Simmel performed a famous experiment.[13] To Smith College students, then all women, they showed an animated cartoon of a large black triangle, a

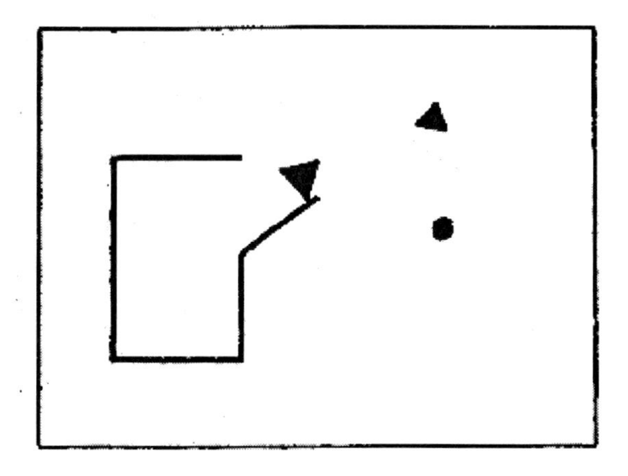

Figure 11-1. Large triangle, small triangle, disk and rectangle from Heider and Simmel 1944.

small black triangle, and a circle. The three of them moved in various ways in and out of a rectangle, including a sequence in which the big triangle hits the smaller triangle, as the experimenters said, "relentlessly." The psychologists told their subjects, "Write down what happened in the picture." Of the 34 subjects, all but one described the movements as actions of animate beings, in all but two cases human beings. When another group of 36 subjects were asked questions like, "What kind of a person is the big triangle?," the students responded with great uniformity (97%) in terms like, "quarrelsome," "dominating," "taking advantage of his size," and the like. Eight per cent even went so far as to assert that the big triangle had a lower I.Q. than the smaller one. The experimenters concluded, not unreasonably, that the subjects organized the movements "in terms of actions of animated beings, chiefly of persons." And "acts of persons have to be viewed in terms of motives in order that the succession of changes becomes a connected sequence."

A long line of experiments confirms Heider and Simmel's findings and indeed, extends them from students to very young children. Thus, infancy experimenters Premack and Premack report:

> We show an infant two bouncing balls. The one that bounces higher and faster is preferred by the infant. The preferred ball moves into the vicinity of the other and demonstrates its superior bounces several times, as though offering an example. It even assists the other directly, placing itself below, lifting it, helping it to bounce higher. The infant will interpret the actions in this and the previous example as helping, coding them both positive.[14]

I notice that these experimenters themselves cannot avoid using the language of agency and motivation ("relentlessly," "demonstrates," "offering") to describe these merely geometrical objects. Unless we write carefully like self-restrained literary critics, none of us can escape the inference that these objects have the attributes of human beings—for a very good reason.

Even in the first few months of our lives, we begin to attribute causality, probability, and realism to events. Even as infants, we draw a distinction between objects that move themselves and objects that are moved by other objects. For example, billiard balls that simply knock one another about are objects that move because they are acted upon. We adults would say they are inanimate. The infant understands these inanimate objects through a causality based in what the psychologists call "naive" or "intuitive" physics. By contrast, infants explain the movements of self-moving objects (which we would call "animate") through intentions. In the psychologists' language, infants have a "naive" or "intuitive" psychology.[15] As the Heider and Simmel experiment and many others show, even as infants, we make the inference that triangles that scurry by themselves and balls that bounce by themselves have to be understood as persons.

One answer then to our oddly humanizing mere words into characters or even real persons comes from our own "intuitive psychology." However we encounter Hamlet, "in" the pages of a book or on stage or screen, he is self-moving. We therefore interpret him as animate. We give him intentions and motives. And just as we attribute intentions to explain his actions, when we imagine his body, we give him the normal complement of human digits. We may even give him an oedipus complex.

I feel his pain

The mere fact that we read Hamlet as animate, however, does not tell us whether we or the psychoanalytic critics *should* be doing so. Can we justify our saying he has an oedipus complex? Is that intellectually sound?

Hamlet *feels* real to us, because we feel real emotions toward him. We may share his perplexity and frustration. We may feel his disgust at Claudius, at his mother, at Rosencrantz and Guildenstern, at Polonius, at Ophelia—at the world. We may admire him or we may feel annoyed that he is dilly-dallying instead of getting on with revenging his father. Feeling is believing. When we feel an emotion, we generally point to some object outside ourselves as causing it. Here that object is the Hamlet we read about or witness.

For thousands of psychological experiments, researchers have used pictures and other representations to stimulate emotions. And even though the human subjects in these experiments know quite well that they are perceiving representations, not the real thing, they feel the appropriate emotions.[16] We saw, in considering the emotional component of our "poetic faith," that we feel real emotions toward fictional characters because our cognitive knowledge that they are fictional is prefrontal and cortical and our emotional systems are limbic and sub-cortical. We feel an appropriate emotion even if we know (if we think about it) that we are looking at a representation, not the real thing.

We can agree that we feel real emotions about Hamlet, but does that entitle us to call him real? Our very real feelings of disgust scanned in an MRI machine don't make the psychologists' picture of dog droppings or garbage as real as what they were pictures of. Do our *emotions* justify our giving Hamlet a childhood oedipus complex before the play? I think it would be very odd to claim that.

Hamlet's markers

Finally, I think we can find an answer to the nature of imagined literary characters by combining linguistics and neuropsychology. The linguist Morris Halle once suggested to me a surprising resolution to the paradox of literary characters. Halle noted that linguists (in the 1960s) imagined as part of our language skill, a lexicon that we carry in our heads, in effect, a dictionary. But this is not an ordinary dictionary. Besides the usual information about meaning and pronunciation, this dictionary contains information about usage and the idiosyncrasies of words, "features."

Halle said that the entries for verbs and nouns, including proper nouns, have "markers" for the various properties that can be assigned to those words. In the case of nouns, for example, there are "count nouns," those which one can enumerate. "I have five straws." And there are "mass nouns" that you cannot count. You can't say (in English), "I have five hay."

As an example of these lexical markers, the entry for "prince" might say that it has the syntactic features: [+Noun], [+Count], [+Common], [+Animate], and [+Human]. "Prince" can go with verbs that require a common noun, a human noun, or a countable noun. But sentences become ungrammatical if "prince" is put with verbs that require a non-animate noun. Thus, you can say, "The prince died," but "The prince elapsed" is ungrammatical because "elapse" calls for a non-animate noun.[17] Notice the similarity to Kelly and Keil's discovery of limits to predicability in myths and fairy tales (ch. 7).[18]

Halle suggested that a literary character is a proper noun, and, like the prince, countable, animate, and human, but the character noun lacks a feature that ordinary people's names have, specifically, *location*. The straws and the hay and the prince can all be located, but the fictional character Hamlet cannot. He is not in the actual Elsinore in Denmark—to say he is, is to assume he has historical reality. Shakespeare's Hamlet is not "in" the text my students were holding. He is not even "in" the Branagh movie, since he is simultaneously "in" the Olivier movie or the Gibson movie or any number of stage productions and "in" the text on my shelf.

The question, "Where is Hamlet?," then, makes no more sense than asking, "Where is literature?" We cannot say where either is, except figuratively. "Literature is in the hearts and minds of humankind." So with Hamlet. "Hamlet is in the hearts and minds of humankind."

We can, then, predicate for Hamlet a big toe or a childhood with an oedipus complex. But we cannot predicate for any of these a location. He has a big toe, but you cannot, so to speak, put your finger on it. He has a childhood but you cannot witness it or read it or know it the way you can witness or read or know Hamlet himself.

Hamlet himself has an odd kind of reality, though. While Morris Halle's idea does seem to me to solve the problem in a technical way, it also seems rather more linguistic than psychological. Hamlet's having or not having a linguistic feature doesn't really speak to me as a human being having feelings about Hamlet in a book or on the stage. Something in my brain makes Hamlet real for me, big toe, childhood, oedipus complex, and all.

Hamlet on my mind

Interestingly, however, Halle's purely linguistic proposal, that the word Hamlet lacks a marker or feature for location, corresponds to what goes on in our brains. With a literary character or a character in media, a writer capitalizes on the way our brains and minds function.

Our sensory organs transduce into our brains data about a world "out there" beyond our skins (ch. 4). To process that data, our brains use two pathways (see Figure 4-1). The sensory information from our eyes and ears and body travels on two different neural systems, a "what" path and a "where" or "how" path.[19] This "how" or "where" system acts quickly to give a crude picture of our environment. It rapidly activates motor systems to improve our chances of survival and reproduction.

The "what" path is where we decide "what" the object we are seeing is. That is where we put the name Hamlet to the figure before us on a stage. It is where we "know" Hamlet's location rather than perceive it. Halle's linguistic feature separates our brains' knowledge of a character's non-location from our perception of other perceivable attributes like a character's being animate or human. Halle's linguistic marker exactly matches the brain's separation of "what" from "where."

The paper Hamlet

I want to put the stage or screen Hamlet aside for a moment and address only the Hamlet we imagine from the pages of an edition of the play, the paper Hamlet. Imagining that fictional Hamlet is not quite the same as construing our sensations into a three-dimensional book "out there" with weight that we can heft and pages that we can feel.[20] Brain science tells us about the literary character that, since there are two pathways, *we can separate in our minds our perception of the "what" of Hamlet from our perception of the "where" of Hamlet.* That must be what we are doing when, by an act of imagination, we create a fictional Hamlet from the pages of a book. We are imagining a what-Hamlet in our minds. That what-Hamlet (our knowledge of Hamlet) does not include a physical location, only a fictional one. Our "where" system can add no real location to that fictional Hamlet.

To be sure, it is true that when we imagine a spatial event, the same brain areas light up as when we perceive such an event. But with an imagined literary character, whatever tells us we are imagining, not seeing, a spatial event (that our "where" system is not active) steps in, as it were, and tells us this literary character's "where" is imaginary.[21] This is a literary character and, as such, he, she, or it is nowhere at all. In other words, where in ordinary life, the "what" of semantic knowledge and the "where" of visuospatial perception confirm each other, in reading a book, the "what" and "where" pathways dissociate. Our "what" knowledge that we are reading a book rules out a location for characters and events as part of that "what" knowledge. And our "where" system does not supply one.

If we think of the "where" pathway as a "how" pathway,[22] the brain filters or calls up sensory information from the posterior lobes according to what we need to do. The "how" system pulls up sensory information to serve motor programs. But, as we have seen again and again, our brain's cognition that we are dealing with literature or some other art rules out motor action to change what we are perceiving. We are not going to stand up, throw down our book, and cheer Hamlet on to his revenge. A "how" pathway is just as irrelevant to a fictional Hamlet as a "where" pathway.

I have been writing as though these two pathways were wholly separate. They are not, of course. In everyday life, the two brain systems combine their information in the frontal lobes.. They talk to each other so as to coordinate actions toward what is being perceived. But in the literary situation, we are not going to move. The "where" or "how" pathway has less to do; it says less to the "what" pathway. There is little use in the "what" pathway's combining its information with the missing information in the "where" or "how" pathway, since we are not acting on the stimulus.

In sum, this centuries-old debate between formalists and realists arises from the very nature of our brains. Because, when we are transported with a story or a poem, our brains separate "what" from "where," we can have the illusion that the literary characters we meet in books or other media are real people with big toes and childhoods and oedipus complexes. if we cease being transported, we know that these representations are not real people. Nevetheless critics can build on the feeling that characters are real people to produce psychological studies of entities that they also know are just tissues of words.

Non-fictional characters

Suppose I read in a newspaper about the Dalai Lama, and it simply says that he is "on tour." When I read that way about the Dalai Lama, I do not acquire a location for him from a "where" perception any more than I do when I read about Hamlet. But I do acquire semantic or "what" information about him. Part of that semantic or "what" information about the Dalai Lama includes a real location for the man in time and space, even if I do not know where it is. If I knew, I could go there. I could move toward him, and conceivably I might have to, for he is part of the real world that I must deal with. But no matter how much I know about Hamlet's Elsinore, I could not find him there. I cannot act and I know I cannot act toward what is represented in a literary work.

Non-fictional characters in books embody real information about real locations in space and time, and we can believe in a "where" for them even if our brains' "where" system has not sensed that "where" physically. When I read about Hamlet, though, my "what" information about him does not include a belief that he existed in real time and had a real location. (It is an interesting question whether the brain of a nineteenth-century reader with a more historical or realist notion of representation would have worked differently.) Fictional characters in books lack not only "where" information from our sense organs but a believable, semantic "where" as well. We could say, then, quite simply and reasonably, that the difference in our experience between fictional and non-fictional characters in books consists of a difference in semantic or "what" information about them. We know whether or not they are fictional.

The theatrical Hamlet

I have a different relation to a Hamlet on a stage or a screen, different from my relation to either a fictional or a non-fictional character that I read about. With a Hamlet onstage or onscreen, our "where" path endows the actor with location just like any other person we see in life and the real world. He is right there, eleven rows in front of me or on the screen in the television set in the den.

"If you prick us, do we not bleed? If you tickle us, do we not laugh?" Shylock's rhetorical questions pose precisely the philosophers' problem of the ontological status of whatever actor is playing him. What is the relation between the character Shylock and this actor playing Shylock?

Which are we entitled to call "Shylock"? I don't doubt that if Laurence Olivier as Shylock were to stick a needle in his arm, there would be blood. But I would know it was Laurence Olivier's blood, not Shylock's.

The staged Hamlet is thus the reverse of the Hamlet we create from a book. The book Hamlet has a "what" but not a "where." The staged Hamlet has a "where" but his "what" tells us this isn't Hamlet. This is Evans or Olivier or Branagh. The instant that we try to pay attention to the "what" of this Hamlet, we recognize that we are pretending that this actor really is Hamlet. I begin thinking about the physical reality of the theater and the actor on the stage and the blood on Olivier's arm, and my "poetic faith" or "anomalous suspense" stops. The transport fails. I know I am sitting in a theater, watching an actor pretend. I may lose even the emotional reality of this Hamlet.

Radio, iPods, tapes, and other audio media give us an intermediate case. There is a "where"—the performance is coming from whatever device produces the sound—but the "where" information is limited. We can only hear, we cannot see, the staged location of performer and performance. Contrasted to stage or screen performances, these aural media come closer to the what-but-no-where situation of a written text. They leave more room for our imaginations than a performance on stage or screen does. I think that is why I have always felt that the performances of Shakespeare that are "truest" to the play as he wrote it, are those that occur in radio or recordings. My imagination replaces the "where" information I would have gotten from stage or screen.

Breakdowns

Sometimes people lose track of the "what" we make from a staged character. For example, a play in Chicago in 2004 portrayed a cold, self-serving, bureaucratic Cardinal

Law, unrepentant for the sexual abuse committed by Boston priests and covered up by him. The play made the audience furious at the hapless actor, Jim Sherman, who played Law. One woman swore at him after the performance, and a Bostonian told Sherman, on learning that the play was going to Boston, "You're going to need bodyguards at the stage door."[23]

We can see another failure of that "what" in a peculiar episode in recent psychiatry. The American Psychoanalytic Association gave a diploma-like award to the actress Lorraine Bracco who played the psychiatrist Dr. Melfi in the *Sopranos* television series. Because the analysts see her as doing a credible job of psychotherapy, *The New York Times* reported, "To the analysts she is Dr. Melfi."[24] The analysts had not really integrated the "where" information about what they were seeing on their television screens with their "what" information. If they had, they would not have given the award to Ms. Bracco but to the writers of the show.

The analysts, though, were not as badly off as Ms. Bracco's father. Again, I quote the *Times*: "After the episode in which Dr. Melfi is raped, Ms. Bracco recalled that her father called her and pleaded with her 'to tell Tony Soprano [her mobster-patient] what had happened so that he could go and whack the rapist.' He yelled: 'Tell him! Tell him!' She had to remind him that it was just a TV show—she herself had not been raped."

A larger issue

Literary characters have posed a conundrum to literary theorists for two centuries. Why do I think and feel that this character I am reading about is a real human being when I know she is not? Does Hamlet have a big toe and an oedipus complex? Can Shylock be pricked with a needle? Our confused perception of the literary character arises from the very nature of our brains. Because our brains have separate "what" and "where" systems, we can "know" that that a character both has and does not have a location. If a Hamlet-in-a-book has a "what" that includes a location, we know it is a "where" that we imagine, not a "real where" from our brain's "where" system. A Hamlet-in-a-theater has a "where" that we perceive with our "where" system, but that "where" is inconsistent with his "what," that is, our knowledge that this is an actor playing Hamlet.

In daily life, what and where do not separate this way They work together as part of one perception. It is only when we imagine things, as in literature and the arts, that "what" and "where" contradict each other.

There is, though, a larger point to be made here. The literary character is like an optical illusion for our brains, like a Necker cube that seems to turn inside out or a vase that looks like two people facing each other. Our brains want to choose one of two alternatives, but each is equally valid. We have no rational way of deciding between our two perceptions: characters as people; characters as figments of authorly imagination. Naturally, then, we critics and thorists cannot settle the question.

Consider, then, the philosophers' "ontological" problem with the physical reality of a work of art.[25] Philosophers debate what "is" *Hamlet* or a Brahms concerto or *Tristram Shandy*. Is it a physical performance of the play or the concerto? Is it a printing of *Hamlet* or *Tristram Shandy*? Or is it some abstract entity *Hamlet* or "the" concerto or "the" novel? Is this perhaps another brain illusion? Simply another inconsistency between our "what" and our "where" systems? Are all our puzzlements (dating back to Plato) about the nature of abstractions—are all of them a reflection of our brains' different handling of "what" and "where"?

Part III

Enjoying

12 | How We Expect

On ne peut désirer ce qu'on ne connait pas.
— Voltaire, *Zaire*, 1.1.

SO FAR, WE have been looking at what we might call the interface between ourselves and a literary work, that is, the relation we have to it as a seemingly separate object. In this part, Part III, we will be considering in more detail the narrative of our experiencing that work. That story begins before we have read or heard a word. It begins with our expecting, because of memories going back to earliest childhood, to be gratified and not to have to do anything to be gratified. Memory is key to expectation.

We go to a theater. We pick up a book. We await a poet's reading. What happens first? First, we perceive the literary work as part of what we take to be a world "out there" beyond our skins and senses (ch. 4). Because it is something new in our environment, we pay attention to it.

Then, however, we bring our expectations to bear. As Voltaire says, We cannot wish for what we do not know. Solms and Turnbull put it in the terms of today's neuropsychology: we "all automatically reconstruct the reality we perceive from models we have stored in our memories." "We do not perceive the world anew every moment of the day and try afresh to . . . decipher meaningful words from the undifferentiated din of stimuli that constantly impinge on us." Rather—

We expect

We, Solms and Turnbull continue, "*project* our expectations (the products of our previous experience) onto the world all the time, and in this way we largely *construct* rather than perceive (in any simple sense) the world around us."[1] Neurologist Adam Zeman puts this important point this way:

> Perception is always shaped by our past. The world is not "given" to us as a stream of uninterpreted colour and unreconstructed line: instead, when we look around, we see a world we recognise, which we have learned to 'read.' This has an interesting implication. If the new is always informed by the old, 'what we see' cannot be specified purely in terms of raw physical stimuli. Perception is always metaphorical: everything, in fact, is 'something else.'S[2]

Zeman's comment that what we currently perceive we read in terms of our past experience states the neurological basis for the kind of understanding of the literary process that I, as a psychoanalytic critic, have. The world that we sense through layers of memory includes works of literature, and, therefore, we sense them, too, with expectations based on memories. I understand the words of a poem or story or any work of literature as not simply "the text." I build my literary experience from expectations based on a stream of memories and associations going back, ultimately, to childhood.

Expectations—specific

Before we even buy a ticket to a movie or play or pick up a poem or novel, we are wishing for something—that is why we are buying the ticket or picking up the book. We have an expectation based on previous experience. We have an expectation of the genre. We expect seeing a movie to feel different from reading a poem from watching a staged play. We expect different things from a romantic comedy, a mystery, a farce, a satire, or a lyric poem.

We also have expectations of the characters. We expect detectives to detect, spies to spy, and lovers to love. We expect movie stars to do what they usually do: Cary Grant or Sylvester Stallone should behave like Cary Grant or Sylvester Stallone. But we don't want them to be too predictable. We want some novelty—how much depends on the kind of people we are. (Are we risk-takers or not?) Similarly, we expect certain things of authors, John Milton or Virginia Woolf or Elmore Leonard; but again, we do not want them just to do the same thing over and over. Then there are the myriad expectations and predictions and memories we bring to bear as we understand puns and murders and all the multitudinous events and words of the work itself. These are far too various to be specified by any mortal critic.

Expectations depend on memory (a confusing word, since it refers both to the faculty and to a thing remembered). Some expectations depend on memories of what we have experienced before with, say, Virginia Woolf. These are "episodic" memories. Some depend on what we have learned in school about Woolf. These are "semantic" memories. And some depend on our habits of reading (my own habit, for example, of trying to fit things together into a unifying pattern). These can be "procedural" memories. Neuropsychologists distinguish these (and other kinds of memory) because they involve different systems in the brain. They give rise to different kinds of expectation when we enjoy literature. To understand what and how we expect when we are experiencing literature, we need to sort those brain systems out.

Thanks for the memories

Memory does not consist of taking a mental photograph of an event and wedging it into some cerebral file cabinet to be pulled out later. Memory, like all the other activities of our brains, is designed ultimately for moving our bodies. Memories guide actions. Our actions in turn are supposed to ensure our survival or otherwise better our chances of passing on our genes. Toward these ends, the most important thing memory does, then, is tell us when something is unexpected. Something new has come into our environment. Something has changed. It might be a danger. It might be something we hunger or lust for. We have to decide what, if anything, we are going to do about it.

As any one of a dozen neurology textbooks will tell us, there are several different kinds of memory, and they are separable. Brain damage can disrupt one and not another. When I set them out in the next paragraphs, I am following Solms and Turnbull's very readable presentation of this complicated topic.[3] They relate the various categories to a normal brain, while the neurology textbooks mostly relate them to damaged brains. But all agree on the broad outlines of memory.

Remembering something follows the famous "Hebb's Law" from 1949. In Steven Pinker's easy-to-remember phrasing, "Neurons that fire together wire together; neurons that don't synch, don't link."[4] Neurons that repeatedly activate one another thereby permanently change their cells so as to make that activation easier. Eric

Kandel received the Nobel Prize in 2000 for proving that temporarily reverberating groups of neurons, that is, neurons that are dealing in a simultaneous and coordinated way with perceptions or movements or memories, produce lasting biochemical changes in the synapses between those neurons even in so lowly a beast as a sea slug. Thus are memories made—and kept.

Many psychological and neurological experiments have shown that we have several different kinds of memory processes. We can first divide them into two broad categories. We can distinguish long-term memory and short-term memory, often called working memory. Working memory refers to the sentence you are reading, that is, whatever you are conscious of right now. Working memory usually holds experiences of a few moments previous. As we read a novel, we bring to each sentence what happened in the last few sentences, perhaps the last few pages. Reading a poem, we remember the preceding lines. Short-term memory lasts a few seconds or minutes, and it has a limited capacity.

Solms and Turnbull divide short-term memory into a passive, perceptual kind ("immediate memory"), like reading a telephone number, and an active kind ("working memory") used in cognitive tasks (like using that number to dial a telephone).[5] Both kinds are conscious. We can say what we are remembering out loud. And both are preliminary to storing something in long-term memory if we choose to do so.

Within the long-term memory processes, neuroscientists then make a second division variously phrased: declarative as opposed to non-declarative; explicit and implicit; conscious and unconscious. They are drawing a distinction between memories that we can put into words (Freud's "word-representations" leading to consciousness) and those we cannot express. These memories may therefore remain unconscious.

We can tease out two different kinds of declarative (or verbalizable) memory. One the neuroscientists call "semantic memory," that is, memory for general information about the world, the kind of thing we learned in school: "who, what, where" memory or "third person" memory. I know, for example, that Virginia Woolf was an English writer, a feminist, and that she committed suicide.

The second kind of declarative memory is "episodic." We remember things that we have experienced: "first person" memory. I remember feeling bowled over by *Mrs. Dalloway* but not by *To the Lighthouse*. Often semantic memory is coupled with episodic, as when we remember where and when we learned a piece of semantic information. I can remember, for example, learning about Virginia Woolf in an old, dusty, unraked lecture hall with a couple of hundred other students, a raised platform, and a lectern from which an aging professor dryly spoke.

The hippocampus plays a crucial role in encoding episodic (and all) memories, passing them on for long-term storage and tagging them with emotional value.[6] As we develop from embryo to fetus to baby, the brain gets squeezed into the skull forming the sulci and gyri that give the brain its wrinkled appearance. A special instance of folding pushes what began in the embryo as the ventral medial surface of the temporal lobe inside that lobe. This is the hippocampus, an evolutionarily early part of the cortex compared to the more frontal parts that are devoted to naming, assessing consequences, and, importantly, inhibiting actions.[7]

In adult humans, the hippocampus serves as a portal from short-term to long-term memory, directing information to storage systems and assigning links, between, for example, the experience of acquiring the memory, the emotion felt at the time, or the memory's several sensory aspects. The hippocampus does the same for other mammals when they learn behaviors. Hippocampal storing is what makes it possible for your cat to come tearing into the kitchen at the sound of the can opener. The hippocampus, because it gets information from a grid that records places in the environment, ties our memories of experiences to particular locations.[8]

For humans (and perhaps for your cat), *episodic memories are intrinsically emotional*, because we mark all our conscious experiences with plus and minus values ("valences") of emotion: pleasant and unpleasant. Then old episodic memories color new experiences of literature.

Also, episodic memory is necessarily conscious. I cannot think "I remember that" without being for a moment that "I." "Episodic memories," Solms and Turnbull put it, "are not simply stored but, rather, *lived*."[9]

Any given episodic memory probably combines a perception with an emotional response with a place. (Is this why we often remember passages in novels as being in a certain position on a page?)

Unspeakable memories

We can put episodic and semantic memory into words. Other long-term memories we cannot, yet some of them bear as much or more on literary experiences.

A rather straightforward process leading to unconscious or nonverbal memory is *priming*. A simple definition is "the influence on performance of previously presented (but not consciously identified) information."[10] In what must be hundreds of experiments, psychologists have shown, say, a word to a subject. Often they show it subliminally, that is, too rapidly or too faintly to be perceived consciously. They then show that the subject more readily recognizes or remembers that word or a related word on a later presentation, even though the subjects are not conscious of having seen the priming word. Other priming experiments show that people imagine that they have seen the primed word in a series of later words when they have not ("false belief" experiments). Animals can be primed as well. All these experiments lead to the same conclusion: we have unconscious memory (at least for a time) of percepts and concepts, and this unconscious memory affects later perceptions.

In literature, we meet priming as "foreshadowing." Thomas Hardy likes us to sense in his novels an ominous fate hanging over his characters. He gets us to have that feeling by presenting us early on with prophecies or brooding landscapes from which we get the idea that there are disasters to come. Chekhov is often quoted as saying, You can't put a loaded gun onstage in Act I unless someone is going to fire it in Act III.[11] The sight of the gun primed you, and. to fulfill your expectation. somebody has to fire it.

Priming also has a lot to do with rhyme and other verbal forms, as in this limerick by Edward Lear:

> There was an old man of Tobago,
> Who lived on rice, gruel and sago
> Till, much to his bliss,
> His physician said this—
> To a leg, sir, of mutton you may go.

The odd sound of the last two words is foreshadowed (primed) by the sound of the last word of the first line. The foreshadowing rests in turn on my semantic memory of what a "limerick" is. Or perhaps it rests on my episodic memory that whenever I have read "There was an old man of . . . " a limerick followed. Then, after reading the poem, I get a feeling of satisfaction or even relief when the priming (foreshadowing or expectation) is completed.

Another kind of long-term, non-declarative (implicit,

unconscious, nonverbal) memory is *procedural.* In general, it is "how" memory as opposed to "who, what, and where" information. Procedural memory includes bodily skills like knowing how to tie one's shoes, ride a bicycle or swim, but also perceptual skills, like judging distances.

One of those perceptual skills, of course, is reading, even though procedural memory is nonverbal. Knowing how to move one's eyes back and forth and up and down to read a page and knowing how to perceive the shapes of the words and letters, these are procedural memories. Knowing how to form with one's mouth the sounds of English or any other language uses procedural memory as does some of our knowledge of the rules and sequences of language. Since procedural memory stores motor patterns, it surely involves the basal ganglia interacting with the frontal cortex.[12] But since procedural memory involves both sensory and motor skills and their synthesis, it probably diffuses widely in the brain and diffuses differently depending on the skill involved.

Procedural memory develops much earlier in hominid evolution than semantic memory. Apes swing from trees using procedural memory, and even invertebrates have lots of procedural memory. Procedural memories are, obviously, preverbal. We cannot put procedural memories, like knowing how to swim, into words. Rather, we have to learn such skills through many repetitions of actions over extended periods of time. We acquire procedural memories more slowly than semantic or episodic memories. Conversely, then, procedural memories resist decay. Alzheimer's patients, for example, usually retain their motor skills even in the advanced stages of the disease. Though speechless in other respects, they can often recite things learned as procedural memory like the days of the week, nursery rhymes, or the Gettysburg address. I am sorry to say that sometimes elderly professors suffering from dementia can speak whole lectures, because they have repeated them so often they have become rote. In this context, Rodolfo Llinás describes a patient in a coma (one of these professors' students perhaps?). Most of this person's brain is functionally dead. The coma has lasted twenty years. Yet, from time to time, the patient will utter words (because parts of the thalamus, the basal ganglia, and Broca's area are still intact).[13]

We have another type of long-term memory relevant for our literary expectations: *emotional learning* or *conditioning*. Antonio Damasio and his group have demonstrated it elegantly with a series of disturbing, emotionally arousing slides and neutral slides. Patients with frontal lesions do not respond emotionally the way normals do to pictures that one would expect to evoke fear, disgust or sadness. They can even comment on the fact they are not responding normally.[14] Evidently we remember emotional experiences frontally.

Thus, another line of experiments by Damasio, Antoine Bechara, and their associates uses a card game with stacked decks, the Iowa Gambling Task. Some decks lead to small gains, others to large losses. Normal players, wired to sensors, showed bodily evidence of avoidance emotions as they contemplated drawing from the bad decks. They developed "hunches" or "gut" feelings that gradually led them to prefer the more profitable decks—without knowing why. Players with ventromedial frontal lesions did not form these emotional associations, these "somatic markers," that translated into cognitive hunches and "gut feelings" and what Freud called "signals of unpleasure."[15]

The Iowa Gambling Task and its associated experiments show that we have a long-term, nonverbal, *emotional* memory system that associates real-world actions with previous pleasant or unpleasant body sensations. These emotional memories speak to the autonomic or "visceral" nervous system, giving us a "gut" feeling. The ventromedial frontal lobes play a key role in these emotional associations and evidently some increase or decrease in excitatory or inhibiting neuromodulators does as well. Solms and Turnbull sum up: "It is in this brain region [the ventromedial frontal lobes, BA 32 and the midline aspects of 10 and 9] that the fiber pathways from the various sub-cortical systems for emotion begin to interact with the cortical (and more cognitive) systems of the frontal lobes. This offers a mechanism by which core emotional information can access the highest-order and most sophisticated parts of the mental apparatus."[16] I mention the neurology because, it should be obvious, *these long-term, nonverbal emotional memory systems govern how we feel as we create or experience literature in our characteristic ways.* For example, previous negative experiences of Lady Macbeth will probably lead us to feel her first entrance differently from, say, Cordelia's. I've noted my "gut" negative feelngs toward the actor Malcolm McDowell. (ch. 10)

I've mentioned that the hippocampus encodes episodic memories, experiences, into long-term memory. Episodic memories are declarative memories; that is, we can put them into words. The hippocampus also combines sensory experiences (retained as episodic memories) with the emotions we felt at the time to form nonverbal emotional memories associated with verbalizable information.

The hippocampus, however, does not fully function in the first two years of life. Hence it is not possible for us to recover memories from that early in our development. (This is the real reason for the "infantile amnesia" that Freud tried to explain.) This fact, note Solms and Turnbull, "implies . . . that the memories we *do* encode during the very early years will take the form of habits and beliefs (procedural and semantic knowledge) rather than explicit, episodic memories. Infantile knowledge is stored as 'bodily memory' and implicit knowledge about how the world works. We therefore have every reason to expect that early experience has a decisive impact on personality development."[17]

That is, *as nonverbal habits and beliefs, early experiences stored as "memory traces" will affect personality unconsciously and preverbally*. Early memory traces will create habitual ways of reacting, more like procedural memories than episodic or declarative memories that can be put into words. They form, perhaps "character."[18]

Memory and literary expectations

I have made an all too brief summary of a complex subject. Perhaps a simple table will help keep straight these different memory processes that we draw on when we respond to literature:

- Short-term memory (conscious)
  - Immediate memory
  - Working memory
- Long-term memory
  - Explicit (declarative, verbal, conscious)
    - Semantic
    - Episodic
  - Implicit (non-declarative, nonverbal, unconscious)
    - Primed
    - Procedural
    - Emotional (conditioned or learned)
    - Infantile (memory trace)

All these different kinds of memory enter into our perception of literature.

Memory and literary experience

Consider so simple and elegant a piece as A. E. Housman's sly poem, "Infant Innocence":

The Grizzly Bear is huge and wild;
He has devoured the infant child.
The infant child is not aware
It has been eaten by the bear.

Notice how many kinds of memory one uses in enjoying it. Short-term memory keeps all three propositions in mind at once. I have to remember, for the length of the poem, the rhyme-sounds of /wild, child/ and /aware, bear/ in order to get the rhymes and Housman's whimsy. I have also to remember the meaning of the words, "infant," "aware," and, most interestingly, "innocence"—semantic memory. (The root meaning of "innocence" is not knowing, but Housman uses it in two senses here.) We also use semantic memory for "getting" the rhymes. We may bring episodic memories to bear for whatever grizzly bears we have known but more probably for experiences with infant children. I, for example, supply missing ideas like being cute and lovable, but also noisy, irritating, and needing diapers changed. (Housman was a confirmed bachelor—a semantic memory of mine—and therefore probably not overly fond of "infant innocence.") And probably, too, we bring to bear "deeper" or "earlier" memory traces about aggression or oral satisfactions or fantasies of devouring or being devoured. Indeed, this poem nicely illustrates Freud's idea about jokes: a verbal form and pleasure licenses (defends) the teller of the joke so that Housman can share in an exhibitionistic and gleeful way his gloomy view of life, which evidently includes summarily dispensing with adorable newborns. He can get his audience to share an aggressive or contemptuous attitude toward the child that might well have been unconscious, at least so far into this text as, "The infant child is . . . "

Imagine, if you will, a hypothetical reader of *Hamlet*, a man who has the following memories:

semantic: People say my father has a harsh temper.
episodic: My father beat me with a rubber hose.
procedural: If a father-figure threatens you, give up or escape.

The first two are conscious memories that this hypothetical reader could put into words. The third may have become an habitual form of dealing with threats, a defense mechanism that is now unconscious and, because habitual, part of character.

Now imagine that such a man reads *Hamlet.* He will bring special expectations to the tragedy, based on his personal experience. He will probably have expectations toward the various father figures in the tragedy, expectations rather different from those of someone with a milder experience of being fathered. He might have more fear of Claudius than most people, he might see Polonius as more of a threat than a comic figure, or he might see the ghost as more powerful than most people do. I say "might," because we can only learn what his expectations are from him and what he says about the play. Free association is the process psychoanalysts use to discover one's less-than-conscious thoughts, and I do not know a better method.[19]

I offer this imaginary example because it is is important to remember that *we cannot determine any one person's expectations toward a text by thinking only of the text or social conventions or anything but that person.* We can guess that an American man of the twenty-first century would have certain expectations toward Shakespeare, toward tragedy, toward this particular tragedy, but what this particular man's expectations are, only he can tell us. And our best way for understanding the unconscious elements in his expectations and experience is free association.[20] For such a person, for all of us, our perception of either the terrific tragedy or Housman's sardonic little poem depends on memory, because it is through memory that we construct the world around us, including or perhaps especially, the language we meet.

We should remember, too, that the different kinds of memory come from different systems in the brain. Semantic memory, while in part widely distributed, relies heavily on the verbal systems of the left hemisphere. Episodic memory relies on, not only words, but also sensory memories. Hence this kind of memory relies on information (probably) distributed among the posterior lobes. The systems involved in priming would vary, depending on the kind of information presented: verbal or sensory. Procedural memory, involving motor skills, must draw on the motor systems of the frontal lobes, the basal ganglia, and the pathways from cortex to spinal cord, as well as a variety of sensory memories from the posterior lobes. Emotional learning and the memory traces of early, pre-verbal childhood experiences certainly involve the limbic system and probably, as we shall see, the deep, central regions of the frontal lobes as well.

Expectations—general

When we pick up a book or enter a theater or start to listen to a writer recite or read, we have certain expectations. I have mentioned those derived from our specific memories of this or that genre, writer, or actor. I think there are also two general expectations that cut across all the genres and are common, probably, to all human beings.

First, we expect not to *do* anything. We expect just to take pleasure in the experience of the words. This is Kant's *interesselosigkeit* (ch. 4). We are disinterested; we don't have any purpose; we know we cannot change the literary work. We don't expect to change the world around us while we are enjoying literature. We will be, as we say, passive. We will simply read for pleasure, or we will sit in the theater and enjoy. That is the second general thing we expect: we will enjoy; we will be gratified; we will take pleasure. More precisely, we will not feel more unpleasure than pleasure.

What gratifications we hope for are quite individual, as we recognize when we call them our "taste." We shake our heads at our friends' lamentable failure to appreciate the things that we think wonderful, and we sigh, "There's no accounting for tastes." *Chaqu'un à son goût. De gustibus non disputandum.*

These wordstems, *goût*, *gust-*, (based on the the Indo-European root *geus-*) combine the ideas of choosing and taste, thus phrasing the deepest unconscious core of "the pleasure of the text." Psychologist Victor Nell in his study of reading for pleasure describes how readers "savor" or "bolt" their books.[21] We have seen (ch. 5) the oral metaphors used by Bacon, Shakespeare, and the Book of Common Prayer for reading. Camus wrote, "*Plongée dans la beauté, l'intelligence fait son repas de néant.*" His phrasing ("Sunk in beauty, the mind dines on nothing"), like so many others, evidences the link in our minds between being transported by literature and our earliest experiences with our mouths.

We come to literature wishing to have again some satisfying prior experience of "taking in." In a crude sense, we are asking to be fed. Such experiences build on the first of their kind, our experience of passive satisfaction in the arms of a nurturing mother, not feeling separate from that gratifying person ("sunk in beauty"). When transported by literature, we re-create that merged, undifferentiated self. We absorb and become absorbed in the literary experience as once we absorbed and were absorbed in our "primary caregiver." We get gratification from literature, as we did in earliest infancy, without doing anything except letting ourselves enter the matrix of the literary work. In my heart of hearts, I am to literature as infant to *alma mater*, nurturing mother. I hunger for pleasure.

Expectation and literary experience

These, then, are general and particular expectations that we bring to literary works. They go on in our mind-brains before we ever begin the experience. But they continue as we read or listen or watch. In fact, as we shall see, they drive the whole literary experience. As the founder of modern neuropsychology, Aleksandr Luria, noted, when we actively expect in relation to a task, the tiny voltages that course through our neurons as we are involved in that task become measurably larger.[22] When we expect in relation to a literary work, we thereby heighten the experience.[23]

Expectation of a passive pleasure brought us to the theater or the book in the first place. The same expectation makes our brains more sensitive to the experience we are about to have, an experience in which our brains use such literary entities as form and content.

13 | Form and Control

> . . . for me,
> In sundry moods, 'twas pastime to be bound
> Within the Sonnet's scanty plot of ground;
> Pleased if some Souls (for such there needs must be)
> Who have felt the weight of too much liberty,
> Should find brief solace there, as I have found.
> —William Wordsworth, "Nuns fret not."

WHEN WE TURN to a literary work, form is what we come to right away. We feel the heft of a novel. We see the lines of poetry stopping partway across the page. We watch the curtain rise on a play. It is through form that we first begin to experience that poem, story, or play. Form works with such basic functions in our brains as attention and perception to establish certain responses as typical. Even more importantly, however, form can work, if successful, with our normal defense mechanisms to allay any anxiety or unpleasure that might disrupt the literary rexperience.

Form raises the basic question of control. Sometimes,

form strongly controls, as with omission. What is omitted we cannot perceive, and we cannot respond to. At other times, we are strongly in control, as when we shut the book or walk out on a movie.

Who's boss?

Even before the curtain rises, even before we turn the first page or read the first line, form has fixed our most basic relation to a literary work. Are we in control, or is the work? We can see the difference in the way we respond to a movie when we see it in a theater as opposed to the way we see it, playing a DVD through the television set at home. Writing about films with improbabilities, film critic Anthony Lane notes, "Watch [them] on DVD and you find yourself scoffing at the unlikely curves and switches in the plot, whereas the same setups, viewed in the dreamy imprisonment of a movie theatre, feel like the machinery of fate."[1]

At home, we are in control. We can stop the DVD, get up and get a glass of wine, and resume where we left off. In a theater, the movie or play is in control. The "dreamy imprisonment" continues regardless of what we do. Listening to a poet read, the poet is in control. But reading a book, we are boss. We can put the book down any time we feel like it. Victor Nell speaks of the "sovereignty" of the reader over the book. Claims of the "power" of literature or cinema or drama oversimplify and overstate the case. It is this fundamental difference in control that leads to the wholly different "feel" of television from movies, even when the television program simply shows a movie. As we have abundantly seen, if our minds know that we cannot change the work (as is usually the case when we see a play or movie in a theater), that leads to our being transported (unaware of body or environment), to freeing us from the skepticism of reality-testing, and to arousing emotional response from our limbic systems.

When we yield control to the artistic work, then it can control us through low-level systems in our brains. Consider the following excerpt from the "final shooting script" for the opening of Alfred Hitchcock's classic, *Rear Window* (1954):

> FADE IN:
>
> INT[ERIOR]. JEFFRIES' [Jimmy Stewart's] APARTMENT - (DAY) - LONG SHOT
>
> Although we do not see the foreground window frame, we see the whole background of a Greenwich Village street. We can see the rear of a number of assorted houses and small apartment buildings whose fronts face on the next crosstown street . . . [I omit a long, atmospheric description of the scene.]
>
> THE CAMERA PULLS BACK until a large sleeping profile of a man fills the screen. It is so large that we do not see any features, but merely the temple and side of the cheek down which a stream of sweat is running.
>
> THE CAMERA PANS OFF this to the right hand side of the window, and MOVES TO a thermometer which is hanging on the wall just outside the window. It registers 84.
>
> THE CAMERA MOVES ON into the open [the courtyard outside Jeffries' window], and brings nearer to us a room with a large studio window. We

> are able to see inside this room. A short, balding man is standing near the window, shaving, using a small bowl of water and a portable mirror which he has set up on a shelf. To the right of him is a battered upright piano. On top of the piano is a radio. The music selection coming from the radio stops, and the announcer is heard.
>
> ANNOUNCER
>
> The time - 7:15 A.M., WOR, New York. The temperature outside, 84 —[and a commercial begins.][2]

This script combines statements about what we viewers see with directions for the cinematographer to move the camera, because, watching the movie, we will see what the camera sees.

We will see the backs of the dwellings opposite Jeffries' window. When THE CAMERA PULLS BACK, we will see Jeffries' (Jimmy Stewart's) sweating face *and nothing else.* When THE CAMERA PANS OFF, we will see the thermometer *and nothing else.* When THE CAMERA MOVES ON, we will see the man across the courtyard shaving and the objects in his room. Then we will hear the voice of the announcer and learn (again!), the temperature, but the voice is something new, and therefore we pay attention to it.

The movement of the camera (and the later editing of the shots) constitute the "form." The "content" is what we see in the various shots. This bit of filmplay tells us, then, two things about the relation between form and content.

Form's two principles

First, the camera's movement gives us one new thing after another to look at: the windows of the dwellings opposite; Jimmy Stewart's cheek and sweat; the thermometer; the man shaving. Then the sound track brings us the announcer's voice. Because of the form, *we are continually perceiving something new.*

We have noted before that our brains are wired, as every animal's must be, to divert attention immediately to whatever is new in our environment. Do I have to cope with this and, if so, how? Continual newness carries us—our attention—along from scene to scene and page to page so long as we choose to give ourselves over to the literary experience. The sequential nature of literary and dramatic works grabs our minds even though we know, at a conscious level, that we are not going to act on this novelty and even though, at an unconscious level, action is inhibited.

The second thing to glean from this fragment of filmscript is that each shot *determines what we will be aware of at any given moment.* When the camera pulls back so that Jimmy Stewart's sleeping face "fills the screen," we no longer see the dwellings opposite. When the camera pans to the thermometer, we see only the thermometer—no more Jimmy Stewart. The director has simply eliminated what is outside our field of view, which equals the film frame (which is part of "form").

The general principle is: *form directs our awareness.* And awareness involves two things: *form directs 1) our attention and 2) our perception.* It determines what we will and will not perceive and what we will pay attention to because it is new. Form has to do with *where* we are paying attention. Content, which we usually pose as the opposite of form, has to do with *what* we are aware of. But form determines what that what will be.

Movies are where one can most easily see form as managing attention, and there have been fine, detailed studies of how film form works, for example, by David Bordwell, Kristin Thompson, Noël Carroll, and many others.[3] The movie director controls what parts of the story we are aware of by cutting from this to that, by flashback or flashforward, by camera angle (what is beyond the screen we cannot see), or by close-up (thereby excluding the larger picture, demanding, so to speak, that we pay attention to this one detail). It is not quite that the film director controls us, for we can choose to shut the film out entirely by closing our eyes or leaving the theater. But if you are "willing," you will willy-nilly follow the movie director's dictates.

To take an example as dramatically different from a Hitchcock film as possible, consider classical French tragedy, the drama of Racine and Corneille and Voltaire. The dramatists had to follow strict rules. The stage must never be empty. No deaths onstage are allowed. No low or insignificant objects (like handkerchiefs) can be be crucial to the plot. (They disapproved of *Othello*.) No social inferior can show excessive villainy. *(Othello* fails again.) The story must be single, and it must be completed in a matter of hours in one locale. (Hence much of Shakespeare fails.) Again, the playwright who follows these rules controls the degree and focus of our awareness just as totally as the movie director does (or Shakespeare!) with a far more fluid medium.

Non-dramatic writers do the same thing. George Eliot will break into her plot with a disquisition on the ethics of marriage. D. H. Lawrence will interrupt his novel for an extended description of wildflowers. But with a book, the reader has "sovereignty." You might become annoyed and put the book aside. If not, though, you will become aware of those things and cease to be aware of the plot. For example, recall the rhymes in Housman's little ditty:

> The Grizzly Bear is huge and wild;
> He has devoured the infant child.
> The infant child is not aware

It has been eaten by the bear.

You can let the rhymes take over from the complex of feelings you might otherwise bring to that breezy approach to an infant eaten instead of eating. In all these situations, I say "you can," because the control is dual: you can always opt out, but if you don't, the text controls.

An experiment from Israel may show that, at this basic level, form works similarly for everybody in the audience.[4] Once again the way basic form functions shows most clearly with movies. The experimenters used Sergio Leone's 1966 spaghetti Western, "*The Good, the Bad, and the Ugly*.[5] They set up no complicated psychological "null hypotheses." They simply showed thirty minutes of the film to five different people as each was lying in an MRI scanner and scanned their brains.

The scans showed that the brain activity of each of them correlated to a remarkable degree with the others. What the viewers shared were the regions of the brain important for basic visual and auditory processing (the things form controls) and what they paid particular attention to were moments in the film that were emotionally arousing or surprising (gunshots and explosions).

I think it is particularly interesting that viewers perked up for three categories onscreen. The posterior fusiform gyrus "lit up" for faces, and the collateral sulcus (adjacent to it on the ventral surface of the temporal lobe) lit up for indoor and outdoor scenes, including buildings. Another region in the middle postcentral sulcus (near Brodmann area 5, also a sensory processing area) showed activity in response to hands manipulating objects—a confirmation, it seems to me, of the "mirror neurons" line of research.

I hypothesize that these three categories stand out because they match motor activity. Faces raise the question, How should I act in relation to this person? Buildings and scenes define spaces I can locomote to and in. Hands and objects in hands relate to my activity in handling things. As we saw in ch. 3, *motor needs guide perceptions*. But this is simply my guess.

Perceptions are what these movie viewers shared. What they did *not* share was activity in the supramarginal gyrus, the angular gyrus, and prefrontal areas. These "consistently failed to show intersubject coherence." The first two of these are polymodal areas where our brains put perceptions together to achieve a synthesis of a whole environment. The prefrontal areas presumably directed the viewers' emotional and intellectual understanding of what they were seeing.

In later experiments, Hasson's group contrasted brain activity in response to a highly edited film (produced by Hitchcock) with response to a totally unedited film of people just milling about. The team was able to show that a director could increase activity even in frontal cortex, high-level processing, through techniques like editing or camera movement. Hasson concluded that different movies vary in the amount of control they have over viewers.[6] Shared activity amounted at its highest to 65% of cortex, but one should remember that the correlation between viewers was only partial. Also, some areas within the 35% showed individual, idiosyncratic responses.

Hence these experiments say something about form in the sense that we are using in this chapter: *form has a widely shared effect in directing brain activity but the total aesthetic experience will vary from individual to individual.*

Two kinds of form

I think of form and its control of awareness in two broad categories. One is large or structural form: the ordering of events, shifting between two plots, omitting large segments of the action, the twelve-and-two (Shakespearean) structure of a fourteen-line sonnet. The other is "technical" form, that is, form that is smaller and more involved with the particular writer's technique. Technical form focuses our attention on the virtuosity of an artist in the medium, as when a movie director astonishes us by artful camera work or a poet dazzles us with an unexpected but right choice of words.[7]

"Poetic" devices create form in this smaller sense. Rhyme, alliteration, consonance, internal rhyme, rhythm, and meter all draw our attention. Consider this little *tour de force* that appears on various internet sites:

> Seduced, shaggy Samson snored.
> She scissored short. Sorely shorn,
> Soon shackled slave, Samson sighed,
> Silently scheming,
> Sightlessly seeking
> Some savage, spectacular suicide.

By sheer technique, the non-Milton who wrote this uses sibilants to suck our focus away from Samson's sad sitution.

One general principle holds, though. The poet, the film director and *writers of every kind limit by means of form what you will be aware of—if you choose to submit to the work's control.* When we allow it to work, form in the arts changes how we perceive the "content," the things we think of as "in" the work of art.

Making it strange

A second general principle also holds. Whether we are reading a poem line by line or hearing a drama speech by speech, seeing a movie shot by shot, or reading a book page by page, we are always seeing something new. Always, therefore, that new thing draws our attention.[8]

Newness controlling attention formed a key concept for the group of literary theorists known as the Russian Formalists. In particular, Victor Shklovskii put forward the concept of "defamiliarization," or "making strange." He was rebutting theorists who claimed that good literary form economizes on its reader's effort. Rather, said Shklovskii, economy of effort leads to habituation, and that is the mark of the prosaic and the everyday, not the poetic and the literary. "If one remembers the sensations of holding a pen or of speaking in a foreign language for the first time and compares that with his feeling at performing the action for the ten thousandth time, he will agree." Writers should not make perception quick and easy but slow it down (as by "poetic" language). Writers need to prolong perception and thereby loosen up the reader's habitual, automatic relation to objects, situations, and poetic form itself. With habituation, writes Shklovskii, "Life is reckoned as nothing." "Habitualization devours works, clothes, furniture, one's wife, and the fear of war. . . . And art exists that one may recover the sensation of life; it exists to make one feel things, to make the stone *stony*."[9]

Shklovskii is telling us that aesthetic form makes the words and meanings of a literary work seem strange or, I would say, new. If they are new, defamiliarized, non-habitual—whatever words you choose—we will pay attention to them. The cliché, the stock character, the predictable turn of plot, we will tend to ignore.

Shklovskii was writing in the early twentieth century, but the idea is much older. Coleridge, for example, asserted that poetry not only "produces the strongest impressions of novelty," but it "rescues the most admitted truths from the impotence caused by the very circumstances of their universal admission."[10] Shelley claimed that poetry "purges from our inward sight the film of familiarity which obscures from us the wonder of our being."[11] A century later, "[T]he function of imagination," wrote G. K. Chesterton, "is not to make strange things settled, so much as to make settled things strange; not so much to make wonders facts as to make facts wonders."[12] All these writers are saying that literary form ("poetry") serves to make things new.

Theorist David Miall has shown in experiment after experiment how defamiliarization plays an essential role in literary response.[13] And brain science tells us that poetic form makes us pay attention to the newness of this new thing. Accordingly, we will bring to bear mental (not physical) ways to cope with it .

Coping, defense, and adaptation

"To cope" means, in our inner worlds, invoking "defense mechanisms." Writing in the psychoanalytic tradition of ego psychology, H. P. Laughlin offers a straightforward definition: "a specific defensive process, operating outside of and beyond conscious awareness. It is automatically and unconsciously employed in the endeavor to secure resolution of emotional conflict, relief from emotional tension, and to avert or allay anxiety."[14] Freud thought of defense mechanisms as mediating between the inner and outer worlds, serving the individual's basic drive to avoid "danger, anxiety, and unpleasure."[15] Nowadays we would assume that defenses in gaining pleasures and avoiding unpleasures are serving the evolutionary aims of survival and reproduction.

We use many defense mechanisms. Grete Bibring and her colleagues list forty-eight defenses.[16] Laughlin lists fifty-one.[17]

When an individual applies an inner-world defense to the outer world, the psychoanalytic ego psychologists of the mid-twentieth century spoke not of "defense," but of "adaptation." They noted that *the form of the defense (or adaptation) was likely to be the same whether applied inwardly or outwardly.* A person who denies the facts of the outer world will also refuse or repress knowledge of the inner world.

Repression, denial, reversal, reaction-formation, undoing, projection, introjection, identification with the aggressor, turning against the self, regression, splitting, isolation, symbolization, sublimation, rationalization—these are some (by no means all!) of the tactics we human beings use as our major defenses and adaptations. If directed to inner realities, we are usually unaware of them. They are unconscious and directed against unconscious impulses. Yet we use these same tactics in acting toward the outer realities of our everyday lives. In therapy, seeing how they affect one's relationship to the therapist often begins an insight into the way we use them with other realities, both outer and inner.

Literary form as defense

With literature and media, *we see these defenses in forms.*[18] Notice how all those *s*'s in the Samson doggerel displace attention from his unmanning haircut and subsequent enslavement and suicide; unpleasant ideas are turned into a joke.

Less obvious formal tricks also work like defenses. Freud compared repression to omissions in a text or distortions.[19] Jacques Lacan, to stress the linguistic nature of psychoanalysis, listed a series of rhetorical tropes: periphrasis, hyperbaton, catachresis, antonomasia, hypotyposis, and so on. He asserted that these would serve as the best labels for the defense mechanisms, since they are the "active principle" of the patient's associations.[20]

Repression, in effect, buries alive an impulse or fear or feeling or fantasy, buries "alive," because the drive does not lose its push toward expression. *Denial* is akin to repression. Repression defends against danger from within; denial defends against danger from without. We refuse to see something in reality it would be unpleasurable to see. In the same way, literature omits.

Irony in literature, either as figure of speech or plot, is

saying or doing one thing but meaning the opposite. Irony thus corresponds to a defense of *reversal* or *reaction-formation.*

Undoing means canceling out what one has done, like saying, "Knock on wood!" Often, in literature, pointing a moral at the end of a story, as in Aesop or Ovid, is a way of replacing the story by an abstraction. The similar defense of *isolation* deals with a threatening combination by separating one item from the rest. In literature, we often see it in subplots or "comic relief."

In *projection*, a literary work represents an impulse or reality as outside rather than within some person where it really is. It becomes fate or the gods or a heartless society or a hostile universe. The opposite of projection is *internalization.* Intensely psychological writers like Henry James will give us the thoughts of the characters almost to the exclusion of the external world (thought of as less motivating than the internal world). Another way we internalize is *turning against the self*: An impulse intolerable if directed toward some outward object, we redirect inward against the self. Hawthorne's "Young Goodman Brown" punishes himself for others' sins, because he cannot tolerate the idea of their guilt.

A literary work can also represent one impulse or feeling or thought or identification as several. Psychoanalysts call that defense *splitting* or *decomposing.* Shakespeare can multipy father- and son-figures in *Hamlet* or *Henry IV*. Different psychological attitudes split into different characters, their common ancestry retained as kinship or juxtaposition.

The only defense which is more important to literary form than splitting is *symbolization*, In this day and age, few of us have not heard of phallic and vaginal symbols, but they are more subtly thought of as representations of our biological destiny: male, female, parents, children, birth, death. But anything can become the symbolic expression of some unconscious impulse or feeling, just as in figures of speech, anything can serve in a simile or metaphor, the forms of language that correspond to the psychological process of symbolization. And what do literature and art deal with but "biological destiny"?

In short, we can understand that an author's arrangement of parts (as in sub-plots or flashbacks) or representations of character resemble defenses in the mind. That is, writers use large, structural forms to manage material for the writer's and reader's aesthetic and psychological satisfaction. Characters' patterns of behavior and speech also act out defenses that handle material. So long as we are engaged, as readers or audience, with a literary work, those same forms become our way to handle that reality. They permit us to perceive some things and not others. They direct our attention and perception on the basis of what is new or "defamiliarized." We can, of course, opt out, but so long as we commit ourselves to a story, poem, film, or drama, *form functions in our experience of literature and media as defenses do in life.*

Four things about defenses

Literary forms, like our own defenses, direct our awareness here or there toward this, that, or the other "content." Psychoanalysts list three other properties essential to a defense properly so called and that apply, to some extent, to literary forms. One, a defense is *unconscious.* We do not, ordinarily, pay attention to forms as such. Unless we are scholars, we do not single out an author's digressions or a film director's cutting. Two, a defense comes into play *automatically*, and forms are surely beyond our control so long as we are transported. Three, a defense occurs after a *signal* of internal or external danger or, more generally, what Freud called "*ein Unlustsignal*,"[21] a signal of unpleasure.

This kind of signal is the "somatic marker" found in

the Iowa Gambling Task (chs. 10, 12), the normal players' bodily evidence of avoidance emotions when they think of drawing from the bad decks. Literary evocations of guilt, shame, depressive feelings, overwhelming emotion, change, pain, one's wish to eliminate "the infant child," and so on presumably evoke similar somatic markers or signals of unpleasure that mobilize our own inner defenses.

I hypothesize a fourth property: defenses are motor actions "mentified." That is, repression and denial are, I suggest, mental forms of flight. Splitting suggests physically dividing or multiplying an object. Undoing and isolation seem like mental equivalents of physically separating objects. Reversal and reaction formation look like turning the impulse around, perhaps like a move in jujitsu or kung fu. Turning against the self, projection, and introjection seem mentifications of various other movings of objects. We can imagine defenses inside our minds as the mental equivalents of motor actions on the world outside our minds.

Defenses are unconsciously, automatically triggered at a signal of unpleasure. They are perhaps mentified physical movements. Literary forms resemble defense mechanisms. Then what systems in our brains do defenses or literary forms involve?

Defenses as memory

When we say a defense is *unconscious*, that means, in psychoanalytic terms, that it does not have a word-representation. Lacking conscious control, a defense is *automatic*. That is, we invoke it without thinking about it, like a reflex. A defense resembles a motor habit. Perhaps, then, defenses involve "procedural memory." This is memory for skills (ch. 12), like knowing how to play tennis, knowledge that exists not as words but as programs in our brains for movement. We learned such programs (and, I suggest, our habitual defenses) by practicing them over and over until they established permanent pathways.[22]

Observations of young children show that our defensive patterns have taken shape by the age of 12 to 18 months.[23] When we are newly born, normal parents mirror our emotional states to us by their reactions to us. They and we together establish emotional interactions and with them, representational systems in us that begin to perform defensive operations.[24] These develop and ramify as we mature. Grigsby and Stevens point out that procedural memory can involve not only motor behavior, but perception of patterns, cognitive judgments, and reactions to interpersonal situations. In other words, you or I as adults may *perceive* situations a certain way and react to them according to *procedural memories* laid down in childhood,[25] which have become a repertoire of habitual defense mechanisms. These inured ways of dealing with inner and outer reality become our character, as various as we humans are. Freud said of each individual's repertoire of defenses, "These become fixated in his ego. They become regular modes of reaction of his character, which are repeated throughout his life whenever a situation occurs that is similar to the original one."[26]

I have hypothesized that defenses may be actions "mentified." If so, then bringing our own defenses into play with a literary work may provide substitute actions for the actions inhibited by our disinterest, our knowledge that we will do nothing to change the literary work.

Whatever the psychological, psychoanalytic, neurological, or Hollandian explanation, our brains are always trying to manage our awareness so as to minimize unpleasure and maximize pleasure. Each of us has preferred patterns of defense and adaptation for doing so, and these make up important aspects of our character. We do not shut these off when we come to literary works even though the form of the literary work may manage our attention.

Literary forms imitate for all readers or audiences human defense mechanisms like denial or reversal, but our individual human defenses play a different role. Freud noted long before there was any neurology to support his clinical observation: "The adult's ego, with its increased strength, continues to defend itself against dangers which no longer exist in reality; indeed it finds itself compelled to seek out those situations in reality which can serve as an approximate substitute for the original danger, so as to be able to justify, in relation to them, its maintaining its habitual modes of reaction."[27] Neuropsychology confirms Freud's observation. *The adult seeks out situations in which childhood defenses will work*, because, in neuropsychological terms, the cell assemblies (and probably the neurotransmitter pathways) conditioned in childhood are still there.

Freud has stated a paradox. *We perceive the world as one we can cope with in order to cope with the world we perceive.* So far as the worlds of literature are concerned, this paradox means that *we perceive a work of literature as one that requires our defenses so that we can bring our defenses into play.* Our defenses themselves, like literary forms, direct our perceptions of a literary work.

Two paths to enjoying literature

When we read, then, two systems are at work. The form of the literary work provides the first. It establishes what we are likely to pay attention to and what we will perceive when we do pay attention. The second comes from within us, our own defenses. *We perceive the work in such a way as to use our own defenses to guarantee our pleasure.*

This second system comes into play, so to speak, alongside the first. That is, the direction from the first we cannot override. What the author does not show us, we cannot perceive. But what the author does show us, we can and do re-understand in terms of our own defenses. *Both systems have to work for us to take pleasure from the work.* Reading a book, we need to be able to blend the text's control with our own for the work to succeed.

With written literature, two defensive systems need to work together, one derived from the text and the other coming from within ourselves. Being in a theater adds a third.

At the theater

Our primate brains are specialized for social behavior. We are herd animals, and we are built for intersubjectivity. We and other primates have "mirror neurons" that react the same way when we watch someone perform an action as when we perform it ourselves[28] (chs. 6, 10). Our minds are porous,[29] with shared knowledge and shared feelings. Our brains include social systems that mean we will probably respond to an action on stage or screen as our fellow-humans do. The individuals assembled in a theater merge into a special, new collectivity that we call the audience (as though there were only one!). But we can be more specific.

The presence of an active (laughing, sighing, fidgeting, weeping) audience presses the disparate individuals that make up that audience toward a consensus. Producers and directors have known this for centuries and paid for claques and catcallers and canned laughter accordingly. Today, we can see why claques and even the television laugh track are effective.

The form of the text and my own defenses combine to shape my individual experience of a text. In a theater, I combine my individual experience of the physical play or film in front of me with my experience of my neighbors' reactions in the theater. The people around me are laughing. They are moved. They are crying. They are restless.

They are muttering and walking out. They think this is awful. To each of us in the audience, the audience as a whole is an impromptu critic. Each of us in the audience may perceive the others' reactions as confirming our own or not at the very moment we perceive the dramatic work itself.

Mel Brooks' 1968 film *The Producers* uses this principle masterfully. Two theatrical producers hope for a total loss for tax purposes. To get that loss, they have put on a musical comedy that is bound to fail because it glorifies Nazis and the Third Reich. At first the opening-night audience sits there in shocked, stunned, and stony silence, appalled. A few people indignantly walk out. Then someone laughs, then someone else, and finally the whole theater explodes in laughter, which continues for the rest of the performance. The audience has provided itself with a defense—treat this monstrosity as a joke. To their horror, the producers, who counted on a loss, have a hit on their hands.

Suppose you, as an individual member of that audience had disagreed with the people around you. Suppose, for example, you had laughed when they were horrified or you had tried to shush them because you were moved but they were laughing (as the pained Nazi playwright does in *The Producers*). Then something is added to what your usual defenses must cope with. You have ceased to be in an audience; you are now the subject of an audience. You now risk the disagreement of your fellow primates. You are acting in relation to the work, ending "transport." Conversely, if you feel as the rest of the audience does, you have that much less to cope with. You have at least the tacit approval of your fellow audience members. This way, the audience around you presses on your synthesis at precisely the most delicate phase of your reaction, delicate because your defenses must find agreement with the defensive form built into the work.

Outer form, inner defense, and liking

To sum up, form works by a complex mixture of outer form, that is, the form we perceive in a literary work, and our own inner defenses. The setting (television at home, theater, book in hand) determines the balance of control in that mixture. The "sovereignty" of the reader of a book contrasts with the passive relation of someone in a theater seeing a play or movie or hearing a poem read.

To the extent that the literary work controls, it manages, first, perception, controlling what we see and the order in which we see it. Second, through novelty, it controls what we pay attention to and therefore what we are aware of.[30] These are large, structural controls. Third, technique, "poetic" language, dazzling cinematography, or artful staging, can draw our attention away from the "content" of the work toward its "surface" properties.

Psychologically, however, works of literature, because they continually present us with new things that are a bit strange, serve to evoke unconscious signals, warnings of unpleasure, that bring our own inner defenses into action. The characteristic defenses in our minds are unconscious, automatic, and they come into play from "gut feelings" or signals of possible unpleasure. They alter our conscious awareness to avoid that unpleasure. Thus, literary form "in" a text outside us functions alongside our own psychological defenses inside us. Form, too manipulates conscious awareness to avoid unpleasure. And, in a theater, the reactions of our fellow audience members can add to or subtract from our own tactics for achieving pleasure.

There is no guarantee, however, that the defenses mimicked by the literary work will mesh successfully with my personal system of defenses to ward off unpleasure. For example, if my preferred defense is denial (mental flight), I might go along with an author's simply dropping some plot element. But if my defense is watchfulness, being alert, I am likely to feel unpleasure. Whatever happened to that character who appeared in the first chapter?

If inner defense and outer form do not match, which is master? Inner. I and other reader-response critics have shown again and again that individual readers will shape and edit what they see, hear, or read to suit their own inner psychological needs, "misreading" as need be.[31] If readers cannot succeed, they cannot enjoy the work, and they reject it.

Then, *for you or me to enjoy a literary work, the outer form that directs our awareness of the work must enact for us defenses that combine effectively with the defenses characteristic for each of us individually as we seek to avoid unpleasure and gain pleasure in everyday life*. Our need poses a delicate and subtle precondition for a satisfying literary experience. It is, notice, a precondition whose satisfaction no writer, and not even the most astute literary judge, could predict from studying the literary work itself. Nor is it the only ticklish precondition for enjoyment. Form's traditional opposite, content, also engages our very individual ways of responding to literature but in a quite different way.

14 | Endings

> "They don't pay you for the sex, you know," a worldly wise madam tells Heidi when the fledgling call girl wonders why actors and rock stars would hire prostitutes when so many gorgeous women are available free. "They pay you to leave."
>
> —Alessandra Stanley, Television Review[1]

NARRATIVES AND PHILANDERING movie stars alike need a proper ending. Without an ending that completes a story, we will not enjoy it. In poetry, too, we find satisfaction in the couplet that rounds out a Shakespearean sonnet or such a resounding finale as Keats'

> "Beauty is truth, truth beauty,"—that is all
> Ye know on earth, and all ye need to know.

We want, as we say, "no loose ends," the way the media celebs want no entanglements with their sex. Proper endings gratify basic human drives. We want to find consummations through the brain system described by Jaak Panksepp as SEEKING.

Closures

In 1927, E. M. Forster in his classic *Aspects of the Novel* distinguished a plot from a story. "'The king died and then the queeen died,' is a story. 'The king died, and then the queen died of grief' is a plot." "If [the death of the queen] is in a story we say 'and then?' If it is in a plot we ask 'why?'" A story is a narrative of events in their time-sequence. It appeals merely to curiosity: what comes next? A plot involves mystery, and it requires of its reader intelligence and memory.[2] It requires of the writer a sensible answer to the reader's "why?"

For me to have a satisfying literary experience, I have to be able to bring the plot to closure, and that means completing my expectations. I would be disappointed if the little Housman poem (from ch. 12) went:

> The Grizzly Bear is huge and wild;
> He has devoured the infant child.
> The infant child is not aware
> It has been eaten like a hare.

I would be similarly disappointed if the Edward Lear limerick (of ch. 12) went this way:

> There was an old man of Tobago,
> Who lived on rice, gruel and sago
> Till, much to his bliss,
> His physician said this -
> To a leg, sir, of mutton you say go.

It comes to an ending, but not one that seems to me to solve the problem of a rhyme to "Tobago" that makes sense. There is a loose end.

Frank Kermode's celebrated *The Sense of an Ending* (1967), gave this issue an elegantly concise statement: "The clock's 'tick-tock' I take to be a model of what we call a plot, an organisation which humanises time by giving it a form; and the interval between 'tock' and 'tick' represents purely successive, disorganised time of the sort we need to humanise." Kermode claims that we feel compelled to impose form or sense (basic human "paradigms") on an essentially disorganized world and, in particular, on time. "Right down at the root, [these paradigms] must correspond to a basic human need, they must make sense, give comfort . . . "[3] We humans demand closures.

We use a cluster of memories to enjoy these little poems (ch. 11). We can add one more. We remember our own expectations. I expected, and you did too, that Housman would bring his poem to a logical conclusion, no loose ends; that Lear would somehow find a rhyme for "Tobago." We need those expectations gratified. We need what Kermode called "comfort." In Forster's terms, we need an answer to our "why?" We need to have the loose ends tied up, with no dangling entanglements and no annoying whys left over (like the movie stars in the epigraph). We need closure. If we don't get closure—well, you may remember the hullabaloo when the wildly popular television series, *The Sopranos*, ended without a real conclusion.

Theorists

One key question for theorists of narrative in literature and film has been, how do plots arouse emotions and endings resolve them? As a result, they have linked endings (and other plot events) primarily to emotion (chs. 8, 10). Also, they have generally favored the so-called "cognitive" theories of emotion. For example, theorist and novelist Keith Oatley asserts that emotions depend on evaluations of perceptions in relation to the individual's goals or subgoals (which combine as a plan leading to a goal). Emotions in turn lead to impulses to action and prioritizing or hierarchizing competing actions, plans, goals, and subgoals.[4]

Oatley goes on to claim that, in narratives, we identify

with characters' goals and thereby feel the emotions they feel. I can see that in an adventure plot I will share, for example, James Bond's emotions as he tries to escape Dr. No and to perform the various feats that he must perform (as subgoals) to achieve that goal. But in, say, Browning's "My Last Duchess," do I share the aristocrat's murderous disgust at his wife's easy courtesy and smiling?

Film theorist Ed Tan sophisticates this approach by suggesting that readers or audience members formulate goals for themselves in relation to the work.[5] They establish a "preferred final outcome." In a boy-gets-girl story, boy may want girl, but what *I* want is *to see* boy get girl. In another kind of narrative, "My Last Duchess," say, my goals may conflict with the character's. I would like to see the super-supercilious Duke get his come-uppance. In Tan's account, "interest" aroused by the "tension" of plot events becomes the general and dominant emotion, with other emotions like fear or anger aroused by the relation of particular events in a plot to the preferred final outcome. Patrick Hogan added the idea of goals related to personal associations.[6]

The problem I see with these "cognitive" accounts of emotion is that they are indeed *cognitive* accounts. Yet one of the best explanations we have of an emotion, Joseph LeDoux's description of fear circuitry, finds that the emotion arises from a rapid *sub-cortical* path with only a slower path to the frontal lobes where appraisals and judgments would have to take place.[7] Similarly, as we saw in considering the Hasson and Malach experiments with films, directorial techniques of form caused shared activation even of prefrontal cortex. But the prefrontal activity that was not shared evidenced a complex intellectual and emotional experience that was different for different viewers.[8] That does not accord with a common goal *cognitively* derived from appraisals of the plot.

In general, the literary theorists' accounts tend to focus on texts. Texts are, after all, what literary scholars like to talk about. These theories, I think, do not fully allow for the activity and control of the reader (Victor Nell's "sovereignty") nor for the great variation among readers. The theories tend to predict a text-driven, automatic, and uniform response. Ed Tan, for example, calls film an "emotion machine."[9]

I would also ask whether these accounts are really "cutting nature at the joints." Do the processes we literary theorists reason out in our book-lined studies actually correspond to systems in our brains that are discovered by experimenters in their laboratories?

In the brain

I think the neuropsychological concept most relevant to endings is Jaak Panksepp's SEEKING. We are always reaching for things in the world. We feel, in Panksepp's words, "engagement and excitement as we seek the material resources needed for bodily survival, and also when we pursue the cognitive interests that bring positive existential meanings into our lives."[10] That is why reading feels good. It gives us engagement and excitement. We enjoy SEEKING. When we sit down to enjoy a work of literature, then, we are performing a process that goes on in us physically and *mentally* all the time. We are SEEKING consummation, and in a poem or story that means seeking a proper ending, one that gives closure. And SEEKING itself gives pleasure.

In technical, neurological terms, Panksepp identifies the crucial circuits for this function in "the extended lateral hypothalamic . . . corridor." This is a system that responds unconditionally to signals of bodily needs like thirst or hunger. The system runs from the ventral tegmental area in the midbrain (the upper brain stem) to the nucleus accumbens at the limbic-motor interface. The nucleus accumbens responds to dopamine, and dopamine is a neurochemical essential to this circuit (ch. 9), although many other brain chemistries may also be involved in the overall SEEKING system.

SEEKING is not the "pleasure center" or "reward system" of a now-doubted neurological hypothesis. Rather, the SEEKING system controls "appetitive activation—the search, foraging, and investigatory activities" that animals must carry out in order to get actual enjoyment. SEEKING is not "liking," but "wanting."[11] The feeling that goes with SEEKING is "the energization organisms apparently feel when they are anticipating rewards."[12]

We have this feeling more or less constantly. In Panksepp's technical language, it is "tonically" or continually as opposed to "phasically" or transiently active. Panksepp relates the neuropsychological concept of SEEKING to the psychoanalytic concept of libido. As a constancy in the well-functioning individual, this feeling also resembles, I think, what psychoanalyst Erik Erikson described as "basic trust." Erik Erikson described this "basic faith in existence" as "the recognition that there is an inner population of remembered and anticipated sensations and images [wishes—nnh] which are firmly correlated with the outer population of familiar and predictable things and people."[13] That seems to me an accurate description of SEEKING. From a psychoanalytic point of view, a person acquires basic trust in early infancy, from experiences in the oral stage of wanting to be and being fed. Writing in 1950, Erikson saw this feeling and the actions that express it as coming about in the course of development. Writing after "the Decade of the Brain," Panksepp found them innate, and he provides evidence unavailable in 1950 to prove his view. Either way, though, both the psychoanalyst and the neuropsychologist are telling us that we have, starting very early in life, this pleasurable urge to seek satisfactions and the confidence that we will find them. And that, I think, is why we pick up novels and go to theaters.

If I have acquired basic trust (and if I am not severely disturbed, I must have), I approach a story, a poem, a film, or a play with a confidence that outer reality will coincide with inner need and desire. This is another expectation we bring to literary works. (That confidence is, of course, not always justified.)

Note that this account of our desire for proper endings resembles in broad outline the literary theorists' focus on goals. It distinguishes, however, wanting (the theorists' "interest" or "tension") from liking, that is, the emotions associated with the satisfying outcome. This "wanting," moreover, is anchored in a particular brain system, while "liking" comes from the different consummatory systems. SEEKING itself gives pleausre, but, as we shall see in later chapters, my SEEKING is not your SEEKING. We differ in characteristic ways in what and how we want. We have styles of being.

"This harmoniously operating neuroemotional system," writes Panksepp of SEEKING, "*drives* and *energizes* many mental complexities that humans experience as persistent feelings of interest, curiosity, sensation seeking, and, in the presence of a sufficiently complex cortex, the search for higher meaning."[14] It underlies, according to Panksepp, our infantile drives to understand the world through a naive psychology and a naive physics, and hence, not only SEEKING a satisfying ending but our filling in the "content" of literary works.

15 | The Content Fallacy

> What do I care what Cervantes did or did not mean to put into that book, or what he actually did put into it? The living part of it for me is whatever I discover in it—whether Cervantes put it there or not—and it is whatever I myself put into or under or over it, and whatever we all of us put into it.
>
> —Miguel de Unamuno, *The Tragic Sense of Life in Men and Nations*

POOR UNAMUNO! HE is troubled about what is "in" a text. He is thinking about what it "contains" or its "content." But, "content" locks him—or us—into a bad metaphor, as Unamuno's difficulty with "into or under or over" suggests.

Since ancient times, people have been assuming that words carry or contain meanings. It follows, then, that a word has a meaningful inside and an outside of sound or writing. As one of Shakespeare's competitors, Thomas Nashe, quaintly put it, literature can be good for our morals because it is "sower pils of reprehension wrapt up in sweete words."[1]

Given this metaphor, a literary work also has a physical outside and a psychological inside. A reader, given that outer physical text, takes from it the psychological inside, the "content." A poem becomes a pipeline. The poet puts something psychical in at one end, and the poem's readers take it out at the other. There is a pre-packaged meaning (or deconstruction of meaning) that the text simply delivers like the Post Office.

But this is just not the case. A book written in Mandarin Chinese says nothing to me. Neither does an Iranian film in Farsi unless it also gives me subtitles in English. Clearly I must at least process the language to get at "content." Psychologists and linguists have spent a lot of effort trying to figure out how we process ordinary discourse.[2] How did you know that the pronoun "we" in that last sentence refers not just to you plus me but to humans in general? When my wife says to me, "Can you take out the trash?," I wish I could just answer, "Yes." How do I know that my wife wants more than just a statement of my abilities? When someone says to me, "A priest, a minister, and a rabbi walked into a bar," I understand that I am not going to learn anything about the tippling habits of the clergy.

The linguist Michael Reddy identified and named the thinking that Unamuno was trying to resist. He called it the "conduit" metaphor for language and, therefore, literature.[3] Ideas (or meanings) are objects. Linguistic expressions are containers. Communication is sending. "The speaker puts ideas (objects) into words (containers) and sends them (along a conduit) to a hearer who takes the idea-objects out of the word-containers"—that is how cognitive linguist George Lakoff and philosopher Mark Johnson sum up the cluster of metaphors that leads to the idea of "content."[4]

Words, so understood, surround meanings as the covers of books clasp pages.

Response: three models

Trying to understand "content" poses two basic questions. First, how do we get some kind of representation of a literary text into our minds? The second question addresses the puzzling variability of "content." Why is it that the representation in the mind will be in some ways the same for all readers and in other ways different for different readers? For example, just about all readers would agree that Hamlet is a Danish prince, but readers and scholars disagree about why he delays or even if he delays.

Simply as a matter of logic, I think there are only three models that people can put forward to answer these questions. I call them text-active, reader-active, and bi-active, two extremes and a compromise position in the middle. In a text-active model, like the conduit metaphor, the text simply delivers its content to a reader, as in Figure 15-1.

Figure 15-1. A text-active model of reading.

The book just pushes its information into readers' minds. This is a bit extreme for most people thinking about literature, since it does not allow for the variation among readers. The text may be the same, but individuals do, after all, differ in their responses to it. This model doesn't deal with the second of our two questions.

Also, it does not fit with what we know of our brains or human psychology. There is no psychological process that simply imprints an external object on consciousness. As any elementary neuroscience textbook will explain, between stimulus and percept the brain is doing a whole lot of active processing. In so simple a thing as perceiving the outside of a book (let alone the inside!), the calculations begin in the retina, the image is split into quadrants, and allotted to the two hemispheres of the brain. The brain processes color, shape, edge, three-dimensionality, motion and so on in separate modules in the occipital cortex, finally bringing all this together to what we perceive as a "book." This is not a god's eye view of what the book "really" is. It is what our fallible, mortal, human senses tell us. A Martian with different sensory organs would no doubt perceive something different.

The other extreme is a reader-active model, that we could picture as in Figure 15-2. In this model, as in the text-

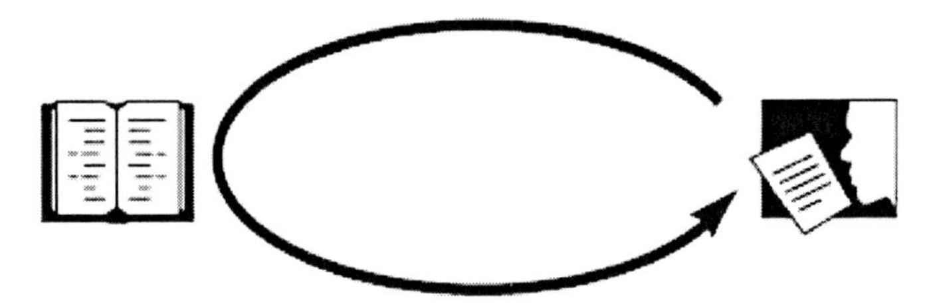

Figure 15-2. A reader-active model of reading.

active model, the arrows suggest information being transferred. Here, the reader supplies everything from the most rudimentary process of putting letters together together to form words to sophisticated interpretations of character. That is, the reader initiates the transaction at the beginning, exploring the text by means of hypotheses about letters, words, paragraphs, and so on. The reader then gets feedback from those hypotheses about the text, good feedback or bad, and modifies his or her reading strategies accordingly.

Many people thinking about literature find this too

extreme. Some say that this implies that the book doesn't exist, that there's nothing "out there." They invoke Bishop Berkeley and his peculiar ideas about trees appearing and disappearing depending on whether we are watching them or not. Clearly, however, this model does take into account the brain's work. And it does account for the variation in readers' responses. But does it account for the samenesses?

Most people who think about literature prefer the compromise position, the bi-active model shown in Figure 15-3. In this model, the upper arc images how the text "causes" or "limits" or "controls" part of the response; the lower arc images how readers are free to supply the rest. The information that the text imposes, everyone perceives the same way. Hamlet is a Danish prince. We all agree on

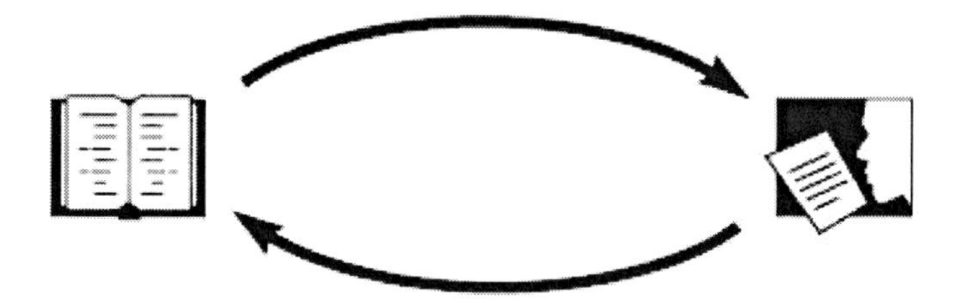

Figure 15-3. A bi-active model of reading.

that. But then readers supply things that differ from reader to reader. Some will say, like Goethe, that he just has too sensitive a nature for brutal revenge. Others will say, like Freud, that Hamlet delays because of an oedipus complex. And some will say that he doesn't delay at all, that if you look carefully at the time scheme of the play, there's really no delay.

This bi-active model seems the most satisfactory, because it takes into account both the similarities and the differences in readers' responses. The similarities come from the text, and the differences come from the different readers. And this is the way many literary critics and theorists talk about literary works. They say things like, Such-and-such a poem *invites us* to do so-and-so. "Invites us"—the text does something, and the reader does the rest. The play *limits* or *controls* the images we can form of Hamlet. As the German *Rezeptionsäthetik* critics used to say, The text sets certain boundaries, and then we are free to fill in the details within the boundaries as we like.

But this bi-active model introduces two big problems. First, it specifies two psychological processes. That is the way it acknowledges that people will respond in some ways the same and in some ways differently. But it doesn't tell us where or why the one psychological process leaves off and the other begins. That is, at some point, apparently the text stops controlling and leaves us on our own. But where is that transition point? And why is it where it is?

There is a second problem. The idea that texts control or limit response includes the text-active model in its upper arc. The upper half of the model simply *is* the text-active model, and that, we have seen, does not correspond to any known psychological process. External objects do not imprint themselves on our brains. The bi-active model is half wrong, and therefore it fails. We are thrown back to what seems an extreme position: the reader constructs everything.

Now, clearly, the reader-active model answers our first question. We know a lot about how our eyes and ears process information to create in our brains a representation of the outer world, which includes the books that we read. We know something about the way the brain processes the language we read or hear.

But how about that second question? How does the reader-active model explain the samenesses and differences in readers' responses? Pretty clearly, the reader-active model can account for the differences, but how can it account for the samenesses? How does it explain that every normal English-speaking person will agree that Hamlet is a Danish prince?

We can start with a simple question. Why do we all agree that this page is white, and and the little squiggly marks on the page are black? We agree not because the page is white—we would think it white even if the luminance (perceived brightness) were such that it was merely gray. We think it white because we are all using the same or a very similar sensory apparatus of rods and cones in the retinas of our eyes. And we are using the same visual areas at the back of the brain to compensate for luminance to establish black and white.

Why do we all agree that A is the letter a? Because we all learned the same alphabet in school. Again we are using (that useful word—*using*) the same codes we learned for letters and for words.

When Hamlet talks about his "inky cloak" and his "customary suits of solemn black," we agree that he is talking about the same color as the marks on the page. Why? Because we are using the same codes for the meanings of the words.

In short, the agreement in our readings comes about because we are looking at the same thing *using the same ways of looking at it*. But when we say that Hamlet has an oedipus complex, some people will strenuously object. We agree about words like "inky" and "black" and disagree about oedipus complexes. Some people believe in the rules and definitions of an oedipus complex, but only some. A lot of other people do not, and the two groups will, naturally enough, disagree. And we could say the same of almost any interpetation of *Hamlet*. The *Variorum Hamlet* collects hundreds and hundreds of different interpretations, many of them claiming to be *the* interpretation.

We can think of readers (and people in general) as perceiving the world by posing questions of it—using hypotheses—that our experience of the world either confirms or disconfirms. At the simplest level, Is this letter a *c*, this an *a*, and this a *t*? Does this spell *cat*? (One can see this in children's first attempts to read.) This young man in the play, is he Danish? Yes. Is he just a student? No. Even at the level of simple perception of, say, color, we can think of it as a testing. When you look at a tomato, you can think of the retinas in your eyes asking, Will this stimulate the blue-green sensitive cones? No. Will this stimulate the red-sensitive cones? Yes. And you perceive red.

If large numbers of people all use the same tests or hypotheses to look at the same thing, the red-sensitive cones, the knowledge that c-a-t spells cat, that p-r-i-n-c-e spells prince, then they will come to the same conclusions about the color, the word, and the play. When we consider something more complicated, Hamlet's delay, then we will differ in the hypotheses we use to read the play (as Freud and Goethe differed), and we will get a difference of opinion. *Different hypotheses distinguish different groups of readers*, "interpretive communities," in Stanley Fish's apt phrase.[5] Goethe's hypothesis fits a Romantic thinker, Freud's a psychoanalyst.

In short, we can answer *both* the first *and* the second questions by means of the reader-active model. We can understand when people will have the same response, and when they will differ. We understand the similarities and differences, not by focusing on the work—that we can never know except through our own hypotheses. We understand the similarities and differences by focusing on the tests and hypotheses that people are using to perceive the work. In this way, the reader-active model, although to some it seems extreme, does in fact answer both the questions that the inaccurate word "content," the bi-active model, or the text-active model cannot answer.

Bearing on this reader-active model are the experiments with films by Rafael Malach, Uri Hasson, and their associates. They found a good deal of shared response (up to 65% for an artfully edited film like a Hitchcock).[6] But they also found brain activity in regions that were not shared, that showed idiosyncratic, individual responses. In general, viewers showed a mix of similar and dissimilar brain activity, with more similarity for the more tightly edited films. Similar brain activity indicates, then, that viewers were responding to the movie in the same way, presumably because of directorial control. Dissimilar brain activity could mean simply that spectators had tuned out and were daydreaming, or it could mean that the film (an art film for example) evoked highly variable activities of understanding, interpretation, and emotional response. The areas where the subjects differed, write the experimenters, "are linked to unique, individual variations."[7]

These experiments bear particularly on the second of our two basic questions about "content": how do we explain samenesses and differences *and uniquenesses* in readers' responses. The samenesses come from the viewers' using basic perceptual processes that they mostly share. The differences and the uniquenesses come when more advanced parts of the brain that interpret information come into play. Notice too how this experiment is deeply consistent with the reader-active model and not with the bi-active model. Even a tightly edited film does not have final control. It is not something about the text that determines when responses are shared and individual. It is something about the way our brains function when confronted with different degrees of directorial control.

For complex literary works and even for the simplest utterances, I am doing a lot of the work, supplying causal connections, filling in grammatical slots, providing information about present and past contexts for what is being said, and adding in my own associations and wishes. "Content" is something *I* generate, *using* the materials the writer provides me, as Unamuno said in the epigraph.

For any chunk of written language, we put sounds or written letters together to form words, words to form sentences, and sentences to form paragraphs of discourse. There are excellent accounts of the brain's activities in converting the eyes' saccades across a page or the ear's processing of frequencies into an understanding of phonemes or letters and converting them into larger verbal entities.[8] Rather than duplicate them here, I'd like to assume, simply, that we have heard (or read) and formulated a *plain sense* for the words of a poem, story, or drama, that is, a meaning that most speakers of English would agree on. We have understood the discourse as discourse. What next?

From "discourse" to "story"

Large domains of psychology and linguistics called "pragmatics" or "discourse analysis" address the questions of what I am doing when I assemble words into "content" and how I do it. Psychologist Victor Nell describes a number of mental procedures that convert individual sentences into coherent narratives, procedures hypothesized by such discourse theorists as Teun Van Dijk, Walter Kintsch, Robert de Beaugrande, Carol Colby, and many others. Nell suggests that these rules or procedures are ways of creating macrostructures that "fill" episodic memory.[9] That is, they make sentences into experiences that we can remember.

Among literary theorists, Patrick Colm Hogan and David Bordwell (for film) have given good syntheses of how readers and audiences create "content."[10] Two terms sum up the issue: story and discourse. Hogan nicely illustrates the difference between them by a murder trial. Discourse is what you perceive; story is what you make of it.

Imagine yourself in the jury box. You will hear a succession of witnesses. A policeman reports the finding of a body. A kinsman identifies the body and reports that the dead man had a violent argument with the defendant. A ballistics expert testifies that the bullet found in the dead man matches a bullet fired from a gun later found in the defendant's possession. And so on. All this is "discourse": what you hear and see as a spectator (or as a reader). And, as Hogan says, "The order of the testimonies is not the same as the order of the events in real life."[11] What you make of them, though, is a story: the night before the murder the victim and the defendant quarreled; the next day the defendant went to the victim's home; the two of them got in the defendant's car; the defendant drove the victm to a nearby woods and there shot him.

From the discourse, we make the story. Discourse includes what we have called "form" (ch. 9) plus fragments of story. The whole story is the coherent narrative you put together from the bits and pieces of story perceived in the discourse.[12]

Lyric poems as well as narratives commonly require us to make inferences. We need to interpret metaphors, to observe patterns of imagery, and to connect words and sounds at one point in the poem to words and sounds at another, perhaps distant point. Particularly with the poetry of the twenty-first century, the reader of poetry does much more than the reader of story.

Basic assumptions

For a fiction (or, more generally, a literary representation), we assume, Hogan points out, that the world of the representation and the world of our daily experience are alike. We will, unless told otherwise, assume that people and physical objects behave in the represented world as they do in our reality. Adopting an idea of Marie-Laure Ryan, Richard Gerrig calls this "a principle of minimal departure."[13] Even if what we are reading is totally unreal, science fiction or mythology or *The Waste Land*, we will assume as much as we can that the fiction is life-like. Angels, for example, are just human beings with wings added and navels removed. Zeus does throw thunderbolts and impose destinies, but otherwise he is just another old man with a beard who believes, with Henry Kissinger, that power is the ultimate aphrodisiac.

Psychologist Victor Nell agrees with the novelist-philosopher William Gass, who says "Our imaginings are imprecise and misty." Having to imagine details about a character's looks interferes with "entrancement." "Readers are reluctant imagers," concludes Nell, " and prefer to have ideas about characters rather than sensations."

> James Bond entrances us because we have been to his London flat, have met his secretary and his housekeeper, and know that he keeps his hand-rolled cigarettes in a gunmetal cigarette box (though we do not much enquire whether gunmetal is blue, black, or silver). In other words, propositions liberate the reader from the vagueness of imaginings and allow the use of propositional thought modes, which, for reasons that psychology has yet to explore (but which are bound up with comprehension processes), are more readily evoked and more richly evocative than the often colorless and wispy pictures we are able to make in our heads.[14]

I suspect that these "propositional thought modes" correspond to the very general way that we navigate reality.

In reading characters and events, we use what cognitive

psychologists call *schemas*, an idea that goes back, ultimately, to Kant. To navigate our world, we carry a great many detailed schemas (or, for classicists, schemata) in our heads, scripts for how the events of our world normally work.[15] Normally, we enter a restaurant, we are led to a table, we are handed a menu, we make a choice, it is brought, we eat it, we get the check, and we pay the cost of the meal plus an 18% tip (or is it 20% by now?). By means of such schemas, we understand how to behave and what to expect from others. Were the server to insist on the tip before we could have a menu, I would be startled at the novelty, the violation of my restaurant schema, even if the server were in a novel. Similarly, I have many schemas about people that I bring to bear to understand literary characters. Excessive detail from a writer can interfere with the normal way I apply schemas.

We also make assumptions of identity. We will assume that the "Horatio" whom we see in the opening scenes of *Hamlet* is the same Horatio who pronounces Hamlet's epitaph at the end.

We also make assumptions about time. Think of *Citizen Kane*, a film with as jumbled a time scheme as one could imagine. Welles' masterpiece precisely raises the question of going from discourse to story. We begin with one of Welles' amazing shots that tracks in from a pair of iron gates and in and in and in through a window and finally closes in on Kane as an old man dying, dropping the glass ball with snow in it, and uttering the famous first and last word, "Rosebud." Cut to a newsreel in *March of Time* style that gives the highlights of Kane's career. This is the public Kane. Then a succession of narrators provides the discourse: his personal manager, his best friend, his ex-wife, finally the sinister butler, all in flashbacks at various points in time. Each tells something about the private Kane. How do we go from what the various narrators tell us (discourse) to the "real" man? We, as viewers put together a story: the trauma of Kane's being given away by his mother, his angry boyhood, his purchasing a newspaper, his marriage, his political career ended by sexual scandal, the disastrous second marriage, and so on, until we catch up with Kane as recently dead. We assume that Kane's life trajectory takes place in ordinary time. We convert the various tales told by the interviewees into the ordinary sequences of a life.

Just as we use schemas to think about time, we use them to organize space. Usually, we understand spaces through human agency, actions like swimming (pool), walking (road or street), flying (airplane), or sleeping (bedroom), as in the responses to *The Good, the Bad, and the Ugly*.

We have other schemas associated with particular genres or period styles or personal styles. If we are reading a detective story, we assume that, at the end, the detective will solve the crime. If we are reading a romance or a romantic comedy, we assume that eventually the heroine will marry Mr. Right. The Victorians liked to read about saccharine heroines like Little Nell and villainous men preying on them. That is a schema, and, knowing it, we expect (and tolerate) certain things from a Victorian novel.

Authors also imply schemas. We expect Hemingway to write in a laconic style about men testing their manhood. We expect Toni Morrison to write about people of color in a remarkably metaphorical language. Similarly, we will understand characters, at least initially, through stereotypes: the cowboy, the gangster, the detective, the crazy scientist, the even more crazy psychiatrist, and on and on.

Colin Martindale has shown, and, remarkably, mathematicized, the way, over decades and centuries, artists will complicate these schemas and stereotypes, making them more and more extreme.[16] The simply good cowboy of the early westerns has to acquire neuroses. The merely foolish psychiatrist must become in later films a homicidal maniac. Artists change and develop schemas so as to make them new to us.

Schemas in the brain

Neuroscientists agree that brain activities like understanding a narrative rely on schemas. But they debate how the brain embodies these schemas. Some say the brain acquires schemas by learning from the environment (a view favored by arts professors like Bordwell, Hogan, or me). Others regard schemas as "emergent" properties of neural networks. From that connectionist or PDP perspective, a schema is not what organizes brain activity at the neuronal level. Rather, a schema is what results from the self-organizing activity of a neural network without supervision from, so to speak, "above,"[17] that is, from higher cortical processes responding to the environment.

For our literary purposes, we need not decide. We need only note that we use schemas widely distributed in the brain to read literature, to watch movies, and, indeed, to understand our world. They enable us to turn a mere text into a literary experience. No matter how fantastic a story, no matter how abstract a poem, by understanding it through schemas, we make a human sense of it.

In short, the literary work does not deliver "content." We construct "content." We begin a literary experience by deploying a basic brain process to perceive the sense impressions within our bodies (of, say, a book or a stage or a screen) as "out there" in the world outside our skins (ch. 4). We use that same process to project the content we have constructed into the book or stage or screen "out there."

When we use basic physiological or widely shared cultural codes, all of us construct content in the same way.

When we use more complex, not widely shared, ideas, we construct differently. At the highest level, we apply our individual needs, concerns, and memories to achieve a purely personal "content." But at all these levels, *it is we who construct content, it is a reader-active model that will explain that "content," and it is we who create the illusion that the "content" is "in" the literary work.*

16 | Literary Language

> There is then creative reading as well as creative writing. When the mind is braced by labor and invention, the page of whatever book we read becomes luminous with manifold allusion. Every sentence is doubly significant, and the sense of our author is as broad as the world.
>
> —Ralph Waldo Emerson, "The American Scholar."

THE READER-ACTIVE MODEL with its processes of inference describes not just literary works, but all discourse. Meaning is not "in" sound waves or spots of ink. Rather, we actively "make sense" of the speech we hear or read by means of extensive brain processing, Emerson's "creative reading." Psychologists and linguists have devoted a great deal of as yet inconclusive study to "discourse analysis" and "pragmatics," developing model after model to describe how we assemble the succeeding parts of a narrative or an argument to get the "plain sense."[1] As before, I'll simply assume that we do in fact, some way or another, get the plain sense of what we are reading.

But when we are responding to literature, especially to poetry, it feels as though we are responding to more of the language than just "plain sense." We have seen in the reader-active model that the reader supplies plain sense plus that something more. Plain sense we are surely aware of. It is conscious. But I think that the something more is both conscious and unconscious. The something more comes from the memory-based wishes of our own brains, like the confabulations of patients with frontal lobe damage. It comes from a complex interaction of the language centers in the right and left hemispheres, the left being more focused on plain sense, the right more on the aspects we think of as poetic or literary. Spreading activations to the right hemisphere, taking advantage of the switch-words and category associations that we perceive in a text, lead to more right hemisphere processing of the language.

The "literary" in literary language

Consider a simple example of that something more: two ways of saying the same thing. First,

A woman does not need a man.
A fish does not need a bicycle.
These two situations are analogous.

Second, "A woman needs a man like a fish needs a bicycle." That is, of course, a well-known slogan that sometimes appears on feminist T-shirts. It is a witticism, a *mot*, in short, a mini-work of literature. I see two reasons why it is literary or even poetic.

First, it has a literary form. That is, the statement of the plain sense of the witticism leads to a different sequence in my mind from the straightforward three-sentence statement of propositional content. I have to work harder to "get" the abbreviated form. There is a "defamiliarization," in Shklovskii's term, a "making strange" (ch. 13). I take it, this happens because of the unusual juxtaposition of fish and bicycle. As a result, I pay extra attention to it. Then, I have to think out what the analogy might be between the oddly combined equation: woman is to man as fish is to bicycle.

Form thus leads to the second reason that I think the sentence is "literary." If I consider my own response, I try to imagine a fish on a bicycle. The problem is that a fish cannot straddle a bicycle. It has a one-piece tail instead of legs. A woman, however, does have legs. A bicycle—or a man—could go between them. But the aphorism says, she doesn't need a man. I become aware of a meaning that goes beyond the "plain sense" given by the three bare-bones propositions. A woman doesn't need a man for sex; she has other ways. The image of a mermaid comes to mind, also the slang meaning of "tail." Knowing that this is a radical feminist saying, I feel a certain dismissal and resentment of men. Men are of no use to women. Other people, I am sure, might have other associations, for example, to a fish swimming in the sea instead of riding a bicycle over land.

My point is that, with literary language, we do not simply pay attention to "what the words say." Our minds consciously (and unconsciously) develop other, related ideas. Of course, we do this in non-literature as well, but less, I think. Form focuses us more intensely on the literary aspects of this text than on its straightforward propositional statement.

Content as confabulaton

My slightly bawdy associations to a mermaid on a bicycle resemble confabulation. Patients who suffer from anterograde amnesia cannot lay down new memories. But these patients do not simply say, "I don't remember" some event that happened a few minutes before. They will make up some kind of fantastic explanation for what they do not remember or understand. They confabulate.

They confabulate in two situations. They may produce a "provoked" confabulation, that is, one induced by a doctor's question or a psychologist's prompt. Or they may produce a "spontaneous" confabulation, in which the patient simply comes up with some fantastic idea out of nowhere. And patients who confabulate believe in the truth of their confabulations, just as we have "poetic faith" in our readings of literary works.

Mark Solms describes one patient in detail (among a group of similar patients).[2] As a result of brain surgery that went wrong, this fifty-year-old executive showed the two symptoms classic for Korsakoff's syndrome: anterograde amnesia and confabulation. One day, the patient called for a certain computer chip to repair his shattered memory. Listening, as a psychoanalyst would, to the patient's words, Solms was able to conclude about this patient's confabulations that he was showing a glimmering awareness of his deficit. "He is trying to find a certain thing, but what he finds instead is a whole lot of things around it that are *symbolically connected*, in the broadest sense, to the topic that he is actually looking for. It is like being in a dream, as we understand dreams in psychoanalysis, where the images are not random." But Solms heard more in this patient. "[H]e replaces what he observes . . . with something more bearable and more tolerable. Thus, it is not simply a cognitive defect." "The reality-monitoring part of the mind is weakened, and some other force, which is usually held at bay, rises up, commensurate with the weakening of that reality-monitoring force."[3] As a result, the patient called up a less troubling confabulation and believed it.

What is this reality-testing system? (In technical language, Solms lists "the dorsal medial thalamus, hypothalamus, basal forebrain nuclei, and frontal cortex.") He is pointing to a system that reaches back and forth from relatively deep and early regions involving emotions and programmed actions expressing emotions (laughing, blushing) to evolutionarily more advanced systems for frontal thinking and planning of actions.[4]

Solms forwarded the recordings of his sessions with this patient to two experimental psychologists. Oliver Turnbull and Akaterina Fotopoulou excerpted some 155 confabulations by this patient and paired them with the actual state of affairs. For example, the patient replaced memory loss with a sports injury: that would be one item on the list of 155. They then gave the list to judges, who did not know what these phrases were, and asked simply, Which of the pairs seems better? The judges said 80% of the patient's confabulations described a more pleasurable situation. This patient's (and other patients') confabulations, the experimenters concluded, were "wish-fulfilling" in the psychoanalytic sense. They resembled wish-fulfilling dreams.[5] With these patients, as in dreams, Solms points out, when the systems that tie us to reality are turned off or damaged, something else that is normally held down is released. Solms follows Freud in calling this disinhibited something "the system Unconscious, the primitive, wishful, reality-ignoring aspect of the mind."

What does all this have to do with literary language? We have seen the connection when we considered "poetic faith." When we are "transported" with a literary work, we are not going to act on what is represented in the work, and we omit our testing of the reality of that representation. We are then in somewhat the same situation as the Korsakoff's patient. The systems in our brain that would normally consider acting on what we are sensing are shut down. These systems would normally inhibit unconscious wish-fulfilling fantasies in favor of realistically planned action. But they are inactive (as in dreams, where we also do not move our bodies and our reality-testing systems are weakened or shut down). Our wishes and fantasies emerge. In effect, then, responding to a literary work, we confabulate. And we believe our confabulation as the patients do.

It is a general physiological rule that, if higher-level control is removed from a system that responds to a stimulus (a so-called "irritable" system), the lower-level system becomes hyperactive. A muscle, for example, goes into spasm or cramp. In experiencing literature, the inhibiting of motor programs weakens or negates the reality-testing systems of the frontal lobe. As a result, the emotional systems whose actions the reality-testing systems would normally inhibit become more free. Because our brains are not reality-testing in the normal way when we respond to events depicted in literature, we project more wish-fulfilling fantasies into the literary experience.[6]

When we are really "into" a work of literature, then, we use the materials of the text to imbue it with our own wishes. In other words, we generate a *provoked confabulation.* We are free to project into *Oedipus* (the provocation) our own version of the oedipus complex or into Keats' poems our own wishes about mouths and mergers or into Ben Jonson's or Anthony Burgess' writings our own wishes about rules and language. The neuropsychological evidence justifies what psychoanalytic critics have been observing for a century in themselves and in authors and in other readers. *We project unconscious, wish-fulfilling fantasies, clusters of wishes, into works of literature.*

Notice that these projections will be *our own fantasies*, which may be more or less connected to what we take to be the plain sense of the text. We may even daydream about something else entirely. The plain sense does not control or limit our projecting, because texts can only limit or control us by formal devices like inclusion or omission (ch. 13). Even so, as in a provoked confabulation, what we project into the text will probably, to some degree, reflect the provocation.

A Shakespearean interlude

In this connection, I recall one of my favorite tactics for interpreting Shakespeare, a method invented in 1794 by Walter Whiter based in Locke's psychology. Whiter found in many passages of Shakespeare clusters of images that had no logical connection. These were "words and sentiments," Whiter wrote, "prompted by a cause, which is concealed from the poet," "forced on the recollection of the writer by some accidental concurrence not necessarily dependent on the sense or spirit of the subject."[7] (We would say the cause was unconscious.) In now-familiar examples, he found Shakespeare associating love with binding books and dogs with candy and flattering.

In the 1930s and 1940s, Edward Armstrong and Caroline Spurgeon found more of these associations, or "image-clusters," for example, pinching linked to death or beetles to cliffs and birds.[8] The "New Critics" in the 1950s and 1960s went on to apply the method to many authors besides Shakespeare. Some image-clusters arise from what Jacques Lacan called *pleine parole* ("full speech") following Freud who wrote of "switch-words" (or *Wechsel*). Switch-words have double meanings with which our minds can start two unrelated trains of thought. "Clasp," for example, might refer either to an embrace or to part of the binding of a book (as in an earlier sentence of mine: "Words, so understood, surround meanings as the covers of books clasp pages"). "Clasp" could thus be a switch-word for one of the associations Whiter pointed out: books and love and (less overtly) sex, as in this passage from *Romeo and Juliet.*

Juliet's mother is urging Juliet to accept Paris, the husband her father has picked out for her:

> Read o'er the volume of young Paris' face,
> And find delight writ there with beauty's pen;
> Examine every married lineament,
> And see how one another lends content;
> And what obscur'd in this fair volume lies
> Find written in the marg[in] of his eyes.
> This precious book of love, this unbound lover,
> To beautify him, only lacks a cover.
> * * *
> That book in many's eyes doth share the glory,
> That in gold clasps, locks in the golden story;
> So shall you share all that he doth possess,
> By having him, making yourself no less (1.3.81-94).

Lady Capulet points to Paris' riches. Then Juliet's bawdy nurse spells out the sexual innuendo in the mother's idea of her covering and clasping and being "no less" by Paris: "No less! nay, bigger! women grow by men."

I suspect that if I, in my role as psychoanalytic critic, were to suggest that a book's cover clasping its contents were a sexual image (a symbol for a vagina), I would be accused of "reading in" or something even more heinous. Yet, as in this Shakespearean passage, such are the ways of the human imagination.

Switch-words typically lead us to unconscious fantasies. Evidently here, we are seeing one of Shakespeare's fantasies about books. It is not surprising that, for an author, a finished, that is, a bound or clasped book, would represent a physical consummation of one's desires. I am suggesting that both writers and readers carry in their minds a variety of possible fantasies, some widely shared, some highly individual.[9] These will be about one's body, one's work, or one's relationships with parents, siblings, and lovers, in short, what Charles Rycroft called "our biological destiny."[10] And these we bring to bear when we produce "provoked confabulations" in our responses to literary language.

Spreading activations

This kind of free association beyond the specific meaning of a word becomes what is called in neuropsychology a "spreading activation," a broader set of meanings for a word than those we take to be its plain sense. These slippages become all too clear in schizophrenic speech. Brendan Maher, who has long studied the language of schizophrenics, gives examples like these:

> "I have no way of knowing how much difference of opinion different editors, politicians, historians, sexologists, astrologers, theologians . . . "
>
> "I have put some beautiful things, the bust of Lincoln, the bust of Washington, the Thinker, strawberry teapot and sugar bowl, some ashtrays."
>
> "Thanks everlasting and Merry New Year to Mentholatum Company for my nose, for my nose, for my nose for my nose."[11]

Maher sees these oddities as coming from the "strong associational bonds" that some words have with other words in the minds of these patients.

For example, if I ask you to say the first word that comes to your mind when I say, "black," you are likely to say "white." If I say "dog," you are likely to say "cat." And so on. The words are strongly associated in your (and my) minds, even though they are not alike in meaning. They are associated because they belong to the same "supraordinate" category, color or animal. Hence they have a category association (some call it "meta-semantic"), and that is important for understanding the psychology of these spreading activations. These patients follow out the category associations, abandoning ordinary criteria for making sense. Further, according to Maher, these strong associations can take over at "vulnerable points" in the sentence, where the speaker has formulated the thought but not yet the language for the next segment.

But these switch-words do not occur just with schizophrenics. Brendan Maher gives several examples of how these spreading activations affect ordinary discourse:

The speaker intended: A career in art has problems.

The speaker said: A career in art has *draw*backs.

Intended: This book, written by a man awaiting execution in Sing Sing prison, is quite amazing.

Said: This book, written by a man awaiting *execution* in Sing Sing prison, is quite *electrifying*.

Intended: China is a giant looking cautiously at the world.

Said: China is a giant *peeking* cautiously at the world.

In 2003, in the U. S. Supreme Court, the justices were hearing arguments about the state of Texas' anti-sodomy law (or anti-gay law). The lawyer representing Texas and defending the law was not answering questions very well. According to *The New York Times*, "Justice Breyer said at one point in frustration: 'I would like to hear your *straight* answer to those points.'"[12] There was a ripple of laughter in the courtroom, the reporter noted.

These spreading activations do often seem to us like jokes. For example, at a conference conducted in both French and English, I was describing to an audience a rather crazy 1960s production of *Othello* in which the play proceeded on the assumption that "Desdemona had been balled by all the sailors on the way to Cyprus." My French translator (fatigued? bored?) rendered this as, "*Elle était chauve* . . . " 'She was bald.' And, of course, everyone burst out laughing.

Two things about these incidents pertain to literary

language or "content." One, the errors revealed what Justice Breyer and the translator were thinking but would certainly not have said right out loud. Two, when the audiences laughed, they too made the macaronic connection: balled—*chauve*; they too used the slang meaning of "straight." They too released half-repressed thoughts. Jokes, which release these skewed unconscious thoughts and feelings, form a handy prototype for more elaborate literature.[13] In literature in general, both authors and readers supply "unconscious content," and these spreading activations often strike us as joke-like.

"Unconscious content"

Generally, throughout this book, I have been applying two ways of approaching a psychological phenomenon like these confabulations and spreading activations, the neurological way and the psychoanalytic way. In the instances of Justice Breyer or my translator, the speakers said something slightly aggressive that they would not consciously have said. Such an unconscious process is, in Freud's term, dynamic; it has a force. An unconscious idea was pushing for expression and, because of fatigue, boredom, or some unconscious concern, that unconscious thought got expression by means of a switch-word.

The best way we have for getting at such unconscious ideas is the psychoanalytic method of free association. Together, analysand and psychoanalyst find the analysand's unconscious concerns and themes by listening for themes in the analysand's free associations (and, nowadays, in "interpersonal psychoanalysis" in the analyst's associations as well). In an encyclopedia article, Freud described the method formally:

> The treatment is begun by the patient being required to put himself in the position of an attentive and dispassionate self-observer, merely to read

> off all the time the surface of his consciousness, and on the one hand to make a duty of the most complete honesty while on the other not to hold back any idea from communication, even if (1) he feels that it is too disagreeable or if (2) he judges that it is nonsensical or (3) too unimportant or (4) irrelevant to what is being looked for. It is uniformly found that precisely those ideas which provoke these last-mentioned reactions are of particular value in discovering the forgotten material.[14]

The odd or unpleasant associations are of particular value for two reasons. First, they are important enough to have driven the spreading activation. Second, they are the associations the individual would ordinarily want to suppress or repress, pushing them out of awareness. They are now brought into speech and consciousness through the dynamic pressure characteristic of unconscious ideas. You could put the process of free association another way: simply say what comes to mind long enough, and you will come to something, one, unexpected and two, unwelcome.

Unconscious thoughts acquire word-representations in free association. A leading contemporary analyst, Christopher Bollas, gives an example of the process. He describes one patient's free associations and his way of listening to them:

> A patient talks about listening to Bach's Mass in B Minor; then, after a pause, talks about going to Selfridges to buy a cricket bat for his son; then talks about a conversation with a friend in which the meaning of loyalty was the object of discussion; then talks about a memory from his youth when he found an abandoned car that proved to have been stolen a few days earlier, a topic the patient now realises is connected to a dream from the previous

> night; and so it goes . . .
>
> What is the link between Bach/Mass and Selfridges/cricket, and so on? Hard to tell, isn't it? If time permitted, we should just drift along with the patient's other associations until we reach a revelation—a point when suddenly we are struck by a pattern of thought, composed of those connecting threads between the disparate ideas.
>
> Looking back, the logic of this brief sequence might reveal the following thought: 'I would be in a mess if as a consequence of my wish to enrich myself ["self-rich-es"] I did not play cricket [fairly] with my friends, especially if I were [car]ried off by stolen ideas abandoned by other people.'
>
> This would inevitably be an incomplete understanding of the associations, however. Certain words, such as 'Selfridges', might call forth other words, so that in addition to the above we may also hear the words 'elf', 'rigid' or 'frigid' . . . .
>
> As the analyst assumes the position of evenly suspended attentiveness, he or she comes under the influence of the unconscious order. Guided by the logic of the patient's chain of ideas, the analyst at some point will retrospectively discover what the patient has, in part at least, been talking about.[15]

In other words, like Brendan Maher's schizophrenics, like Justice Breyer or my translator, what this patient says carries in his own mind a whole host of associations or, in neurological terms, spreading activations. These are what Bollas infers. They deal with the patient's current worries, like questions of money, being fair, or stealing ideas. These thoughts are the kind that produce a certain amount of anxiety. They are thoughts that the patient, without free association, would have kept out of awareness.

Psychoanalytically, then, *words can express for writers or speakers and elicit from readers or hearers unconscious fantasies.* Psychoanalysts usually picture a thought expressed in words as an iceberg. A little bit of it shows above the surface, and there is an immense amount of other, unconscious thinking underneath, as with Bollas' patient..

We can draw a more detailed analogy: our minds are like an apartment building. Imagine that we are on the roof, the surface of consciousness. There, any group of words corresponds to one location among many on the flat plane of the roof of the bulding. It has connections to other rooftop areas, and that broad, flat plane represents the broad network of ideas in or near consciousness. If one were to drill straight down from one particular point or idea on the roof surface, through lower and lower storeys, one would come to the meanings of that surface idea at storeys representing the network of consciousness at earlier and earlier times and stages of life. Adjacent spaces at each storey would represent associations and context at that particular time. Finally one would come to the murky preverbal level of the cellar. Free association begins at the roof, but what is going on in all the lower storeys influences what goes on at that surface.

Psychoanalytic evidence shows that any conscious word, image, or idea has an "unconscious dimension" that is very large and deep like the storeys of that apartment building. In writing literature, many writers have told us, this unconscious dimension is what a writer draws from. "Composition," writes Louis Menand, one of our most talented essayists, "is a troublesome, balky, sometimes sleep-depriving business. What makes it especially so is that the rate of production is beyond the writer's control. You have to wait, and what you are waiting for is something inside you to come up with the words."[16] In reading as well as writing, this uncontrollable, unconscious dimension colors our response, creating "spreading activations" that may well never be put into words.

From a psychoanalytic point of view, spreading activations represent dynamic, unconscious thoughts pushing toward expression. But we can also understand these slips, unintentional puns, and free associations neurologically.

Literary language in the hemispheres

As we saw when considering "poetic faith" (ch. 7), when we are "transported" by a literary experience, perhaps always when we are in a situation of "flow" where our attention is directed entirely to what we are doing, we do not pay attention to the things we normally heed: the real world of our bodies and our environment. And, when "transported," we have let form take over (at least partly) the directing of our attention (ch. 13). Our own defenses are busy coping with novelties from our ongoing perception of the work and our unconscious associations to those novelties. Our defenses therefore are less occupied with warding off those alternative and perhaps slightly taboo meanings of words. But these alternative meanings come from someplace in our brains.

Neurologists, starting with Broca and Wernicke in the nineteenth century, have discovered much about how (in most people) the left hemisphere processes language. The left hemisphere performs what we might call ordinary language processing: getting the plain sense of speech or writing. It is the kind of processing that the theorists researching "narrative comprehension" or "discourse analysis" or "pragmatics" try to model.

Many researchers agree that the right hemisphere also has at least rudimentary language processing capabilities, as words are passed from the left hemisphere across the corpus callosum to the right hemisphere. "With corticocognitive maturation," writes Jaak Panksepp,

> the diverse emotional musical communications of infants begin to bifurcate into two seemingly distinct streams—propositional, logic-constrained, low-affect speech consolidates within the left hemisphere, while the prosodic-emotional poetic streams flow more forcefully through the right . . . . However in well-functioning brains, more so in females than males, the two remain functionally entwined.[17]

It is to the right hemisphere, then, that we must look for the processing of literary language.

Right hemisphere language processing

Neuroscientists have studied these right hemisphere language abilities extensively. For example, Christine Chiarello and her associates have performed a long series of complex experiments with priming.[18] That is, one word is presented (sometimes subliminally). Then a second word is presented and the subject is asked its meaning. The question is, What is the effect of one's conscious or unconscious knowledge of the first word on the meaning one gives to the second? The experimenters present, for example, word pairs like *king-duke* or *nose-arm*, words that share a category but that we would not normally associate with one another (as we do with *black-white* or *cat-dog*). The experiments show that the right hemisphere's language centers respond more to these categorically related words than the left hemisphere's language centers do. The neuroscientists have extended this kind of research with a wide variety of experiments and with analyzing other researchers' work using still other kinds of experiments. In general, these researchers conclude that, *when a word is presented, the right hemisphere activates a wider range of meanings than the left hemisphere does* (the "coarse coding hypothesis"). In current thinking, the right hemisphere develops meanings that are less "salient," that is, less obvious or less likely to come first to mind.

Lisa Aziz-Zadeh and Antonio Damasio summarize research studying conventional as opposed to novel metaphors (clichés as opposed to literary or poetic language). Contrast, for example, "leaders grasp situations" with "leaders grasp nettles." These studies indicate, the authors write, "that different brain areas process the two kinds of metaphors, with the right hemisphere specifically more active for novel metaphor processing."

> This finding has been related to the Graded Salience Hypothesis (GSH). GSH predicts that salient meanings are accessed more quickly than less salient meanings. Thus highly familiar meanings that are represented in the mental lexicon are accessed more readily. According to this model, [in] conventional metaphors, such as "grasp the situation," the metaphorical meaning (to understand) is more salient than the literal meaning (a grasping action). Thus it is the figurative meaning that would be activated first, without needing to access the less salient literal meaning. Because the metaphorical meanings of novel metaphors are not salient—that is, they are not yet stored in the mental lexicon—these representations would not be activated first. Instead, for novel metaphors, the literal meaning would be more salient and accessed most readily.[19]

The difference in timing between more and less salient meanings also supports the "coarse coding hypothesis" developed by Christine Chiarello, Miriam Faust, Mark Beeman, and others. Perceiving a word begins parallel but distinct processes in each hemisphere, processes of word recognition and activation of meanings. The left hemisphere is specialized for word encoding and decoding. It rapidly resolves the heard or read lexical string into a word. Then all meanings of the word are activated and passed to the right hemisphere. The left hemisphere, again rapidly, commits to one particular meaning that fits with the left hemisphere's "model of the current discourse," in the linguist's phrase, that is, the plain sense. The left hemisphere actively suppresses the rest of the meanings. By contrast, the right hemisphere keeps those tentative meanings around for a measurable interval of time.

As a result, if the salient (obvious) meaning that the left hemisphere chose ceases to fit, as in a metaphor or a joke or a "garden path" sentence,[20] the brain does not decode the word a second time to recapture the rejected meanings. That would cost extra processing energy. Instead the brain draws on the less salient meanings that the right hemisphere has already retained, that were at first treated as irrelevant.

Following out this idea, Miriam Faust has argued that the left hemisphere can use, to assist word recognition, information about the word itself ("intralexical" information) plus message-level information contained in the sentence as a whole. The right hemisphere, however, can use only the intralexical-level processing mechanisms. Therefore structural and conceptual restrictions from the sentence level do not constrain the right hemisphere.

Suppose, in a sentence, you encounter a word that doesn't fit, as in "This restaurant serves French fries with *cream.*" The beginning of the sentence primes the left hemisphere for "ketchup" or "vinegar." But then you come to "cream." The left hemisphere priming doesn't work. But the beginning of the sentence did not prime the right hemisphere. The result is, the right hemisphere can handle such sentences.[21] In this context, notice how psychoanalyst Christopher Bollas inferred his patient's unconscious thoughts from word-level puns ("Selfridge's," "self-rich-es," "elf," "rigid' or "frigid"). Bollas put aside the sentences as wholes.

In other words, the right hemisphere seems to have a language system that actually uses, indeed may even be confined to, the spreading activations that Brendan Maher described in schizophrenics and normals. As Maher showed with schizophrenics, these spreading activations are salient for them. Schizophrenics do not inhibit these spreading activations based on category. He concluded that schizophrenic language arises from a combination of factors: a point in their speaking of least attention (a word juncture, for example); high levels of association; and low levels of inhibition.[22] These last two I would associate with right hemisphere and left hemisphere respectively (following Chiarello's and Faust's work). I would note, too, that we found the left hemisphere important in defense mechanisms (ch. 13). It is well established that the right hemisphere matters more than the left in the emotional processing of language (prosody). And finally I would recall that, because we are not going to act on what we are perceiving in a literary work, we weaken our reality-testing. We rely less on the left hemisphere's talent for deriving from language realistic statements about the world. In general, these different evidences say to me that, *when we are "transported" with a literary work, the right hemisphere language centers become more active than usual in language processing, and we open up a richness of meaning that we call "poetic" or "literary."*

One would predict therefore that patients with right hemisphere damage would have trouble accessing nonliteral meanings. And they do. They have trouble understanding figurative meanings (like associating "dull" with stupid rather than a butter knife). They have trouble with phrases like, "heavy heart" or "living high on the hog" or "face the music." They have trouble re-interpreting a character's implicit attitude when the story indicates that it has changed. They have trouble getting the motivation of characters in a narrative or the moral of a story. In a variety of contexts, patients with right hemisphere damage have trouble bringing to bear, on a current sentence, meanings derived from the entire social context of the discourse as well as the figurative meanings of words.[23]

Ultimately, Chiarello concludes, each hemisphere has its own semantic system for meanings. We need both for the proper interpretation of word meanings in context. In general, she, like other researchers in this field, finds an important role for the right hemisphere in interpreting ambiguous words, indirect requests (like "Can you take out the trash?"), connotations, metaphors, idioms, sarcasm, and jokes.[24] To me, these things imply literature. I think these researchers are telling me that the right hemisphere's language centers are important, and perhaps dominant, in our experiencing the literary language of poems, stories, and dramas.

In an encyclopedic paper,[25] Julie Kane, a poet very well versed in neuroscience (note spreading activation), makes the right hemisphere's role very specific. She goes through all the major literary devices characteristic of poetry: imagery, allusion, synaesthesia, metonymy, synecdoche, personification, paradox, oxymoron, irony, litotes, hyperbole, alliteration, and so on. Drawing on the experimental literature, she shows that they are either processed by the right hemisphere or capable of being processed by the right hemisphere.

Neither Kane nor I, however, is suggesting that we "do" literature "in" the right hemisphere. Our brains consist of immensely complicated systems that interact in immensely complicated ways. The right hemisphere can only express its special poetic or literary meanings when it is combined with such left hemisphere abilities as perceiving the words, decoding the grammar, and assigning to a text the plain sense (or "model of the current discourse"). Nevertheless, these lines of experiments make it clear that one can find a neurological system that would make switch-words and ordinary words lead to the associations that poets and other creative writers, literary critics, psychoanalysts, and creative readers find.

Emotions and the right hemisphere

These aspects of right hemisphere processing bear on the emotions readers and writers derive from literary works. Many researchers over many decades have shown how important the right hemisphere is for the processing of emotions. The right hemisphere is dominant in responding to music, for example, in processing the emotional aspects of speech ("prosody" is the term neurologists use), in interpreting facial expressions for emotion, and in expressing emotion through facial expressions. Damage to the right hemisphere can leave people indifferent and emotionless themselves, even though they may be able to infer (in the logical left hemisphere) the emotion appropriate to a given sentence.[26]

In short, a review of the literature on language processing implicates the emotional capacities of the right hemisphere in receiving and expressing ambiguities and emotional communications in words,[27] far more than the left hemisphere that deals with "what the words say." Yet the right hemisphere could not decode these things unless the left hemisphere did its cognitive processing first. And we cannot live with the left's cognitive processing alone; we need the emotional understanding and expression provided by the right hemisphere to get along with our fellow human beings.[28] If we are to survive, the two systems must work together.

Language and SEEKING

We have already seen how important the SEEKING system is to our emotional response to literary works and our wish for a satisfying ending.[29] It enters into the literariness of literary language as well. As Keats saw, bright-eyed fieldmouse or bright-eyed human, we mammals are always SEEKING, either to gain pleasure or to avoid unpleasure. This is Freud's pleasure principle, the core of motivation, perhaps now given a basis in the brain.

But we do not simply seek in a vague, unfocused way. Inevitably, we mix memory with desire. "The mode of operation of the SEEKING system," Solms and Turnbull point out, is "incomprehensible without reference to the *memory* systems with which it is intimately connected. These systems provide the *representations* of objects (and past interactions between the self and those objects) that enable the organism to *learn* from experience."[30] Such memories include not only explicit memories and ideas (like literary opinions), but also fantasies and imaginings that mattered to us in childhood, fantasies that may now be unconscious.

In effect, memories allow vague SEEKING to become a "wish" for something specific. Freud defined "wish" as: "a psychical impulse . . . to re-evoke the perception . . . to re-establish the situation of the original satisfaction."[31] As we go about the world SEEKING what we wish for, our pasts bias our present perceptions, because we remember what gave us pleasure at an earlier time and, as we go on living our lives, we seek that thing. A textbook puts it this way: "Higher vertebrates in particular use the past as well as the present in interpreting current sensory input. . . . . Experience . . . leads to the assembling of a whole repertoire of assumptions and interpretations that have proved useful in the past."[32] We color our ordinary perceptions with wishes and fantasies. We imagine the people we meet, the situations we are in, or events in the news, all as either granting or preventing the particular things we desire. If freed from reality-testing, because "this is only a story," the SEEKING system can produce even more delusional thoughts, wishes and fantasies free from current reality.[33]

When we turn to literature, we are SEEKING a pleasurable experience without motor action on our part. Further, though, *we come to literature for the particular kind of pleasure that the pathways in each of our unique brains wants.* We want to satisfy our "taste." "Taste" is our SEEKING system biased by (as Panksepp notes of animals) our personalities.

In this chapter I have worked my way from the "higher" verbal systems in the left and right cerebral hemispheres that turn discourse into story or spreading activations down to "lower" motivational levels originating in the brain stem. The system in the brain also goes the other way, however. Those lower levels project, using the dopaminergic "reward" system, into higher levels. They project into the frontal regions, biasing higher verbal levels toward an experience of literature that satisfies the clusters of an individual's deeper and probably unconscious drives.

Further, each of our brains was individualized, first by inheritance and intrauterine environment, second by a process in infancy of emotional regulation by early caregivers, later by peers and a wider range of experiences. As described by Solms and Turnbull, this individuation is particularly strong in the right hemisphere. Therefore, I think we can say, *individuation can bias right-hemisphere language systems toward our individual sources of pleasure.* We will interpret jokes, metaphors, figures of speech, in short, literary language so as to give us our particular style of pleasure. *This bias will also favor readings of the literal (left hemisphere) language of a literary work that re-create our particular style of pleasure*, rooted in traces of our earliest unconscious experiences of satisfaction (infantile elation and joy). In short, when readers construct literature, as in the reader-active model (ch. 15), they construct it so as to suit themselves—as one would expect.

Individualized "content"

Psychoanalytic literary critics often describe our fantasies about our biological destiny as "in" the literary work. This way of reading a text began in 1895, when Freud explained that *Oedipus Rex* had "gripping power," because everyone in the audience was once a budding Oedipus in fantasy and now recoiled from that dream-fulfillment acted out.[34]

A century later, we know that reactions are not as universal as Freud thought. Our hypothetical reader of *Hamlet* with the brutal father (ch. 12) might well feel especially threatened by Claudius' efforts to kill Hamlet. Or he might well feel the impulse to revenge more strongly than most people and might therefore especially hold Hamlet in contempt for his delay. When psychoanalytic critics say that people are responding to an oedipus complex "in" this or that work, then, they are really pointing to a wide range of possible responses. Which one any given member of the audience activates depends on that person's personal history. Plays themselves do not, after all, "have" complexes or fantasies, even if they portray them—only people do.

Psychological patterns, then, are not "in" a literary work. They are what our individualized minds and brains actively create, whether we are authors creating words from experience or readers creating experience from words. As the ones who actively give life to the literary process, we achieve our own individualized creations of "content" and our individualized expansions of plain sense into literary language. And we do so within an individual style.

17 | Individual Styles

> Style is not a tool, it is not a method, it is not a choice of words alone. Being much more than all this, style constitutes an intrinsic component or characteristic of the author's personality. Thus when we speak of style we mean an individual artist's peculiar nature, and the way it expresses itself in his artistic output.
>
> —Vladimir Nabokov, Lecture: "Mansfield Park (1814)."

MOZART SOUNDS LIKE Mozart. Hemingway reads like Hemingway. Matisse looks like Matisse. Always. Aestheticians speak of their "style," while psychologists might point to personality and psychoanalysts to "character" or "identity." Key to these styles or any style is repetition. Mozart, Hemingway, Matisse—and you and I—have styles in that we do things the same way over and over, different things, but with the same style. Why? Or more accurately, we have two questions. What is a style? And why do we have them? Evidently style involves repetition, and that suggests an answer to the second question. We have styles because something in our brains, something beginning in infancy, makes us repeat and repeat.

Styles, however, are also group styles: classic, Romantic, modern, or postmodern. These too we compulsively repeat, and they too must exist in our brains. They cannot be innate, however, since they change over the decades. Writers and readers give them an individual form, blending them into a personal style. Individuals use group styles to meet individual needs. We can understand this interaction as a hierarchy. An individual style, developed from infancy on, governs styles associated with physiology, culture, and particular communities within a culture. These group styles, we can further understand as hypotheses with which individuals test and cope with the world. *Styles consist of individual identities deploying tests based on physiology, culture, and community.*

Style as character

Presumably, as Nabokov says, each style is a function of its owner's essence or, less philosophically, his or her personality. Proust describes the language of a book, "each sentence, in essence resembling the others, for all are spoken with the unique inflection of a personality."[1] With some writers, Hemingway, say, or Faulkner, you only have to read a few sentences to be able to say, That's Hemingway, or, That's Faulkner. We demonstrate styles even in far more abstract human pursuits. Chess masters can recognize one another's styles of play, and mathematicians can distinguish differerent styles of proof. We recognize these things, because a given person does things the same way over and over.

Our knowledge of someone's style makes parody possible. Here's a delicious bit from one of the winners of the annual bad-Hemingway contest:

> The rains came early that day. They fell as they always had, downward and in little drops.
>
> I will go inside, the man thought. There one can stay dry. He knew this because he had traveled much and seen many things.
>
> "Hola, Roberto," said the waitress. Her skin was like leather—brown and tough and still in the shape of a cow.

It is Hemingway-ish because it repeats the very things Hemingway himself repeated: short, common words; thoughts as free indirect discourse; stating the obvious; and so on.

Writers and other creators are not the only people who manifest styles. Readers, moviegoers, and theatergoers also have styles, which we call "taste." We re-create literary works in our individual styles. As I and other reader-response critics have shown in more than one book and many an article, readers read and interpret and answer even grammatical questions in characteristic and different ways. My *Hamlet* differs from your *Hamlet*, my *Casablanca* differs from yours, my *Madame Bovary* is not your *Madame Bovary*, and so on and on. One would expect porn to elicit standard responses. After all, it is designed and created with a certain response in mind. But people respond even to porn in quite different ways.[2]

In everyday life, we read other people in terms of their styles of being. We say things like, "Oh, that's just like Jane." Or, "Algernon isn't himself today." Such statements imply two things. One, they imply that we can ordinarily see a certain repetitive pattern in the way someone writes or talks or walks or dresses or makes love. Two, they imply that we see new behaviors against the previous pattern that we have recognized. These new behaviors either fulfill the pattern or vary it. We would have to have evolved some such ability to get along in our hominin troupes. If we couldn't predict, at least to some extent, how our fellow primates would react, how would we know how to act in the group?

These individual styles repeat and persist over time even when the brain cannot function fully. Neurologist Oliver Sacks wrote, commenting on an exhibit of Willem de Kooning's late works, painted when the artist's mind was deteriorating: "Style is the deepest part of one's being, and may be preserved, almost to the last, in a dementia."[3] In another example, he pointed to letters Henry James wrote in a delirium that show signs of the delirium but also James' distinctive prose style.[4]

What is style?

In 1753, the naturalist and polymath, Georges-Louis Leclerc, comte de Buffon, announced to the French Academy in his celebrated *Discours sur le style* the classic answer to that question. *"Le style c'est l'homme même."* We usually translate it, The style is the man himself (or, better, the person). But we should really read Buffon as saying, The style is the *very* person, the essential, fundamental, deep nature of that human being, as Nabokov says in the epigraph. Someone's style expresses that person's *essence*, as Sacks says, "the deepest part of one's being."

By contrast, some contemporary theorists suggest that style is cultural, imposed through society's control of language. Certainly culture and environment play a role in style: there is an eighteenth-century style of writing, a Romantic style, a modernist style, and so on. Part of de Kooning's style obviously derived from the Abstract Expressionist movement in New York in the 1940s. A personal style of being and knowing, begun in infancy, comes to include quite sophisticated ways of reacting derived from our cultural environment.

Styles repeat. They are *habitual.* Sacks' comment suggests that they must exist somehow in the brain at a fairly deep or pervasive level. But before we consider style in the brain, we can go to the other side of the Alp (ch. 2).

Style in the mind

From the beginning, psychoanalysts have focused on their patients' repetitions. In 1900 Freud defined a wish as the wish to re-create and re-experience a previous perception of satisfaction.[5] And in his last theorizing he posited a "compulsion to repeat." We repeat because it is economical to do so.[6] Before seeking a new solution, we try the one that worked before. Finally, Freud generalized this human tendency to repeat into a general biological principle, the "death instinct," the tendency of all living matter to return to its previously unliving state.[7]

Metapsychology aside, repetition became central to the clinical idea of "character." Among the early psychoanalysts, Sándor Ferenczi thought of character as habits, and he noted that these habits generally occurred outside of consciousness. Therefore, he said, "Psychoanalysis can be regarded as a long-drawn-out fight against thought-habits."[8] Otto Fenichel gave the classic definition: "Character [is] the habitual mode of bringing into harmony the tasks presented by internal demands and by the external world."[9] "Character" in this psychoanalytic sense of the term, must be one of the things that leads to the repeated "character" of Mozart's music, Hemingway's prose, or Matisse's paintings.

From a psychoanalytic standpoint, Heinz Lichtenstein has, I believe, provided the strongest way of approaching these habitual, repetitive, characteristic patterns (stronger, I think, than Freud's frankly speculative "death instinct"). Lichtenstein observed that we can think of a person's character or identity (or, in our literary context, "style") as a pattern repeated with variations on that pattern, like a theme and variations in music. We can understand people the way we understand a movement in a symphony. We recognize a theme, and then we hear variations on the theme, and finally the orchestra returns to the theme, but throughout all the variations we can trace the one theme. One theme can have an infinite number of variations: fast, slow, high, low, in the treble, in the bass, inverted, or reversed. But one can always discern the theme within the variations.

You can—and we do—understand a person by formulating such a theme or themes, although rarely do we do it explicitly. "That's so like Norm." We sense a pattern, and then we look at variations on it. However, to understand human identities, unlike music, one uses words to formulate an identity theme.[10] *"Identity" in this strict sense, then, includes a verbally formulated theme plus someone's cumulating variations on it.*

I am using "identity" in a special sense here. I intend *identity-from-outside*, that is, a persistent personal style that we infer in someone else in order to make sense of that person. Identity-from-inside refers to my own ideas and inferences about myself, and, of course, I see myself as constantly changing. Neuroscientists tend not to distinguish clearly between one's fluctuating sense of one's own identity, an identity-from-within, and a stable identity as others think of us, an identity-from-outside.

An identity theme inferred from outside, however, does not entail the problem of fluctuation. We see persistences in others (and sometimes, with psychoanalytic insight, in ourselves). I might observe, say, Ronald Reagan change from being a labor-oriented Democrat to a plutocratic Republican, and I am sure it seemed quite a change to Ronald Reagan. But I can point to his persistent appeals to a hierarchy of strength and merit that appeared in both these opposite positions. Seen from the outside, one could read Reagan as repeating the same themes, no matter how different he may have seemed to himself, inside.[11]

"Character" is an older term for this identity-from-outside, and it is observable and measurable by various tests for "personality" (the psychologists' term). The psychologists, however, divide the indivisible individual. They fractionate character or personality into a series of discrete, measurable traits. Currently favored are the Five Factors or the "Big Five": Openness to Experience, Conscientiousness, Extroversion, Agreeableness, Neuroticism (acronym OCEAN), with various tests for each.[12] While this approach has many uses, I would add holistic method: identity as involving a central theme (Reagan's hierarchies, for example) and constantly changing variations on that theme.

We humans can vary our themes infinitely. We can play variations that are positive and negative, healthy and unhealthy, creative and ritualistic, liberal and conservative, hostile and loving—all the varieties of human life. But, if Lichtenstein is right, an observer, a biographer, say, should be able to trace a sameness, a characteristic style, an identity theme, within all those changes.

Instead of a "death instinct," then, one can explain the deep repetitive tendency of living things by an "identity principle." *The organism, as its deepest motivation, seeks to maintain its own identity—indeed, must maintain it, or die.*[13]

Identity and biology

The well-known biologists, Humberto Maturana and Francisco Varela, advance a similar principle as *autopoeisis* or self-making.[14] As with Lichtenstein, the principle says that an organism's deepest motivation, the one that underlies all others, stems from the necessity of maintaining its own inner nature. Thus, an organism's quests for food, air, water, sex, and information all serve to perpetuate the persistent nature of that organism. Varela puts autopoiesis this way: "Living systems . . . transform matter into themselves in a manner such that the product of their operation is their own organization."[15]

Maturana and Varela adduce a great deal of reasoning and evidence from biology to show that autopoeisis states a fundamental law. It extends evolutionarily from the simplest one-celled animals to the complexities of the individual human being and even to large social groups of humans. An amoeba will absorb new stuff into itself if that new stuff will make more amoeba. It will ignore something that will not. So with an octopus or a dog, a cat, Keats' fieldmouse—or a human being. Each of us eats, drinks, relates to other human beings, breeds, heeds language, and all the rest, so as to satisfy our psychological goals. Those in turn express our biological nature, a physiological identity theme within us of which we are largely unconscious.

Autopoesis applies to social groups as well. We commonly see corporations hiring only executives who will fit into that corporation's style. A culture brings up its children so that they can live in that culture. "A society, therefore, operates as a homeostatic system that stabilizes the relations that define it as a social system of a particular kind."[16] Cultural styles re-create themselves.

In his 2003 book, Antonio Damasio also points to basic biological principles: "All living organisms from the humble amoeba to the human are born with devices designed to solve *automatically*, no proper reasoning required, the basic problems of life," namely getting energy, repairing wear and tear, fending off external dangers, and so on.[17] Like Maturana and Varela, Damasio identifies these biological devices with a concept first discovered by the great French physiologist, Claude Bernard (1813-1878), and generalized by the American, Walter Cannon, in the 1930s. This is *homeostasis*, a purely physiological concept which profoundly influenced psychological thinking, including Freud's and now Damasio's.

Homeostasis sums up the ways the body acts (particularly through negative feedbacks) to maintain a stable internal environment in spite of environmental variations and disturbances. The classic example is the human body's control of its temperature in the midst of changing external conditions like exercise, exposure, or disease. There is a "normal" range between a high and a low that sustains life. As either of the two extremes is approached, the body takes corrective action. The brain adjusts, say, breaths per minute, level of blood sugar, and rate of digestion and metabolism to compensate. This "negative" feedback returns the system to the normal range and keeps it there.

Damasio likens this biological property to Spinoza's concept of *conatus* (translatable as striving or endeavor plus tendency), the relentless drive of each being to preserve itself as itself: "The striving by which each thing strives to persevere in its being is nothing but the actual essence of the thing." "In spite of the transformations the body must undergo as it develops, renews its constituent parts, and ages, conatus continues to form the *same* individual and respect the *same* structural design."[18]

Identity in the brain

Lichtenstein suggested that each of us acquires this identity theme in the early relationship between infant and mother (or "primary caregiver"). As Lichtenstein saw identity, the infant achieves an identity by *learning to be the child for this particular mother*. The infant is born with a certain temperament (excitable, colicky, persistent, or "easy"). The mother responds to that temperament in her characteristic way. The infant in turn responds to the mother by using its temperament to adapt to her traits. In so doing, it shapes within itself its own identity theme. "The infant is imprinted," summarizes psychoanalyst Arnold Modell, "with the mother's theory of being and relating."[19] From then on, the growing child plays variations on that theme, modifying it a lot at first, but less and less as time goes on.[20]

Somehow this "constancy" or "habitual" becomes embodied in our brains. It must be in a distributed brain system, I think, given what we know about the growth and ungrowth of the human brain in infancy and childhood.

Donald Hebb's work in the 1940s showed how experience gets written into the brain.[21] As Steven Pinker neatly phrases it: "Neurons that fire together wire together; neurons that don't synch, don't link."[22] The newborn brain has only a small fraction of the synapses it will ultimately have. Development creates a supercharged brain in latency. Then in early adolescence the excess dies off. Terrence Deacon states the process: "In the context of the developing brain, where the numbers of connections are significantly in excess of what will be maintained to maturity, [Hebbian learning] determines which connections will 'win' in a biological variant of the children's game 'musical chairs,' where the numbers of viable targets decrease over time."[23] Overall, in growing from, say, age five to adolescence, the child develops some brain connections and drops others, forming a personal brain.[24] We can therefore think of *style (or an identity theme) as a system embodied in the brain.*

Jim Grigsby and David Stevens make the interesting suggestion that one can think of character (or personality or identity) as habits *procedurally learned.*[25] Procedural memory is a system that embodies, in particular, motor skills (ch. 12), but Grigsby and Stevens also include perceptual abilities, cognitive skills (like reading or understanding music), and relations to other humans. Procedural memory is non-declarative, that is, it is non-verbal; we cannot put into words the way we walk or swim. Because, for motor memory, many systems must acquire permanent changes in the strength of their synaptic connections, procedural memory must be widely dispersed in the brain. Acquiring a procedural memory, for example, learning to swim or to touch type, requires many, many repetitions. Procedural memories involve both slow learning and long retention. That, I think, is why personality remains stable over time, in the face of crises or even dementia. There is a kind of "inertial quality" to procedural memory and hence to personality. In describing the sudden moments of lucidity among brain-damaged patients, Oliver Sacks concluded: "One's self, one's style, one's *persona* exists as such, in its infinitely complex being; that it is not a question of this system or that, but of a total organization which must be described as a self."[26]

In suggesting a "total organization," Sacks could well be describing a system of procedural memories. Also, the prefrontal cortex is slow to myelinate. Therefore memory in the first few years of life (as Solms and Turnbull point out) consists only of non-verbal procedural memory and memory traces. Personality or character is thus more influenced by procedural learning (repetition) than by semantic knowledge of the world or even episodic memory of experiences, the kinds of memory we can put into words.[27]

Grigsby and Stevens define "character," much as I define identity, as,

> those habitual behaviors that give people their own distinctive styles of being in the world. The foundations of character are acquired early in life but

> undergo change over time in association with experience and neurocognitive development. Nonetheless, certain predispositions (e.g., arrogance or obsequiousness) tend to remain fairly stable despite changes in the precise details of how they may be manifested across development.

"The automatic, unconscious, repeated performance of routine behaviors is the essence of character."[28]

They therefore argue that character "results from the activation of neural networks that have been assembled as a consequence of procedural learning within the context of a specific temperament."[29] On this theory, infants acquire character as an array of procedural memories (or habits) through their relations with early caregivers. These relationships establish, say Grigsby and Stevens, basic neurophysiological regulation, and later in life, the individual uses these same procedurally learned processes to regulate behavior and that way manifests character. "The genesis of character remains obscure not because of repression but because it is in the nature of procedural memories that they are unconscious, have no content, and are completely dissociable from declarative memory."[30] We cannot say how we came to be the people we are.[31]

Affect regulation

Neuropsychoanalyst Alan N. Schore has written about "affect regulation" as the core of the "self," established in the child's growing toward a personality.[32] This core is established in the first year and a half or so of life and provides the armature for the child's growing and ungrowing of neurons in its further development toward adult personality. In essence, the infant's intimate relation with its mother (or "primary caregiver") consists of emotional interactions, body contact, and, in particular, facial expressions. These provide the infant with experiences of joy (in roughly the first 9-12 months) and, in the later period, disapproval, as the toddler becomes able to get into trouble.

From the neuroscientific literature, Schore has established that, in his words,

> the vitally important attachment experiences of infancy are stored in the early maturing right hemisphere, and that for the rest of the lifespan unconscious working models of the attachment relationship encode strategies of affect regulation for coping with stress, especially interpersonal stress. These internal representations are accessed as guides for future interactions, and the term *working* refers to the individual's unconscious use of them to interpret and act on new experiences.[33]

Schore is stating in terms of the brain a familiar psychoanalytic principle: early attachment experiences with a mother (or "primary caregiver") lay down patterns of "affect regulation" for the individual's lifetime. Schore finds a neural base for such patterns of affect regulation in the right orbitofrontal cortex, more specifically, the descending pathway to the limbic system.

As baby-watching psychologists, notably Colwyn Trevarthen,[34] have long pointed out, early maternal interactions regulate emotions. The mother serves as an external regulator of the neurochemicals in the infant's developing brain, hence of emotional experience. According to Schore, there are two critical stages in the development of that brain.

In the first critical period, experiences of joy and reunion activate the sympathetic nervous system that energizes us for fight or flight, exciting the infant. These positive experiences produce neuroendocrine changes, specifically the innervation of orbitofrontal areas, particularly in the early maturing visuospatial right hemisphere. More technically, these positive "attachment" experiences create dopamine-releasing axons in the orbitofrontal cortex and the maturation of the ventral tegmental forebrain-midbrain circuit.[35] If the details of the pathway correspond, these regions could be Jaak Panksepp's SEEKING system,.

In the second year, at say 14-16 months, Schore observes, socialization begins. "Don't throw your peas on the floor." Rebuke leads to inhibition. The child experiences shame and, "Thou shalt not." This second stage, associated with negative experiences, serves to regulate the parasympathetic system that calms us down. This stage gives rise to the expansion of the second limbic circuit in Schore's picture, the parasympathetic lateral tegmental limbic circuit that restrains action. This circuit also becomes wired into the orbitofrontal cortex, creating an inhibitory system.[36]

Together these interactions, internalized in the infant's brain, create, according to Schore, a system and a recurring pattern of affect regulation. This internalized regulation gets laid down in paths that run from ancient parts of the midbrain to the earliest parts of the still-developing frontal lobes. And these paths occur primarily in the right hemisphere, because it becomes active at birth. The left hemisphere "comes online" later. These systems respond to emotions of pleasure and unpleasure in the developing individual. "The attempt to regulate affect—to minimize unpleasant feelings and to maximize pleasant ones—is the driving force in human motivation,"[37] Freud's (un)pleasure principle.

Schore has described, it seems to me, a neurological basis for an observed theme-and-vartiations style or identity. Affect regulation, I suggest, is what regulates virtually all other brain processes. Feelings are what tell you that something you have tried out on the world, a perception or an action, has or has not succeeded. Damasio, Luria, and many other neuroscientists have written about the guiding role of feelings. I understand feelings in this context as what monitors the outcome of the various feedbacks and feedforwards that our brains use to cope with our changing environment. The feeling you get after you look at something or hear something or do something determines what you will do next. If it feels good, you will repeat it. If it doesn't, you won't. And repetition becomes character or identity. Thus, Schore's "pattern of affect regulation" becomes a style of being or an identity as observed from outside.

When we are reading a book or seeing a film or play, responding literarily, line by line and word by word and scene by scene, we are always confronting something new. So too, when creating, the writer keeps confronting new thoughts. We are always trying to fit these new things, these slight challenges, into our normal processing, that is, our characteristic way of thinking. Our emotional response to the literary work, our feelings of pleasure or unpleasure, tell us how successful we have been in getting enjoyment from it. And our feelings of pleasure lead to repetition and thus to our taste, which forms part of our total identity.

Mind and brain

Psychoanalyst Arnold Modell draws on Kurt Goldstein's idea of one central motive, to actualize oneself: "The need to maintain the continuity and coherence of the self is a vital urge of no less importance than sexual desire or the need for attachment to others." "I propose that the continuity and coherence of the self is . . . a psychobiological homeostat."[38] For neurological backing, Modell relies on Gerald Edelman, the Nobel-winning neuroscientist with whom he has worked.

Edelman divides the nervous system into two large systems. One Edelman calls "nonself." This system (cerebral cortex, thalamus, and cerebellum) operates through sensory interactions with the outer world, through experience and behavior. In particular, it develops learned perceptual categories. It learns what is food, a tool, or a human being. The other system, the "self," exists to assure the persistent dominance of adaptive homeostasis within a person. Biologically, it operates through hypothalamus, pituitary, parts of the brain stem, amygdala, hippocampus and limbic system, all evolutionarily ancient parts of the brain. They underlie what is presumably involved in one's fluctuating sense of one's self (identity-from-inside): the frontal and temporal cortices.

One system deals homeostatically with the inner world. The other deals through perceptions and actions with the outer world.[39] They must combine. We need both systems to coordinate diverse sensory inputs. The means for doing this, Edelman calls "reentry." The evolutionary constraints on this internally-directed system, Edelman terms "value"; value acts as a bias on reentry. Through reentry connections in the brain, the organism selects perceptions and behaviors that elicit favorable values. Thus, values (our ratings of experiences) contribute to the fitness of the organism for reproduction and survival.[40]

Previous experiences in the sensorimotor system have inscribed emotional values matched to perceptual categories. Chocolate is good. Castor oil is bad. Keats is good. Edgar Guest is bad. These value-categories connect to current perceptual categories, so that the individual now will *characteristically* seek Keats and avoid Edgar Guest. Connections between the two systems ensure that adult past experiences (like early mother-infant interactions) lay down the values for future perceptions and motor actions.

These remembered value-categories and the systems

for imposing them on current experience correspond to autopoesis or identity, a basis for the evolutionary persistence of species characteristics. They also support style or character or Lichtenstein's identity-from-outside.

Lichtenstein instances his theory with several case histories (all reported in his 1977 book). I have added still more: Ronald Reagan; five subjects of an experiment in reading; Robert Frost; F. Scott Fitzgerald; George Bernard Shaw; a young woman, Ellen, who told me why she thought some cartoons were funny; and Freud's case history of Little Hans, where one can trace an identity from the five-year-old boy to the adult director of operas. Some of those cases show how identity-from-outside persists even through the changes wrought by a psychoanalysis or brainwashing.[41]

18 | Cultural Styles

> Sense data are taken, not merely given: we learn to perceive. . . . The teacher has forgotten, and the student himself will soon forget, that what he sees [in the microscope] conveys no information until he knows beforehand the kind of thing he is expected to see.
>
> —Sir Peter Medawar, "Hypothesis and Imagination"

GIVEN THE NEUROPSYCHOLOGY of a theme-and-variations identity-from-outside we can account for the way we create or enjoy literature in an individual way. We perceive and enjoy within a personal style. But styles are also social. We have a Romantic style, a postmodern style, a French or German style, and so on. Neuroscience can tell us a good deal about the relation between an individual identity, character, or style of writing or reading and the cultural environment in which that style came into being. We can draw on one of the cardinal principles of neuropsychology, the hierarchy or nesting of neural functions.

In the nineteenth century, John Hughlings Jackson, the "father of British neurology"[1] concluded that the brain worked by a hierarchy of levels. The lower levels feed information to higher functions, but the lower levels also are governed by those higher functions, more associated with the limbic system and the frontal cortex. We could say higher functions *use* lower functions. If the control by higher brain centers is removed (through disease, injury, exhaustion, or temporary inhibition), the next lower centers, normally under the control of the higher centers, take over, leading to overactivity of those lower centers.

Freud was much taken with Jackson's thinking. This idea of hierarchy formed his psychoanalytic model of the mind. Reality-oriented, "secondary" processes ordinarily govern "primary," wish-fulfilling processes. But, if the higher control is lost, as in dreaming, moments of creative inspiration or "poetic faith," wish-fulfillment takes over.

Naturally, when we are talking about the creation or re-creation of literature, we are talking almost entirely about functions at quite "high" (frontal) levels. Even so, we can use the principle of hierarchy to think about how individual style and cultural givens interact. Think back to the three diagrams at the beginning of chapter 15: text-active, bi-active, and reader-active. The reader-active model of responding to literature gives us a starting-point. The reader constructs an experience, using the materials of the text. To build that experience, the reader deploys various hypotheses about the text, ranging from recognizing individual letters to sophisticated hypotheses about theme or character.

A hierarchy

We can distinguish four levels. At the lowest, most basic level, we perceive our environment by means of a series of a physiological tests. These are much the same for all physiologically normal human beings: eyes, ears, nose, tongue, fingertips, and the rest of our senses.

At a different level, we deploy our knowledge of our culture. We can recognize a flag, a stop sign, or a fork for what they are. This cultural level is much the same for all of us in a given culture, which can be defined narrowly or broadly, the "South," the U.S., or "Western civilization."

At yet another level, we belong to "interpretive communities," in Stanley Fish's phrase and concept.[2] They can range from informal book clubs to social and political groupings (liberals, feminists) to sophisticated literary schools (deconstructionism, psychoanalysis). People within these communities will apply similar tactics for creating their literary experiences, tactics not shared by others in the larger culture and thus not shared at the other two levels. And they will share tactics not just for literary experiences, but for seeing any data, as in the epigraph.

Ultimately, at a fourth level, I have personal memories and concerns and needs, some conscious, some unconscious, and these I will deploy to complete my literary experience. While all humans share the lowest level and some humans share the middle levels, this highest level no one else shares with me.

According to Freud and Jackson, "higher" levels govern lower levels. That is, I—an individual with a unique identity—use the skills I have learned while professing literature within my interpretive community to form my literary experiences. But to use my specialized skills, I must draw on general cultural knowledge that I share with just about everybody in the U.S.A. And to perceive the literary work itself, I use basic physiological skills of perception and memory that I share with virtually all other humans.

In general, the higher tactic *uses* the lower tactic to accomplish its ends. But the lower tactic can only do what the lower tactic can do. If the lower tactic is, say, the ability to read English, but only English, that is the only thing a higher level, interpretation, say, can use to satisfy its needs. The lower skill enables *but also limits* the higher skill.

We can systematize these four levels of experiencing literature as a hierarchy (in the Jackson tradition). We can imagine a stacking of feedbacks (like the one in the reader-active model). Each feedback loop provides the rule or test or hypothesis for the loop below it. The loops below both *enable* and *limit* the loop above:

at the most abstract level, I have my *identity* understood as an identity theme and a history of variations on that theme (will this satisfy me?);

at intermediate levels, I have tactics I have internalized from culture, of two kinds:

canon-tactics: tactics for understanding followed by my interpretive community; rules with which other people in my culture may well differ (Marxism, psychoanalysis);

code-tactics: tactics followed by my entire culture; rules that no member of this culture would normally believe otherwise (stop sign, fork);

at the lowest level, skills using my *organs of perception and movement* (sights, sounds, etc., that just about all other people share).

Psychologists will recognize that I am offering a version of constructivism or the "personal construct psychology" of George Kelly.[3] Kelly famously said, "Man is a scientist," always trying to predict events by building up and refining theories or models about how the world works. I have called them codes and canons.

Not just individual

Presumably these canons and codes are embodied in widely distributed systems in the brain. They would have to call on semantic and episodic memory systems (knowledge of the world and of one's own experience), language systems, particularly the visual and aural lexicons, and even procedural memory for reading skills.

We can now understand what critics and psychologists mean when they speak of "objective" features of a literary work. They are referring to those features about which everybody within a given culture would agree. They are referring to the two lower levels in this four-level model of response (codes and physiology). Hamlet is a Danish prince.

Ultimately, I suggest, a high-level identity theme governs the three lower levels: my canons, my codes, and my body. Such an identity theme might well exist in the frontal-to-midbrain circuitry defined by Schore, Modell, Damasio, and others (ch. 17). Thinking psychoanalytically, one can formulate a highly abstract verbal theme that describes what an observer would see as the me-ness of me, my "self," the theme I varyingly re-enact over and over. Thinking neuropsychologically—I am drawing on Schore and Panksepp—I suggest that such a theme exists physically as projections from the midbrain and upper brain stem (specifically the periaqueductal gray) up through the limbic system into the lower and midline regions (ventromedial) of the frontal cortex.

My growing identity (the persistent identity theme plus variations on it) sets the standard for my applying the various hypotheses provided by my culture. These are the canon-tactics and the code-tactics in the table above. As E. D. Hirsch has abundantly shown, we need this knowledge (that is, semantic memories) to interpret literary works. What we can bring to bear on what we read determines how much we can understand it.[4] And Hirsch has developed an ambitious program of school reform to give students the culturally shared knowledge (for formng canons and codes) that they need to enjoy or profit from reading.

These canons and codes, in turn, use my eyes and ears to sense the words that I will interpret by means of the cultural tactics applied by my identity. So far as literature is concerned, we apply the term "style" to the tactics associated with an interpretive community and an individual. We might, but probably do not, think of physiological or code-tactics as involving style. We can speark, for example, of Anglo-American or, especially!, French styles of interpretation.

Using this model, we can understand how people agree and disagree in their interpretations. If two people are considering the same work and using the same way of interpreting it, they are likely to agree although they probably do so with different personal styles (enthusiastically, grudgingly, cautiously, and so on). They agree because they share the three lower levels and tactics described above, but not the topmost, personal identity. If enough people agree (and this is easier at the lower levels), we take that to be a "true" interpretation. Hamlet is a Danish prince who wears black clothes. That agreement requires only the two lower levels. Where interpreters commonly disagree are the two higher levels. Marxist critics might regard the psychoanalytic reading of *Hamlet* as socially irresponsible.

Notice how the Hasson and Malach experiments with films[5] apply here. Recording the brain activities of five subjects watching a movie, the experimenters found "across-subject, stereotypical response[s] to external world stimuli." They are describing, in the table above, the low levels of basic visual and auditory processing objects like buildings and guns by means of cultural codes. They found "unique, individual variations,"[6] differences in frontal lobe activity that would correspond to the upper levels of canons and personal identity. Their experiments divide the hierarchy described above between codes and canons, rules and physiology shared by all members of a culture and hypotheses shared by only some. One should also remember that the experiment used films to re-create "natural" conditions of perception and understanding. We do not invoke our personal styles just for literature; we use them to perceive the world. Even scientists looking through microscopes need to be taught and to acquire canons and codes (as in the epigraph from Sir Peter Medawar).

Styles, what and why

A style of being, then, consists of a theme-and-variations identity governing lower and and relatively less low levels of understanding stimuli. It is easy, then, to understand why there are styles: because evolutionarily, neurologically, developmentally, and socially, they become built into our brains. At some levels, these styles are alike, because we humans have to live among other humans. Human societies re-create themselves (fulfilling the identity principle or autopoesis). Our parents who represent society to us as infants cannot help but instill in us the codes and canons by which they test and understand the world.[7] And we in turn pass them on willy-nilly to our own children. That way, we survive in our culture.

Culture reproduces itself because humans do. But we are also individuated people. We have different heredity, had different childhoods, live different lives, and so we accrue different identities. Styles become alike and different.

Styles are what make our human species so variously and endlessly fascinating. Styles are what let humanists like me discuss and discuss endlessly the meanings of literary works. Styles are what allow all of us to enjoy works of literature differently, according to our individual tastes.

19 | Pleasure Principles

> Then I thought of reading—the nice and subtle happiness of reading. This was enough, this joy not dulled by Age, this polite and unpunished vice, this selfish, serene, life-long intoxication.
>
> —Logan Pearsall Smith, *Trivia*, "Consolation."

WE HAVE COME far enough in this exploration of the ways we create or respond to literature to look back.

A review

Enjoying literature is what the neuropsychologists would call a *self-stimulation system*, but, obviously, a far more complicated one than a laboratory rat's constantly pressing a lever to get an injection of amphetamine in its brain. I think we can separate the self-stimulation we get from literature into a cycle of four discernibly different processes. When we do, we can see that the same process describes our pleasure in the work as a whole and as we go through it bit by bit. We can also see that this process, SEEKING and comsummation, wanting and liking, mimics what we do in life. We can also understand why we enjoy painful things, like tragedies, and, conversely, why we laugh. The pleasure comes from wanting followed by liking. As for the four different processes—

Expectation (ch. 12) We come to a literary work construing it as a piece of a three-dimensional world "out there," separate from ourselves. In general, we expect not to act on it, and we expect to enjoy it. Then, based on our memories of similar things, expectations about genre, about this or that author, or about the historical period of the work, we build more focused expectations about this particular text. These expectations color our perceptions and ultimately our whole experience of the work. Declarative memory tells us what is new, and our brains' attention systems focus us on that new thing[1] or, for a literary work, that sequence of new things. For each of us, our preferred balance of the expected and the unexpected will be the gateway to having a literary experience. If we cannot fit the literary work into our ongoing expectations, we will put down the book or walk out of the theater. If it ceases to be novel, we will become bored and leave it. We need a balance: new but not perplexingly so.

Form (ch. 13) Writers so shape the form of the work as to control what comes newly to our attention or what crowds out other elements. The brain demands that we pay attention to what is new, and it mobilizes our own habitual defenses (or ways of coping with our inner and outer worlds) toward this new thing. The form of the literary work and, in a theater, the reactions of other audience members co-act with our own inner defense mechanisms to help us achieve whatever emotional goals we have in relation to that literary work. Ideally, outer form and inner defense combine harmoniously, enabling the pleasure-seeking that was our goal in approaching the literary work in the first place.

Content (chs. 15-16) Our conscious and unconscious expectations about books and media in general and about this particular genre or author or period, have defined our goals to some extent. Then, as we read or hear or see some particular literary work, we generate other goals—wishes—from it. We can distinguish three types of this generation.

First, to make sense of it, we use schemas to fill in the gaps in the work. We infer things unsaid like motives, causes, happenings offstage, or the look of a character in a book.

Second, as the left hemisphere processes the literal language of a literary work, our SEEKING to fulfill expectations takes advantage of the right hemisphere's maintaining of alternative meanings for the words. To the extent we are "absorbed," our reality-testing systems weaken and perhaps shut down. We allow possibilities that would be foreclosed in non-literary discourse by the more logical, realistic left hemisphere. Goal-directed, wish-fulfilling fantasies fill in, adding "unconscious content" to the "plain sense" of left-hemisphere meanings. The ambiguities of literary language allow the right hemisphere's normally suppressed meanings to express unconscious wishes and so enter into our literary experience.

Third, and most important, we project our conscious and, especially, unconscious goals onto the events portrayed. Consciously, we take pleasure in witnessing or imagining a happy ending: boy gets girl or hero defeats villain. It is not so much that we "identify" with the characters' goals. *We ourselves wish to see this or that outcome represented in the literary work*. Perceiving a satisfying outcome gratifies wishes, some of which we have carried forward from infancy. We have goals embedded in our character. And these wishes, like our characteristic expectations and defenses, color our perception of the poem or story or drama.

These wishes and impulses, partly conscious, partly deeply unconscious, involve dopaminergic SEEKING systems that run from the brain stem up into the limbic system and express all over the frontal and perceptual lobes. It seems clear that dopamine (indeed, one particular receptor for dopamine) modulates this exploratory behavior, this SEEKING.[2]

Endings (ch. 14) We find a closure at an intellectual level for the varous SEEKINGs that we have experienced. To do so, we use frontal lobe processes, probably verbal, involving semantic memories, our most advanced kind of thinking as opposed to the brain operations involved in expectation, form-and-defense, or content. When we get the feeling that we have "made sense" of a work, then we feel satisfied. It is ours. When we find closure in the work, it becomes part of our regular making sense of the world. We have coped with the literary work as we cope (or try to cope) with new experiences in life. We can leave the literary work with our original expectations satisfied, as in the epigraph of chapter 14, or I could use Emily Dickinson's lovely phrasing, "There is a finished feeling . . . A leisure of the future."

All these processes coact. If I can find that finished feeling, that closure, if I can make pleasure from the work, I reinforce my usual kinds of wishes and desires and gratify my expectations. I lose track of the ordinary world and make the literary work part of my own mental functioning. I become one with the literary work. If I feel pleasure, that emotional signal confirms me in my defenses. (They are working!) Being able to make sense of the imaginary world of a work of literature also confirms me in my characteristic way of making sense of my own everyday world, and that feels good. It gives me a sense of mastery and being in control. And all these justify my expectations.

If these form-and-content, expectation-and-closure cycles that we are performing feel good enough, we will begin to have those moments when we suspend our connections to our bodies, the environment, and our ordinary testing of reality. We will feel "transported" or "rapt" or (Victor Nell's word) "entranced." Things in the work feel as though they were part of our own mental processes of desire and coping. As they are.

Victor Nell, in his study of reading for pleasure, distinguishes two kinds of literary pleasure. In the one I have tried to explain above, we feel "rewarded" by this kind of cycle, by a proper ending to the whole or by the little miniature closures of a particularly choice metaphor or image.[3] In the other, according to Nell, we read (or go to films and plays) to escape the cares of everyday life. I think that pleasure of escape corresponds to the feeling of being "transported" with the work and therefore unaware of ordinary concerns. It is not the same as the pleasure we get from the very words of the work.

Film theorist Ed Tan suggests something quite like this model. Viewers remain interested in a narrative film to the extent that (1) they can envision "a number of possible structures" resulting from the current narrative situation, (2) they can "continually test their probability," that is, the likelihood that any one of those structures will be realized, and (3) in the course of this testing, they can feel that there is "progress made in the direction of closure or, more precisely, the *preferred final situation*."[4] Tan describes the successful film as balancing a viewer's cognitive and emotional (affective) investment in it by a return in the form of progress toward some preferred final solution.

The pleasure cycle

In sum, when we respond to a literary work we are cycling through well-nigh instantaneous circuits of expectation, form-and-defense, content as schemas and fantasy, and finally a closure or "making sense" that gratifies the original expectation. Jaak Panksepp provides an explanation of this cycling and why we enjoy it.

He notes that when the SEEKING system succeeds in finding the reward it sought, that system shuts down, and a second system, a consummatory system takes over. After hunger has led us to the restaurant, we eat. "Consummatory behaviors" replace SEEKING in "the real-life flow of the underlying brain systems." "When animals eat, drink, or have sex," writes Panksepp,

> there appears to be a chaotic, dancelike tension between the consummatory and appetitive phases of behavior. As the animal momentarily settles down to eat, each swallow is followed by the urge to reach out for more. Just picture yourself eating potato chips . . . . Your hand repeatedly reaches out with with an apparent mind of its own.[5]

"On the perceptual side," Solms and Turnbull sum up, "this [consummatory] system generates feelings of pleasurable delight: 'That feels *good!*' On the motor side, this system switches appetitive behaviors off and replaces them with *consummatory* behaviors."[6] Panksepp is describing *self-stimulating systems*. "Such cyclic urges to reach out and seek rewards constitute the basic adaptive function of the underlying [self-stimulation] circuits."[7]

Our seeking and enjoying literature, it seems to me, is just such a system. I suppose it is sacrilegious to suggest that a highbrow human activity like reading poetry corresponds evolutionarily to a laboratory rat's pressing a bar to get a spritz of an addictive drug. But surely we turn to literature to enjoy ourselves just as the rat turns to the self-stimulating bar. Panksepp suggests "that 'intense interest,' 'engaged curiosity,' and 'eager anticipation' are the types of feelings that reflect arousal of this [SEEKING] system in humans."[8] And they are exactly the feelings I have and that I seek over and over with plays, poetry, stories, and movies.

With literature, though, we do not literally consummate. Books and media do not give us real potato chips. Nor were we SEEKING them. We were seeking an imaginary boy-gets-girl or hero-trounces-villain experience, the kind of "rewards" described by theorists like Nell, Tan, and many others. Knowing this was "only literary," we had shut down our systems for acting on the real world. We only wish to *imagine* a completion to our SEEKING. When E. M. Forster contrasts "The king died and then the queeen died," as a mere story with "The king died, and then the queen died of grief' as a plot,"[9] he is describing this kind of literary consummation. We accept an imaginary gratification of an imagined goal that we assigned ourselves (a rationale for the queen's death). Such goals we ourselves project into the literary work.

Moreover, moment by moment, as we read or as we listen, we project goals and accept gratifications purely in terms of language. Literature, after all, is language.

Literary language again

I've suggested that language becomes "literary" (and differing in degree from ordinary language) because of off-beat ("non-salient") meanings retrieved from the right hemisphere language centers (ch. 16). But literary language also provides much of the joy in experiencing literature.

To take a simple example, in Edward Lear's limerick, I had wondered, How will Lear rhyme to "Tobago"? I wanted the poem to yield an answer. I really did not care whether the old man from Tobago would get a meal he could enjoy; I just wanted that difficult rhyme solved. When I read Lear's clever solution, "may go," I satisfied in that way my interest and curiosity (my SEEKING). Now I know.

Now I have closure. Notice, too, that I accepted an *imaginary* gratification, one in words only. That was in fact what I was SEEKING, because I was not using my systems for SEEKING real gratifications in my real world beyond Lear's limerick. I did not care a whit for this fictional old man's fictional diet.

Edward Lear's limerick and Housman's little poem—these are surely "literary." But we find literary language all around us, not just in the official genres of fiction, drama, and poetry. A sentence caught my eye when I was casually reading *The New Yorker.* Anthony Lane, one of the most entertaining of our movie reviewers, was writing about the second half of Jean-Luc Godard's latest film. "My wish to relate the events of this second half is slightly thwarted by my inability to work out what they are."[10]

Look at the verbal tricks. This is a sentence about being stopped in one's tracks—thwarted. The first half has several *s* sounds: "My wi*sh* to relate the event*s* of thi*s* *s*econd half i*s* *s*lightly . . . " And it has several sounds that I feel in my mouth as lasting a bit of extra time, as continuing, like those *s* sounds: "*My* wi*sh* to *rel*ate *ev*ents *of* this second hal*f* is sl*igh*tly . . . " Together these give me the feeling in the muscles of my mouth of a continuous moving, a lengthening of time. Then I come to the double dentals of "thwar*ted.* " Bump. I hit a wall (the wall of my teeth?). And the dentals are followed by "*b*y . . . *b*ility . . . wor*k* . . . wha*t*"

In other words, as I read the sentence, I feel a movement forward, and then it abruptly stops, carrying out Lane's sense of "thwarted," the key word in the sentence. In effect, the surface of the language captures my attention, while Lane slips in his witty gibe at the obscurity of Godard's film. The sentence feels good to me, because I can use the order of Lane's thought, the passive that at first hides his point, to gain a feeling of success. His thought, at first a little hard to understand, therefore got my attention in the stream of *New Yorker* prose that I was reading. Now, I can finally make it clear and sensible, no longer an attention-grabbing novelty. I have moved from SEEKING to a consummatory meaningfulness, all at the level of language, all of it an *imaginary* gratification.

This kind of play with language, which we experience in poetry or "musical" prose or "literary language," involves the brain in a different kind of processing alongside the logical step-by-step sequential processing of language. Neurology traditionally associates that orderly processing with the left hemisphere language systems, the auditory cortex, Wernicke's area, the arcuate fasciculus, and Broca's area. We fill in the gaps we find in the words' descriptions. But when language gets tricky, as in Lane's sentence, the momentary novelty and uncertainty allows us spreading activations. We include in our interpretation unconscious goal-fulfilling and right-hemisphere meanings we would ordinarily suppress (ch. 16).

Alliteration and rhyme or just the kind of repetition Anthony Lane used—non-ordinary language—must by its very non-ordinariness engage our brains in non-ordinary ways. Some experimental findings suggest particular brain paths for the small parts of language, the parts that we find oddly used in literary language. For example, there is evidence that we process initial consonants differently from final consonants and that we process fricatives (¦f¦, ¦s¦, or ¦z¦) and affricates (as in eigh¦th¦) in a special place in our brains. There is evidence that English-speaking Broca's aphasics tend to omit grammatical morphemes, while German and Italian Broca's aphasics tend to substitute one grammatical morpheme for another.[11] The phonetic, grammatical, and semantic tricks of literary language must induce our brains to behave oddly, like the contradiction in "slightly thwarted."

In general, we process the sound effects of poetry and other details of "literary language" by using our brain systems differently from the way we do with ordinary language. With poetic language we focus a large part of our attention on the language itself as opposed to its "content." And we accept in language, in both meanings and sound effects, gratifications that are imaginary.

The literariness of language is a relative thing, however. The most banal statement can be stunningly "literary" in the right hands, as essayist Louis Menand points out for one sentence in the final, culminating paragraph of perhaps the greatest short story in our language. Writing about James Joyce's "The Dead," Menand comments,

> The difficulty of putting into words the effect a story produces is part of the point. . . . James Joyce called the effect an "epiphany," . . . . What Joyce meant by an epiphany was, he said, just 'a revelation of the whatness of a thing,' a sudden apprehension of the way the world unmediatedly is. Language being one of the principal means by which the world is mediated, the epiphany is an experience beyond (or after, or without) words. 'Snow was general all over Ireland.' The sentence is as banal and literal as a weather report. (In fact, in the story it *is* a weather report.) But if "The Dead" works, then that sentence, when it comes, triggers the exact shiver of recognition that Joyce wants you to have.[12]

Menand neatly phrases this effect as "the expected unexpected." Ralph Waldo Emerson asked writers to omit everything but "the spirited *mot* which amused or warmed you when you spoke it—because of its luck & newness." "Then all the words will be sprightly, and every sentence a surprise."[13] Robert Frost wrote of a poem's ending as "unforeseen [but] predestined."[14]

The usual thing that we say about literariness in language that succeeds is that it is "surprising but right." Something seems offbeat ("non-salient"), and then we make sense of it. It feels somehow "expected," "right," "a sudden apprehension of the way the world unmediatedly is." It has denouement. It has an outcome that, though unforeseen, was predestined from the first image of the original mood—and indeed from the very mood. Neuropsychologically, "surprising but right" corresponds to SEEKING plus consummation.

Somehow Joyce's utterly banal but unexpected comment about the weather sums up the deadening Christmas party that constitutes the bulk of this long story. (Is it because Christmas is the traditional time for ghost stories and these are the walking dead?) I project onto that flat sentence all the loveless repression and mediocrity that has gone before, onto the snow coldly covering and smothering.

Anthony Lane's confession that he is going to fall short as a reviewer of Godard's film surprises me enough to gain my attention. I wish to resolve the surprise, and his conclusion allows me to do so (and, incidentally, to gratify my aggressive impulses by a poke at Jean-Luc Godard's annoying obscurity). "Tobago" in Lear's limerick surprises me—how on earth can he rhyme to that?

Writers can easily surprise. It is harder to write "right," to leave us feeling that what surprised us has subsided into satisfaction. As Mark Twain famously said, "The difference between the right word and the almost right word is like the difference between lightning and the lightning bug." (And that is itself a nice example of literary language.) Yes, I feel a little as though lightning had struck me when I read the "right" word. I have to remember, though, that it is I who have to make it "right." If I did not know that what Twain calls a "lightning bug" is what I call a "firefly," I could not get the feeling of rightness Twain wanted me to have.

Where is "literary"?

"Literary" then is not a property of the language as such. The mere presence of rhyme or metaphor does not make language "literary."[15] "Unexpected," "non-salient"—these terms require reference to our mental processes of expectation or familiarity. Joyce's sentence is itself banal, but it is our thinking it through that makes it brilliant. Language only becomes "literary" when it enables *us* to do certain things with it, namely, to make it a *satisfying* part of *our* patterns of expectation, unpleasure-avoiding, goal-imagining, and goal-achieving. Having found it "surprising," we make it "right." That is when it becomes "literary." In other words, we call language literary when *we* can cycle through this miniature literary work, this phrasing, as we cycle through some much longer literary work.

To argue that "literary" is a property of the language as such, apart from our own or someone's perception of it, would require us to step out of our human bodies. We would be claiming that we can perceive something about the language that is quite independent of our human perceptions and capacities. We would have to be able to take, in philosopher Hilary Putnam's phrase, a "god's eye view" of that particular bit of language.

In short, in the familiar formula, "surprising but right," it is only if we readers and viewers can make the surprise "right," that we will feel the presence of something literary. Only then will we go beyond surprise to aesthetic pleasure. In Menand's phrase, the unexpected must return to being the expected. Only then can we make even ugliness into something we enjoy aesthetically.

20 | Enjoying the Ugly

> There is nothing ugly. *I never saw an ugly thing in my life*: for let the form of an object be what it may, —light, shade, and perspective will always make it beautiful.
>
> — John Constable[1]

WE ENJOY UGLY or painful things if they are presented in works of art—why? Think of the paintings of Francis Bacon or William Burroughs' *Naked Lunch* or the sight of Oedipus with his eyes torn out. Aristotle asked that question long ago. His answer was: "[T]o be learning something is the greatest of pleasures . . . . [T]he reason of the delight in seeing the picture is that one is at the same time learning—gathering the meaning of things."[2]

The neuropsychological answer is not that different. We enjoy ugly or threatening things in art, because we are SEEKING—and finding. *Both the act of SEEKING and the act of removing the threat and incorporating painful things into our normal mental functioning yield pleasure.*

SEEKING and pleasure

SEEKING itself is a source of pleasure. We anticipate something good happening. We feel invigorated. Also, we wish (unconsciously, to be sure) to maintain our brains at an optimal level of arousal. Technically, the mesolimbic dopaminergic circuit within the medial forebrain bundle is "tonically active." Animals need always to be SEEKING to achieve their evolutionary goals of survival and reproduction. We, like them, need to be searching for food or sex or to be preserving our lives. We humans, faced with an hour's wait in a doctor's office, will pick up even a years-old *Time* magazine.

Inevitably, our SEEKING will happen on unpleasant thngs. The strange thing is that we even seek them out. Most of us, when we drive by a particularly grisly highway accident, will crane our necks around to see the bodies and the blood. That's odd.

Evolutionary psychology provides, I think, an explanation. Dead bodies, "low" animals, rotting food—these all represent potential threats to our survival and reproduction. Our brains insist that we pay attention to them, because we may need to do something about them. To trigger those actions, we look at the ugly and painful more intensely than we look at blander sights. And that holds true in the neuropsychologists' experiments with pictures of such things.[3]

But we take *pleasure* in seeing them—why? SEEKING carries with it a feeling, "an affective urge that characterizes all motivated behaviors." Jaak Panksepp and his associates call it, "enthusiastic positive excitement," "interest," "desire," and "euphoria," a feeling that "generally tends to counteract negative feelings, even though it may not eliminate them."[4] This is the feeling we have when we enjoy *War and Peace*, despite the pain and loss and bloodshed that Tolstoy portrayed. We feel the negative emotions that

Aristotle pointed to, *but* we also feel that sense of positive anticipation. We are SEEKING to learn the meaning of things.

Why do we go on roller coasters? (Some of us, anyway.) Or go to horror movies? Because good feelings go with SEEKING, they can make a recreation even of fear. Freud seems to have happened on this SEEKING explanation, although he described it as sexual. He noticed how fearful situations sexually arouse children:

> The sexually exciting effect of many emotions which are in themselves unpleasurable, such as feelings of apprehension, fright or horror, persists in a great number of people throughout their adult life. There is no doubt that this is the explanation of why so many people seek opportunities for sensations of this kind, subject to the proviso that the seriousness of the unpleasurable feelings is damped down by certain qualifying facts, such as its occurring in an imaginary world, in a book or in a play.[5]

Books and plays, Freud is suggesting, work like roller coasters. We *enjoy* exercising even our unpleasant emotions, *provided* we can resolve them.

Resolutions

Freud points, then, to a second reason why we enjoy ugly or fearful things if they are presented as art or literature. We are SEEKING to be scared or disgusted—*provided we end up reassured.* We are SEEKING a novelty for ourselves that could be threatening, and it engrosses our entire attention. We imagine (or a work of literature imagines for us) the aversions and dangers. By making sense of what we have seen or read, though, we get past alarming or disgusting novelties and embed them in our ordinary mental functioning. Finally, we survive, and *we return to ordinary life.*

In sum, enjoying a work of literature involves a succession of SEEKINGs followed by consummations followed by new SEEKINGs. *SEEKING, in and of itself, evokes euphoric emotions.* Also, by means of frontal lobe executive functions, we make sense of what we find in these SEEKINGs, making them non-novel and therefore non-threatening. The unexpected becomes the expected. We make them part of our unaroused, ongoing mental activity. And then we start the process again. We cycle in this way bit by bit through the literary work. Then when we have finished it, we have completed this same cyclical process, SEEKING followed by consummation in the form of making sense, now for the work as a whole.

Thus we enjoy tragedies. We bring them from representations of the direst threats outside us into our inner mental processing, and there we fit them into our schemas for understanding the world. By making sense of them, we tame them. In life, we try to do the same and if we cannot, we feel distress and seek harder for answers. We are likely to turn to some fictional "sense," sometimes appealing to a higher power to make our world rational: "It was fated," or "He got what he deserved," or "It was God's will." A self-stimulation process, both in life and literature, enables us to master what we perceive as possible dangers.

With literature, there is also the simple factor of "Thank heavens, this isn't happening to me." As La Rochefoucauld put it in his hard-boiled way, "In the misfortunes of our dearest friends we often find something that is not displeasing." "We all have strength enough to endure the misfortunes of others."[6] Or Alexander Pope, "I never knew any man in my life who could not bear another's misfortunes perfectly like a Christian."[7] And, of course, the literary characters having their eyes torn out (in *Oedipus* or *Lear*) or being led to the guillotine in *A Tale of Two Cities* are not even "our dearest friends." They are not even real. Not only are their misfortunes not ours, we do not have to cope with their predicaments. We do not have to plan adaptive actions. We can have "poetic faith" and even derive pleasure by "making sense" of their misfortunes.

Some of the time, those characters overcome the danger, real or imagined (as when Macheath is pardoned in *The Beggar's Opera* or Brecht's *The Threepenny Opera*). Then we can even laugh, despite the ordeal the characters have gone through. And that leads to another phenomenon, related to the fearful or disgusting in literature.

Why we laugh

There are few things in life more pleasurable than a good, long belly laugh, drawing as it does on a host of body systems in diaphragm, epiglottis, larynx, tear ducts, even the bladder. Furthermore, we humans all have this same physical pattern. Florida professor or Australian aborigine, our bodies do the same things when we laugh.

The visible physical activities of laughter come from still lower and earlier parts of the brain. Interestingly, stroke victims who cannot deliberately move their faces on one side can nevertheless laugh normally—if they laugh spontaneously, that is, involuntarily. That anomaly is evidence that the physical side of laughter comes from a system lower than the damaged cerebrum. The emotion-generating limbic system releases a pre-programmed body activity. Presumably, we laugh by means of the brain stem and basal ganglia, the ancient parts of our brains that govern such "hard-wired" movements like laughing or crying or walking.[8] Our closest primate cousins, chimpanzees, laugh in somewhat the same way we do, and even rats laugh (according to Jaak Panksepp[9]). Evidently, we humans are born to laugh as part of our being mammals.

Then, if we have an inborn physical mechanism for

laughing, what triggers it? *Why* do we laugh? In 1982, I summarized the dozens of traditional theories this way: If we perceive a sudden, playful incongruity that gratifies conscious and unconscious wishes and defeats conscious and unconscious fears to give a feeling of liberation, then we laugh.[10] That sentence describes laughing at a joke or some other form of wit like a cartoon. And it explains joke-laughter fairly accurately, I think. *But most laughter is not joke-laughter.*

Robert Provine has convincingly shown that, in fact, when we laugh, it usually has little to do with jokes or wit.[11] He concludes, from observing and counting people's interactions, that only about 15% of humans' laughter comes from things we would call funny. Rather, we laugh most of the time as a result of social interactions. Provine lists some lines that elicited laughter: "I'll see you guys later." "I should do that, but I'm too lazy." "I told you so!" Pretty clearly, this kind of laughter serves as a kind of social bonding, a way of saying to our fellow-hominins, I mean no harm. I am friendly. And we the hearers want to say, I am friendly, too. So we laugh.

Non-joke laughter can also be caused by physical means like laughing gas, marijuana, or tickling. Tickling is both physical and social, creating bonds between parents and children and between children, not only in humans but in chimpanzees. Tickling is part of the aggressive play in which all young male mammals indulge, and animals' play provides the evolutionary prototype for humans' literature.

Yet we do laugh for purely cognitive reasons; we laugh at jokes, witty remarks, limericks, comedy routines, or something funny in a book. For an example of a stimulus for that kind of cognitive laughing, consider a children's joke, one that, perhaps, only a child could laugh at. "Would you rather have an elephant chase you or a lion?" This grandparent could only answer, "Neither!" My grandson gleefully gave the right answer, "I'd rather have the elephant chase the lion."

In 1982, I approached the matter of cognitive laughter psychoanalytically. (Provine's demonstration that most laughter is social had not appeared at the time.) I showed a group of cartoons by B. Kliban to a subject, Ellen, who had previously told me she found Kliban hilarious. Her response nicely explains not only why we laugh, but why we get pleasure from what one would expect to be displeasing.

Why Ellen laughed

In a seminar probing students' responses to literary works, we had explored Ellen's personal style of reading and writing. We (and Ellen) concluded that Ellen was the kind of person who saw the world in dualities, particularly the duality between self and other. She conceived of that other primarily as a source (rather than, say, as a threat or a promise). She would ensure the other person's giving to her by her own giving. But she does not imagine this as an exchange. Instead, because the other is pleased with Ellen, the other simply, generously gives. The other becomes a freely bountiful source (like a mother).

What Ellen gave, in our university environment, was work, wit, imagination, and intelligence. What she got back was approval and, often, the satisfaction of making others laugh at some of her jokes and stunts. With literature, she enacted that same pattern. She deliberately and consciously invested herself in the literary work so that it would give back pleasure.

She agreed to take part in my cartoon experiment (thus giving of herself). Together, we looked at a book of cartoons by B. Kliban. She had told me she liked Kliban's work, although many people find Kliban's heavy-lined artwork gross and even repellent. I asked open-ended ques-

Figure 20-1. A Kliban cartoon that Ellen found funny.

tions like, Why do you find this funny? Why did you like this one? One really cannot answer such questions, because one laughs for unconscious reasons. Instead, the subject's responses serve as associations to the cartoons. Effectively, I was asking Ellen to free associate to the cartoons she found funny.

When Ellen free associated to her laughing, she showed her basic pattern: I give of myself so that someone will freely give to me.

> ELLEN. Why do I like ugliness? Did I finish that?
>
> NNH. Well, you said because it's there. Because it says that it exists.
>
> ELLEN. Because I know people who look like this [pointing to the cartoon in Figure 20-1]. . . . . his furtive look. Fat. No one's well built in this [book]— Everybody's fat. Everybody's kind of hunchbacked or uneven and— Ugly hair, no one

> has decent hair. . . . And either they're all completely clean, which doesn't fit right with the shape of their faces, or they're pockmarked. Their hair is just—I don't know. It's just so ugly . . . . And you see people who look like that, and you look at them, and you say, "Oh, this is so disgusting." And *you want to think up words for it, and you want to describe it to someone*, and you know if you tell someone, they're going to think you're a horrible person, and in a way *it's funny that you see it, and can't say it, and you know that someone else sees it.* (Italics mine—nnh.)

Ellen wants to give a description and not be criticized for the nastiness of it. She would like not to be given negatively to. She would like to be forgiven, given to positively. So, earlier, I had asked:

> NNH. But why is it funny to take an unpleasant chunk of reality and put it in a cartoon? A grubby, ugly part of reality.
>
> ELLEN. Because it admits that it's there. That's the best part of it, that you see, I see—I am very critical. [My best friend] tells me that I'm overly critical of people and of things, and . . . . this book proves that somebody else sees what I see.
>
> NNH. Sees the world as you see it.
>
> ELLEN. Yeah.

Looking at a cartoon, she wanted to describe it, that is, give it, to someone else. But she is, she says, "overly critical," and it would be a nasty description. She would be seen as nasty. But then she justified the ugliness in the cartoon: "*this book proves that somebody else sees what I see.*" The cartoon originally posed a slight threat to her ongoing mental equilibrium. It was disgusting. But then she was able to embed the cartoon in her regular mental processes of giving and being given to. She found confirmation and forgiveness.

What was mildly threatening, she converted to no threat at all. Neurologist V. S. Ramachandran has hypothesized much the same explanation of laughter at an evolutionary level. He suggests that joke-laughter involves a "gradual build-up of expectation," which he calls a "model." Then the joke provides a sudden twist or anomaly that requires a change in the model, but for laughter the new model has to be "non-threatening." It must have "trivial rather than ominous implications." He calls his hypothesis the "false alarm theory,"[12] suggesting an evolutionary purpose for the physical act of laughing. It is part of the communicative function of emotions. The explosive, repetitive ha-ha sound serves to alert the others in a hominin herd that the anomaly is of trivial consequence. Thus, he explains, the motor paralysis that takes place during laughter would have no effect on survival.

Ellen's laughter, however, did not help a hominin herd. Hers was personal. She was able to work an ugliness that was at first cognitively or emotionally discrepant into a confirmation and reassurance for her overly critical way of seeing the world. That was why she found these cartoons funny when many people do not. She had—and all we advanced hominins have—a *personal* "sense of humor." And her particular sense of humor was embedded in her larger, individual pattern of response to literary and artistic works, her "taste."[13]

Fully to understand why we laugh, then, and, more generally, why we enjoy some works of literature and not others, we need to accept that we have individual identities and styles of being (ch. 17) that lead to individual ways of responding to literature. Readers, no less than writers, have personal styles, which include both a personal "sense of humor" and a more pervasive "taste."

As we have seen, I (like all readers and audience members) come to literature and the other media, expecting to get pleasure while not acting on the work, just reading or watching. That expectation enables me to do the necessary psychological work of responding. Form, acting like a defense, enables me to project personal wishes (SEEKINGs-plus-content) into the work. Enjoying those wishes' gratification justifies the defenses. Finally, I make the experience a regular part of my understanding of the world and my life in it. Sucessfully completing a self-stimulation cycle, I can enjoy even what was at first no fun at all, just ugly or threatening.[14]

"I" and "my" are crucial. Laughing depends on *my* particular sense of humor. Enjoyment depends on *my* expectations, *my* defenses, *my* fantasies, *my* kind of "sense," *my* "taste," in short, *my* style of being. Although critics often talk about wit or meaning "in" the text, both derive from personal styles.

21 | Making Meaning

> Here we have the cause of all the trouble! Words! . . . . how can we understand each other, sir, if into the words which I speak I put the sense and the value of things as they are inside me, while at the same time whoever is listening to them inevitably assumes they have the sense and value that they have in his or her inner world? We think we understand one another, but we never really do understand.
>
> —Luigi Pirandello, *Sei personaggi in cerca d'autore*, I.

WHEN WE GET "the sense of an ending" from a poem or play or plot and especially a joke, we enjoy. If we don't, we don't. From the caption to a Kliban cartoon to the couplet that ends a Shakespearean sonnet, we need that sense of closure, of completion, of the ends being tied up. True. But we also want something more, a "point."

Audiences and readers derive from literary works both the plain sense and the wider range of senses that we get from literary language. We do this at the micro level, word by word, sentence by sentence, as we go through the text. In the same way, readers crave and make meaning for the work as a whole. A poem, Robert Frost famously said, "runs a course of lucky events, and ends in a clarification of life . . . a momentary stay against confusion."[1] We crave that final "momentary stay against confusion." But as Pirandello points out there is a problem. You and I may be reading or hearing the same words, but my "clarification" will surely differ from your "clarification." We will differ because we bring different culturally based hypotheses to bear on the text, those hypotheses embodied and deployed in our different memory systems. We will differ because we are different people whose frontal lobes work differently.

"The" meaning "in" the text

My quotation marks suggest some of the confusions about the idea of meaning in literature. Mostly, when we literary people write about meaning, we assume there are one or more meanings "in" the literary work just as we assume there is form "in" it or content. All follow from the original projection of the book from our sense organs to the book as a physical reality. It is a construction almost impossible to avoid.

Look at the difference between Pirandello in the epigraph and Frost. Frost optimistically assumes there is a "clarification," a meaning, "in" the poem. Pirandello's hero laments that speakers and hearers put "into" speech purely personal meanings that differ for speaker and hearer. Despite their difference, both assume "meaning" occurs "in" the language, not in our construing of the language.

But the work doesn't mean. We have to make literature mean. Texts in Arabic or Mandarin mean nothing to me. As Stanley Fish puts it with characteristic force, "There is no distinction between what the text gives and what the reader supplies: he supplies *everything*."[2] Actually, not quite everything. Expectations we clearly supply. Also, although we perceive words as "in" the text, it is we who make them into discourse, metaphor, figurative meanings, and even the plain sense. To be sure, we have seen that form in the work (as we perceive it) can limit our attention to this part or that, but even the omissions and close-ups of form have to be combined with our own inner defenses to function. A literary work never does anything or "has" anything by itself. For it to become literature—that is, to become a literary experience—we must construe it. Literature has to happen in our minds. Like the sleeping princess in the fairy tale, we must love a literary work into life.

The need for meaning

We want meaning. Jaak Panksepp describes the SEEKING system we share with less intellecting animals as going "from nuts to knowledge." Pretty clearly, our search for meaning in literary works comes from that system. SEEKING gratification, my brain succeeds in construing the "content" of the work to suit my new and old, conscious and unconscious, wishes. I arrive at a "meaning," "a momentary stay against confusion." And I *want* that "point" just as much as I want a joke to have a point.

In the world of neurology, one sees this need to "make sense" of things in patients with frontal lobe damage who experience baffling feelings or emotions. For example, a patient might be given a hypnotic suggestion to go to the umbrella stand and open his umbrella. He does so and explains that he did this odd thing, even though indoors, because he had realized it might rain, he wanted to make sure his umbrella would work, and he had to do so right away in case he needed to get a different umbrella.

Michael Gazzaniga, a leading split-brain researcher since the 1970s, has again and again demonstrated this need to make sense of what doesn't make sense. As described in textbooks and several popular books,[3] his split-brain subjects have had the connections between the two cerebral hemispheres cut in order to control disabling epilepsy. Information sent to one hemisphere cannot reach the other. In one common experiment, a picture is shown to the far left visual field in someone's left eye so that the image goes only to the right hemisphere of the brain. Because the connections between right hemisphere and left have been cut, the left, "languaged" hemisphere cannot "know" about the picture presented to the right hemisphere. Thus, one split-brain patient, a woman, watched (with her right brain) a film of one person throwing another into a fire. She commented, "I feel scared. I feel jumpy. . . . I know I like Dr. Gazzaniga, but right now I'm scared of him for some reason."[4] To another split-brain patient of Gazzaniga's, the experimenters showed sexy pictures, but only to her right hemisphere. She giggled and blushed. Asked why she was acting that way, she explained that she was thinking about something embarrassing. Her right hemisphere had experienced the emotion, the embarrassment, but could not transfer information about the source to the left hemisphere for a verbal explanation. The woman's left hemisphere then invented a reason all by itself.[5]

Both these patients were demonstrating a deep human need. *Homo sapiens* demands an explanation for even the inexplicable. Gazzaniga calls this lust to explain things embodied in the left, languaged side of the brain, the "interpreter." It is closely related, I think, to confabulation (ch. 16). Patients come up with plausible explanations for their mental difficulties. (Remember Mark Solms' patient who wanted a computer chip to replace his ruined memory.)

Solms notes (as other neuropsychologists have) that confabulation occurs with frontal lobe damage. Patients lose the "source" information associated with a given episodic memory. Readers forget that "this is only a story" or poem or drama. The reality-monitoring part of the brain ceases to control earlier, lower systems. Solms describes this reality-testing system as reaching back and forth from early regions involving emotions and emotion-driven actions to evolutionarily more advanced frontal systems for planning.

When we become transported by art or literature, our brains turn off planning for motor activity in relation to the work of art, and, with planning for action goes reality-testing (ch. 7). Then wishes and wish-fulfilling fantasies can come pushing up from sub-cortical emotional systems unchecked by reality. As a clinician, Solms found that patients with Korsakoff's syndrome had this shutdown of reality-testing because of damage to the posterior frontal region of the brain. With literature, we have seen the same shutdown of reality-testing and "source knowledge" when we know that we will not act on the literary work, because action begins in the frontal lobes.

Damage to one or more of the areas Solms mentions allows the release of unconscious, wish-fulfilling thoughts, severed from reality. Inner, psychic reality takes the place of external reality. In the same way, readers flesh out the bones of a poem or narrative with their own wish-fulfilling thought, experiencing the reality of the literary work as their own reality. Solms identifies this kind of thinking with what Freud called "primary process" as opposed to the logical, reality-oriented, and problem-solving thought of "secondary process."[6]

This kind of wish-fulfilling thought comes into play as part of the fantasizing in our perception of sentence-level literary "content." Now, in the larger process of "making sense" of the work as a whole, this same kind of wish-fulfilling thought drives more advanced, secondary-process thinking to seek a "point" for what we have seen or heard or read or imagined or fantasized from a work of literature.

The SEEKING system, Panksepp suggests, may also underlie "the tendency to selectively seek evidence for our hypotheses."[7] We literary critics find evidence in texts and contexts for our favored interpretations and evaluations. And regular readers do the same (although, probably, in a less systematic, determined, and predisposed way). As part of their pleasure, ordinary readers will simply "make sense" of a text, and they will make the kind of sense that feels right and good to them.

SEEKING a "point"

We are always reaching for things in the world. Finding a "moral to the story" feels good because it satisfies our perpetual SEEKING. That is a neuropsychological reason. Giving a work a point also feels good for a psychodynamic reason. When we interpret, that is, when we develop a meaning for a text, we are doing something analogous to what psychoanalysis calls *sublimation.*

In life, we have childish or unconscious wishes that, if we were to gratify them, would involve guilt or shame or fear or the disapproval of someone important to us. We need to do something different instead of acting on those impulses that would be unacceptable to us or to the others-in-us. In infancy those others were our parents or other caregivers and their recurring demands that became part of our personalities. As adults they are our inner feelings of Thou Shalt and Thou Shalt Not (that is, in psychoanalytic jargon, "ego ideal" and "superego"). To satisfy those taskmasters, we defend, transforming our baser impulses. We need to do something different, but not too different: something that will satisfy both our conscience and our social milieu but also partially satisfy those persistent demands. That is sublimation.

When we sublimate in life, we transform risky wishes into something inwardly and outwardly legitimate. Psychoanalysts sometimes call sublimation "the normal defense" because we all do it all the time in all kinds of human adaptations. One person might transform aggressive wishes into being a surgeon or climbing mountains. Another might reverse a pleasure in dirt into housecleaning or gardening or censorship. You are sublimating right now by reading this book instead of gratifying, perhaps, some less licit curiosity. Hemingway's characters and Hemingway himself re-symbolize their aggressive masculine impulses into fishing, hunting, or bullfighting. Hemingway famously said of writing, "It is facing the white bull which is paper with no words on it." Symbolizing writing as bullfighting was *his* special, creative sublimation of aggression.

With literature, the form of the work has already offered us defensive strategies to combine with our own. We can use the symbols in the literary work to re-symbolize our less savory wishes and impulses into something else, something that would work in the world or that feels right to us internally. We avoid the feelings of guilt or fear of punishment that would result if we did not obey the parents we introjected in childhood.

The meaning we find may be something as simple as crime-does-not-pay or loving-others-is-good or something as complicated as the latest lucubration of literary theory. We may achieve some complex act of thematic or cultural interpretation. We may confirm or outrage our political passions or our sense of ethnic pride.

Symbolizations make meaning possible. That is, symbols, be they individual words or multiple images, provide the basis for making sublimations into meanings. Because a symbol "stands for" what it symbolizes, but is not that thing, sublimations are compromises. They serve as partial but ethically and socially viable gratifications of a less acceptable underlying wish. Symbolizing aggression into bullfighting gratifies less, but it gratifies somewhat. We accept partial gratification of the banned wish so as not to incur the penalties that full gratification would entail. And we do get some gratification from the compromise.

We do the same thing with imaginative literature, particularly at that point in the literary process when we find a meaning for a text. In the stage I have described as "content," we fleshed out the words of the literary work with our own impulses and fantasies. But, in order to have a satisfactory experience of the work as a whole, we need to transform the fantasies that we have projected into the text to some acceptable overall "meaning."

Perhaps because these sublimations toward meaning mask things we would rather not think about, we need to feel that we get the meanings from the work. Meaning is "in" the text. It isn't just me. And this projection of the process of meaning from ourselves into the work continues the very basic projection of our sensations of the book or play or movie into the world beyond our sense organs.

That projection we all perform much the same way. This process of making meaning, however, will be personal and idiosyncratic. The "meanings" we find in literary works, were we to explore them psychoanalytically, through free associations, would reveal their continuity with original, deep, unconscious wishes and fantasies of a quite personal kind. My unconscious impulses will very likely differ from yours. So will my defenses. Doubtless my parents issued different Thou Shalts and Thou Shalt Nots from your parents, and surely you and I handle the tension between impulse and control differently.

I have suggested a hypothetical reader of *Hamlet* who had had a brutal father. He might find Hamlet's killing one father-figure (Claudius) in order to revenge another (Hamlet Sr.) a double gratification. Revenge against Claudius and Hamlet's own death would satisfy his aggressive wish for revenge but also seem an appropriate balancing of the scales of justice.

Conversely, that reader might well find the pity and regret lavished on the dying King Lear annoying. Indeed, in Wendy Wasserstein's play, *Third*, a radically feminist English teacher argues that the real tragedy in *King Lear* is the "girlification of Cordelia." Lear himself is a cranky old fool with a bunch of noisy, unruly companions who has overstayed his welcome at his children's castle. He has to be taught a lesson. Goneril and Regan are the real heroes, and Cordelia is a milksop. Such a critic needs to recognize how her interpretation justifies her hostility toward father-figures (unconscious in the play). Her expectations, defenses, fantasies, and their transformation into "sense" lead to a very special reading of that tragedy. But we all do the same. Personal brains lead to personal readings.

That is why five different people will produce five different interpretations of a Faulkner story[8] or a spaghetti Western.[9] That is why no one, no matter how expert, can produce the "right" meaning for a work, a meaning that all other readers will find true to their experience (and sublimations). Of course, we can all produce "wrong" meanings—that is, interpretations that most people will deem wrong. But whether or not people agree with an interpretation, it must be personal, since it depends on someone's particular expectations, memories, defenses, SEEKINGs, and the ways that person transforms them into a coherent experience.[10] Any good literary experience will surely be a "clarification of life," as Frost said, but it may or may not be, as Pirandello knew, one that anyone else will share. That poses a problem for professional interpreters.

Critics

As a means to their pleasure, "common" readers, as they are unfortunately called, will simply "make sense" of a text. They will make the kind of sense that feels good to them. For professional readers, however, for literary critics like me, SEEKING a meaning becomes our occupation. For the last half-century, literary critics (as contrasted to reviewers for newspapers and magazines) have assumed that their main function is interpretation, not evaluation (which is what reviewers do). Critics find or deconstruct a "meaning" typically assumed to be in the text. We critics typically spend our professional (and professorial) time finding evidence in texts and contexts for interpretations and, occasionally, evaluations that we favor. Other critics (I? never!) often ignore evidence to the contrary. The SEEKING system, to repeat Jaak Panksepp's dictum, underlies "the tendency to selectively seek evidence for our hypotheses."[11]

We enjoy our work—at least I do—despite what the Israeli novelist Amos Oz writes about "the literati." "They analyze everything *ad nauseam*, techniques, motifs, oxymorons and metonyms, allegory and connotation, hidden Jewish allusions, latent psychological keys and sociological implications, and archetypal characters and fateful ideas and whatnot. Only the pleasure of reading do they castrate."[12] Oz is pointing out, sharply, that *critics' enjoyment differs from the regular pleasure of reading*. We are actively doing something rather than passively enjoying the text. We are not "disinterested."

As a result, we are enjoying something like Mihalyi Csikszentmihalyi's "flow."[13] We have matched our talents to a task that is neither too easy nor too difficult. To be sure, non-professional readers and audiences also "make sense," but they do so, presumably, in a less systematic, determined, and predisposed, in short, a less "interested" way. They are enjoying the work as such; we are enjoying what we are doing with the work. That is an altogether different kind of pleasure, as different as active is from passive.

Both regular and professional readers use the same physiological feedbacks and the most widely shared cultural codes. But we professional readers apply the canons of our particular critical persuasion: psychoanalytic, deconstructive, cultural, marxist—whatever. These canons (and codes as well) call on widely distributed systems in the brain (ch. 18). Presumably they draw on the declarative, semantic and episodic memory systems, visual and aural lexicons, and procedural memory for the physical act of reading. Most importantly, professional critics work to re-create their own identity themes, their own styles of being, deploying all these other systems to that end.

Consider, for example, Walter Jackson Bate, the very model of a professorial critic, who much influenced me in my graduate student days and for many years after. Bate liked to talk about moral poignance, moral sincerity, and acts of what he called the "moral imagination."[14] Whom did Bate write about? Keats, surely the most moral of the romantic poets, but above all, Samuel Johnson, whom Bate regarded as a great source of moral wisdom. And for years he taught a course in the great critics, from Aristotle to Richards, showing how each elicited moral wisdom from the subjects they wrote about.

By contrast, I can point to a very different kind of critic, my late colleague Leslie Fiedler. Leslie liked to stand conventionality on its head. His great theme, the one that runs through all his work, was bringing whatever was marginal, whatever was outside the mainstream, into the mainstream. Indeed he would replace the mainstream with what was marginal—until he came along.[15] What are the books he liked to work with? Jewish novels. Writings about what he called "freaks." In his most famous essay, he showed that the greatest mainstream American novel, *Huckleberry Finn*, really embodied a homoerotic relationship between two people of different races and that this relationship—outrageous in 1950s America—was true of all the great American novels.

What about me? For me, the important thing is being able to find the unity of a text. My favorite works are those that I can treat as a problem to be solved. I find myself treating literary works as like jig-saw puzzles where my aim is to fit all the parts together in a rational way. I am drawn to works that are in fact obscure and difficult—Kafka, Ingmar Bergman, or *Last Year at Marienbad.*[16] Alternatively, I write about texts that people think are simple but that I can show are complicated and in need of my unifying skill: Robert Frost, Hollywood movies or soft porn.[17] (Perhaps it is true for all critics, that we enjoy most those works with which we best do our particular thing.) For me, literature is a puzzle, a puzzle I have been trying all my professional life to solve. And that is what you have been seeing in this book, me in the act of solving the puzzle that is literature.

Meaning for philosophers

In the world of philosophy, I think this neuropsychoanalytic account of meaning corresponds most closely to that put forward by Hans-Georg Gadamer. In *Truth and Method*,[18] he undertook to describe what we humans do when we interpret anything, especially works of art. He claimed that people in general and scholars in particular have a "historically affected consciousness" (*wirkungsgeschichtliches Bewußtsein*). History and culture are always already at work in the act of interpretation, coloring our very idea of understanding as well as any particular interpretation. In describing codes and canons and the way we deploy them through feedback from hypotheses, I think I am giving Gadamer's concept of interpretation a psychological form that is specific, observable, and even quantifiable. That is, people will agree that an interpretation is valid within a given culture to the extent that they share the same codes and canons (ch. 18). Hamlet, we can all agree is a Danish prince who wears black clothes. Some of us will agree, using psychoanalytic canons, that he suffers from a reactivated oedipus complex; others will not. And I have my own, private understanding of the character that fulfills my identity but may or may not correspond to anyone else's reading.

What must fascinate and puzzle the non-professional reader is the way critics persist in developing interpretations when it is obvious, even to the critics, that there is no one "right" interpretation (although, years ago, in the heyday of formalist or "New" criticism, we thought there was). But we enjoy what we do, and there is a method to our madness.

Necessarily, discussions of humanistic interpretations will always involve some mixture of agreement and disagreement created by the differences in codes, canons, and identities of the interpreters. The sciences can arrive more easily at consensus through repeated experiments and peer review (imperfect though the latter may be). Researchers' discussions in scientific journals eventually lead to some interpretation of results being accepted as fact (at least provisionally, subject, as always in the sciences, to disconfirmation). Knowledge in the sciences cumulates. In the humanities it does not. At least interpretations of events and texts do not. Instead, the humanities offer a continuing conversation. That is their point, and that is their value:

conversation among human beings. But conversation is, by its very nature, ephemeral. My graduate students today have never even heard of the interpreters (like Bate) whom I admired and imitated in my own graduate student days. So be it. The valuable thing is that we are still interpreting and still talking about our interpretations.

Again, we can find a philosopher who formalizes this activity, Jürgen Habermas.[19] He proceeds from the assumption that all our human speech acts have the goal of mutual understanding and that we humans can attain this goal (*pace* Pirandello). Our ability to speak to and understand one another (for example in interpreting literary works) must tie us into three worlds: an external world (as constructed by our brains), an internal world (of identity, I would argue), and a social world of shared codes and canons, in sum, a sociocultural "lifeworld." (I think Habermas' "lifeworld" corresponds to what I call a "style.") Habermas then locates "rational consensus" in structures of free interpersonal linguistic communication among lifeworlds rather than in the structure of either the external world—the literary work in our context—or of an isolated subject. Understanding is neither objective nor subjective. It consists in experiences shared. When we humanists share interpretations, we are, it seems to me, fulfilling his ideal. In my terms, we negotiate agreement based on understanding one another's codes and canons.

The sciences converge into a series of consensuses, while the humanities continue a conversation. Clearly, this book, in which I hope to set out a neuropsychoanalytic description of the literary process, aspires to science rather than humanities. Although I am myself no scientist, I believe others could confirm or disconfirm the model of literary experience I am presenting here. So far as the humanities are concerned, I am hoping to provide a framework within which the kind of rational discussion Habermas advocates can take place. Self-knowledge, that is, understanding our own styles, can lead to that rational discussion.

Meaning—we each create it in our own way as well as in ways we share with others. Meaning thus returns us to personal styles. In writing about style, though, I have focused away from what we usually think of as styles and, indeed, from the first examples I gave: Mozart, Hemingway, Matisse—examples of artists' styles. Presumably, artists have the same brain structures and the same kinds of brain history that readers or viewers or spectators do. Readers read and find meaning within a certain style. So writers write in a certain style because of the same kind of identity that gives every normal human a personal style. A writer's style, like a reader's, deploys knowledge and values and tactics incorporated from a particular cultural environment. But the artist's style involves something much more than what ordinary folk use in the reception of literary and artistic works. The artist has creativity, and that topic deserves at least a chapter to itself. In this account of the literary process, we come at long last to the person who starts it all, the writer and some of the large questions that go beyond literature to life.

Part IV

The Big Questions

22 | Inner Creativity

> Some people have things like that [dance], and they don't have to make money at it. It's something they have to do, or they're not themselves anymore. If you take it away from them, they'll still walk around, and you can touch them and talk to them. They'll even answer. But they're not there anymore.
>
> —Andre Dubus III, *House of Sand and Fog*

YOU AND I develop lifelong styles, evidently embodied in our brains. Styles, both writers' styles and readers', shape our literary experiences from beginning to end.

Literary experiences begin with an act of creation by a writer. Few of us achieve that writerly creativity, and people have long suspected that creative writers' minds function differently somehow from those of ordinary people or "the common reader." How? One short answer is: *key neurotransmitters may be differently organized in the writer's brain.* But there are many other issues involved in creativity.

Writers do not simply "create." They create within a

certain style. As Nabokov said, "[S]tyle constitutes an intrinsic component or characteristic of the author's personality," or, in the word I prefer, identity. But style is not wholly individual. Creative style in whatever domain also partakes of a given time and place.

Personal identity deploys the codes and canons that social environment provides. American writers in the 1960s, for example, derived from writers like Borges and Calvino a radically different way of writing novels (metafiction), and then John Barth, say, or Donald Barthelme created new writings using that new style. A writer's identity draws on prevailing fashions, reader demand, the conditions for publication, and, in general, many things that have nothing to do with the individual writer's psychology.

We can understand this mingling of the personal and the environmental in style by assuming there are hypotheses or guesses with which each human identity questions our world and gets answers from it (chs. 17, 18). Should a poem have endnotes as *The Waste Land* does? Should a novel recount reality or should it point to its own unreality? The answers will come from the writer's literary environment, its codes and canons, and the writer will use them to serve a personal style of thought and diction.

So far as the individual writer is concerned, his or her frontal lobes learn, retain, and use these cultural codes, canons, or hypotheses. The brain deploys them not only in creative, but in ordinary thinking. But we call creativity creativity because we think it differs from ordinary thinking.

Issues with creativity

Our idea of creativity poses a number of questions.

Is creativity just one thing? Are the writer's creativity and the scientist's the same thing?

Why do artists and writers feel compelled to create (as in the epigraph)?

Where do creative ideas come from?
Are creativity and madness linked?
How does creativity that succeeds differ from creativity that doesn't?

Finally, I want to broach a last question that I cannot propose an answer for. I think nobody does and nobody, perhaps, ever will. How do we recognize the creative "gift"?

Creativities?

Is all "creativity" the same or are there different kinds of creativity? Does the creative scientist's brain work the same way as the poet's brain or the painter's?[1] Researchers into creativity generally answer, Yes. Kenneth Heilman, a neuroscientist who has written a telling book on creativity,[2] concludes (like many other writers on the subject) that all creativity is alike: *all creativity involves making connections between disparate ideas that seemed to have no connection with one another.* He speaks of connecting the previously unconnected or of "unity in diversity," a term traditional among writers on the arts.[3] Psychologist Colin Martindale states that all creativity involves an idea "that is both original and appropriate for the situation in which it occurs," "an analogy between two or more ideas or images previously thought to be unrelated."[4] We saw this idea in miniature in thinking of literary language (ch. 16, 19). Louis Menand spoke of literary language as "surprising but right," and Frost called it "unforeseen [but] predestined." William James wrote of a state of mind in which "the unexpected seems only law,"[5] and James thought it common to all creative thinking.

One early writer on the subject, Graham Wallas, separated creativity (of all kinds) into four stages. He listed: preparation; incubation; illumination; and verification.[6] "Preparation" means the long training that goes into the making of, say, an innovative neuropsychologist or a successful poet. One acquires skills and knowledge, *enough to know what the next step is.* "Incubation" means working on a particular idea over a period of time during which both conscious and unconscious thinking goes on. "Illumination" refers to that magic moment of an "Aha!" or a "Eureka!" Most people use the word "creativity" to mean just this instant of insight. Finally, "verification" means submitting one's idea to others in one's field for confirming experiments in the sciences or critical approval in the arts.

Most writers on literary creativity have found Wallas' four phases (or something very like them) a useful way to think about creativity. It is not difficult, for example, to translate Wallas' terms into literary creation. Preparation: writers train (nowadays) in creative writing programs. They used to (and some still do) serve long apprenticeships in journalism or some other activity that requires regular daily writing. Incubation: writers keep notebooks with ideas for future projects. They outline novels and stories and do extensive research on the locales and history they will use. Illumination: this is the magic moment that we shall be looking at in this chapter. Verification: writers (necessarily) seek critiques of their work from others. The writer hopes to hear the telephone ring with a call from Oprah's Book Club or from the *New York Times Book Review* planning a front page paean.

"I must write, I must write, I just must . . ."

Part of the mystique about literary creativity comes from its compulsive quality. Creative people, not just writers, are driven. As Picasso said of his art, "I could not live without devoting all my hours to it."[7] Photographer Maggie Taylor says, "Making images for me is a way of life. I can't imagine not doing it . . . I guess in terms of what motivates me, the best answer would be, if I don't make images I'm unhappy."[8]

As for writers, "I like to do and can do many things

better than I can write," said Hemingway, "but when I don't write, I feel like shit."[9] "I sat paralyzed . . . in a self-induced vacuum," Sylvia Plath agonized to her journal during one of her bouts with writer's block. "I felt sicker & sicker. I couldn't happily be anything but a writer & I couldn't be a writer: I couldn't even set down one sentence: I was paralyzed with fear, with deadly hysteria."[10] Salman Rushdie put the same thing this way: "E]verybody I've ever known who really was a writer had some real fire burning inside them that forced them to do it. They didn't have an option; they had to be a writer because they couldn't *not* be a writer."[11] Chekhov's writer-character Trigorin describes himself: "I'm obsessed day and night by one thought: I must write, I must write, I just must . . . [A]s soon as I've finished one novel, I feel I must start writing another, then another, then another . . . . I write in a rush, without stopping and can't do anything else."[12]

Alice Flaherty, an authority on hypergraphia, sums up this driven, compulsive quality: "For many [writers], there is the primal conviction that they should not do anything but write because it is their vocation, in a nearly religious sense. Writing is what they are meant to do and [the body rebels] when it is kept from fulfilling its destiny."[13] Psychologist Ellen Winner too notes that creative people can't stop writing or painting or composing.[14] If something should happen to make them stop, an illness, say, military service, or prison, they find a way, or, if they can't find a way, they just about go crazy. By contrast, she comments. "Rarely does a lawyer, for instance, insist that she is driven to practice law, that she could do nothing else that her life would be empty or unbearable if she had to enter another profession."[15]

Creativity and identity

Writers *have* to write. I will suggest a reason, although it is only a suggestion. As the epigraph says (describing a dancer), "It's something they have to do, *or they're not themselves anymore.*"

Looking at style, I suggested that an artist's style (or any person's style of being) plays variations on that person's identity theme. That is, from our genetic temperament and our early interactions with others, we embody an identity theme in our brains. All of us are constantly driven to work out variations on our theme to re-create identity. This, we have seen, is the biological principle of autopoesis or a psychological identity principle. Others see in us a personal style. They can understand us as having a "character": we have patterns and consistencies in what we do. For all of us, that identity theme shows in the way we love and work and otherwise live. In an evolutionary sense, without some such predictability, our fellow creatures would not know how to relate to us. How could we humans exist as sociable primates?

This identity, this style of being, forms the deepest level of our motivation. Our particular "autopoesis" is laid down in infancy and childhood in the corticolimbic pathways of our brains as we relate to the people sustaining us in the early, vulnerable years of the human animal. This identity is the something in each of us that seeks the goals and feelings special for you or me or any one of us.

For the creative person, I think, that identity, that style of being, has come to include the medium in which the creative person works: words, paint, microbes, and so on. One is not simply "creative." one is creative *within a certain medium.* An artist's identity re-creation depends on creating within a certain art form.

I believe, and Howard Gardner reports research along these lines,[16] that a person creative in the arts establishes early in childhood a special relationship with the particular kind of seeing or hearing or speaking that marks out that creator's special medium. The future creator gets a self focused on sounds, smeary stuff, moldable stuff, shapes sustaining human activity, or words. Somehow an artist's medium gets entangled with personal identity at a deep, early level. That is why, if for some reason they can't create, as Andre Dubus puts it in the epigraph, "They're not themselves anymore."

Writers write compulsively, but the compulsion does not apply to "creativity" in some vague general sense. I cannot imagine that some writer would suffer from being forbidden to do experiments in chemistry. One can guess that a poet's identity concerns words or a dramatist's involves acting out. The artistic compulsion to create is tied to a particular medium and form and style in which to create (although a few people can create in more than one medium like Woody Allen, who excels both at comic writing and at directing films about intense human relationships).

Feeling, as an artist or writer, that you are successfully creating will be, then, deeply satisfying. Conversely, being unable to fulfill your identity theme will feel profoundly threatening: Plath's "deadly hysteria"; Hemingway's "when I don't write, I feel like shit." For all the complaining about how painful writing can be (and indeed it can be), writers go on writing, and most feel frustration and even pain if prevented.

A writer's or artist's medium is locked into identity, the core character, the same way basic characteristics of a style of being are. Choice of words, sound patterns for poets, this form and not that, repeated character types, recurring themes—all these are *psychologically* characteristic for a writer. We can also see this compulsion in writers' returning again and again to the same psychological themes. As writer Bernard Malamud said to me once, "Every novelist only writes one novel." Virginia Woolf returns to the consciousness of a deprived woman. Hemingway has his macho preoccupations. Fitzgerald writes over and over about some infinitely desirable or powerful woman who withholds. Others revert compulsively to the theme of parents and children: Shaw, Dickens, or the Japanese filmmaker, Yasujirō Ozu. And these psychological themes persist even with some change of medium. Ozu transferred his concerns with family from silent movies to sound.[17] Shaw carried over the parental themes and verbal paradoxes from his early, unsuccessful novels to the great plays he wrote later. The painter Albert Alcalay put it this way: "You paint and paint and paint, and eventually there comes a time when the painting looks back at you and says, 'Hey, this is *you!*'"[18] As we can see in the many, many psychological studies of writers, the psychological themes associated with that person's childhood will recur in all the creations.

Scientists too have that same compulsion to create. Alan Lightman, a prize-winning novelist on scientific themes, has taught at M.I.T. where he constantly sees scientists at work. He writes of their

> . . . pleasure of discovering something new. It is an exquisite sensation, a feeling of power, a rush of the blood, a sense of living forever. To be the first vessel to hold this new thing.
>
> All of the scientists I've known have at least one more quality in common: they do what they do because they love it, and because they cannot imagine doing anything else. In a sense, this is the real reason a scientist does science. Because the scientist must. Such a compulsion is both blessing and burden. A blessing because the creative life, in any endeavor, is a gift filled with beauty and not given to everyone, a burden because the call is

> unrelenting and can drown out the rest of life.[19]

Allegra Goodman's prize-winning novel about a laboratory team, *Intuition*, develops just this idea.

I share Lightman's impression. The scientists I meet are indeed driven, but not so much by a particular medium, as by a generalized curiosity and a subject-matter to be curious about, the brain, for example.[20] Perhaps scientists are driven to measure. In the case of medical researchers, I think this curiosity may be coupled with a desire to help the sick. Among the scientists whom I know, I think any given neurologist or neuropsychologist might be just as happy being a psychologist or a neuropharmacologist. Yet, once matured into their specific fields, they too are driven like the artists. To that extent, I will guess that creativity in the sciences develops as in the arts, the particular field for curiosity becoming part of identity, but perhaps later in childhood development and therefore less tightly focused.

To madness near allied

Most of us lack this compulsion to create, this driven quality. Because it is unusual, this driven quality fits all too well into one of our stereotypes of creative people. They are a little mad. The famous Italian psychiatrist and criminologist Cesare Lombroso, in his best-known book, *The Man of Genius* (1891), argued that genius was a form of insanity. But the idea is as old as Socrates, who persuaded the reciter of poetry, the rhapsode Ion, that either he was crazy or a god was speaking through him. Aristotle (or the "pseudo-Aristotle") asked, "Why is it that all those who have become eminent in philosophy or politics or poetry or the arts are clearly melancholics?," that is, depressives. Shakespeare had his Theseus (the voice of reason among the madnesses of *Midsummer Night's Dream*) describe something more like mania:

> The lunatic, the lover, and the poet

Are of imagination all compact . . . . (5.1.7-8).

John Dryden, describing a character "turbulent of wit" gave us the familiar epigram: "Great wits are sure to madness near allied."

In recent years, psychologists have noticed that a lot of American writers were alcoholic, addicted, or suicidal: Poe, Hemingway, Plath, Fitzgerald, Faulkner, Hart Crane, Burroughs—the list could go on and on. Some are at the extremes of politics or sex, like H.D., Dos Passos, Pound, Mailer, Polanski, or Chaplin. As a result, a number of psychologists and psychiatrists have subscribed to Lombroso's thesis, that creativity is genetic and co-occurs with various forms of mental illness. The favorites have been either unipolar depression or bipolar disorder (manic-depressive illness), particularly with women poets (the "Sylvia Plath effect").[21]

Yet I know successful writers who are as rational and sober as accountants. And a recent, thorough book on this issue by Robert W. Weisberg concludes, "It seems that we need more data before we can conclude that there is a causal link between madness and genius, and the data that are presently available do not strongly support the existence of that link."[22] Neurologists who study creativity seem not to associate creativity with pathology. Nevertheless, all these scientists seem to agree that *the inspirational moment, the "illumination," in creativity involves a special state of mind.*

Creativity and states of mind

For Freud, the artist's abilities simply exaggerated normal people's psychic processes. The artist had an unusual amount of libido (or energy), "a certain degree of laxity in . . . repressions," and an "extraordinary capacity for sublimating the primitive instincts."[23] He thought imaginative art resembled the fantasies of hysterics. But ultimately he threw up his hands. "An artist's joy in creating, in giving his phantasies body, or a scientist's in solving problems or discovering truths, has a special quality which we shall certainly one day be able to characterize in metapsychological terms."[24]

Ernst Kris offered the formulation that most psychoanalytic critics accept and repeat like a mantra. Creativity is "regression in the service of the ego."[25] That is, it is like dreaming or daydreaming. One regresses, that is, one goes back to early or even childish thoughts and earlier ways of dealing with thoughts. One puts aside ordinary problem solving or reality-testing and lets unconscious, wishful fantasizing take over. Then ideas and feelings percolate up from the deeper parts of one's mind, and this leads to "illumination."

To quote essayist Louis Menand again, "You have to wait, and what you are waiting for is something inside you to come up with the words."[26] "I yield to a theme," wrote novelist Robertson Davies,

> Like all writers, I get great numbers of letters and many of them are from students who ask, bluntly, "Where do you get your ideas from?" The answer, which they are reluctant to believe, is that I do not "get" ideas; ideas get me. I do not invent plots; they arise in my mind, beginning usually with some mental picture that will not go away. It demands to be examined and thought about.[27]

One could multiply by the dozens statements by creative writers describing their "inspirations" as coming from what a psychoanalyst would call the unconscious ego.

The unbalanced brain

Among neuroscientists, there is a rule of thumb—I will not call it a principle—that the brain, for all its immense capacity, does have a limit. If one part of the brain is highly developed, another part will be less so. "It is clear to a man who does one thing better than another," wrote Leonardo da Vinci in contrasting painters of faces with narrative painters, "that nature has more inclined him to that than to something else, and on this account he has more love for it and his greater love has made him more diligent. All the love which is concentrated on one part is missing from the rest."[28] What Leonardo found true for painters holds true for writers and every kind of artist—and human being.

Our brains make trade-offs. Psychiatrists and neurologists see this imbalance commonly among autistics. "High-performing autistics," such as those with Asperger's syndrome, can often execute astonishing feats of arithmetic or musical composition or visual art. A remarkable novel, *The Curious Incident of the Dog in the Night-time*, tells its story from inside the mind of just such a person. Gifted scientifically but emotionless, this adolescent boy has to reason his way laboriously through the most ordinary human situations.[29] Typically, autistics' brains have sacrificed emotional intelligence for some other kind. As a result, most neuroscientists agree that autistics, for all their talent, are not creative as we usually use the word.

Doctors treating elderly patients with dementia are surprised to find that, sometimes, as ordinary mental abilities deteriorate, new talents emerge, say, for painting.[30] In the same vein, a Swedish researcher reports a greater incidence of dyslexia and poorer phonological skills among art students than among other university students.[31] Ellen Winner, in reviewing work with gifted children and savants, notes that there is some evidence that gifted children have atypical brain organization, often manifesting as difficulties with language. Social and emotional problems also set them apart. They have "uneven cognitive profiles," because they have so intense a motivation toward their gift.[32] To some extent, this imbalance in the direction of a particular skill fits my hypothesis of a particular medium or subject being embedded in a core identity.

Divergent thinking

Many writers have identified creativity with a large capacity for divergent thinking as contrasted with convergent. When we think convergently, we try to bring disparate ideas together toward a single focus. Convergent thinking finds answers to problems. When I write, I try to find the most exact word, not the most connotative. When we think divergently, however, we let disparate ideas float around, as it were, without settling on one. Divergent thinking makes specific answers wait, letting a lot of unrelated possibilities hover before settling on "the answer."

William James described divergent thinking with particular eloquence:

> Instead of thoughts of concrete things patiently following one another in a beaten track of habitual suggestion, we have the most abrupt cross-cuts and transitions from one idea to another, the most rarefied abstractions and discriminations, the most unheard of combination of elements, the subtlest associations of analogy; in a word, we seem suddenly introduced into a seething cauldron of ideas, where everything is fizzling and bobbling about in a state of bewildering activity, where partnerships can be joined or loosened in an instant, treadmill routine is unknown, and the unexpected seems only Law.[33]

In experimental psychologist Colin Martindale's summary, creative thinking is "autistic, free-associative, analogical, and characterized by concrete images as opposed to abstract thought." "Because primary process cognition is associative, it facilitates" the essence of what Martindale defines as creativity, "the discovery of new combinations of mental elements." In effect, he (and other researchers) are supporting Kris' "regression in the service of the ego."[34]

James went on to link the "fizzling and bobbling about" to a personal style:

> According to the idiosyncrasy of the individual, the scintillations will have one character or another. They will be sallies for wit and humor; they will be flashes of poetry and eloquence; they will be constructions of dramatic fiction or of mechanical device, logical or philosophic abstractions, business projects, or scientific hypotheses, with trains of experimental consequences based thereon; they will be musical sounds, or images of plastic beauty or picturesqueness or visions of moral harmony. But, whatever their differences may be, they will all agree in this, —that their genesis is sudden and, as it were, spontaneous. That is to say, the same premises would not, in the mind of another individual, have engendered just that conclusion.[35]

As James notes, creatives do not simply have a talent. They have an individual style, and this style (I believe) is linked to their core identity, itself embodied in corticolimbic pathways in the brain.[36] *Writers have a talent for being the particular kind of writer that they are.*

Right and left

In another trade-off within the creative brain, a Canadian group finds creativity associated with more rapid processing of signals in the right hemisphere than the left.[37] Ellen Winner, we have seen, found that gifted children and savants often have enhanced right-hemisphere development, with reduced left-hemisphere language capacity.[38] Martindale notes that most of the centers for music and visual art are located in the right hemisphere, as are centers for mental imagery.[39] After one visual artist suffered damage to the right cerebral cortex, the neurologists reported a deterioration in artistic talent.[40]

In general, it is well established in neuropsychology that (for over 95% of people) activity in the left hemisphere tends to be logical and sequential, in the right hemisphere to be holistic and visuospatial. The studies above tend to identify creativity with increased right hemisphere activity. At one time, this led to a lot of fanciful (wish-fulfilling?) thinking on the part of the general public. Pop psychology books promised to enhance creativity by stimulating the right cerebral cortex. I wish!

Nevertheless, when we considered what makes language "literary" (ch. 16), we saw that spreading activation in the right hemisphere elicits more unusual associations and a larger spread of meanings than words presented only to the left.[41] The right hemisphere therefore plays a key role when we enjoy jokes, metaphors, poetry, and "literary" language.[42]

Possibly the bias in creatives toward the right hemisphere bears on the association of writers with alcoholism and depression. The left hemisphere is associated with positive feelings and the right relatively more with negative. We might expect, therefore, the creative writer, whose right hemisphere may be more active, to show depression and its consequences, suicide or self-medication with alcohol or drugs.

A group at the University of Kansas complicates this right-left picture somewhat. They studied verbal creativity in order to test the familiar notion that the creative person has the ability to deal simultaneously with seemingly unrelated ideas, letting them all co-exist. Their experiment suggests that, with creative people, *both* left and right hemispheres coact to maintain multiple word meanings, while in the less creative the brain either does not maintain the offbeat (non-dominant) meanings or maintains them only in the right hemisphere.[43] In the less creative, the right hemisphere's offbeat meanings never get to expression in the left hemisphere. Thus, Robert Lewis found that, in eight patients whose two hemispheres had been disconnected, the operation reduced creativity.[44] *We cannot simply conclude that creative people have more active right hemispheres at the moment of insight.* The right hemisphere has to fertilize the left.

Connections

In the mid 1850s in Germany, researchers studying brain organization and creativity took to looking directly at the brains of creatives. Rudoph Wagner dissected the brains of several professors, including the great mathematician Carl Friedrich Gauss, poking around for the anatomical wellsprings of genius. In America, Edward Anthony Spitzka also did research along these lines, dissecting the brains of notable scientists, a presidential assassin, and, among others, Walt Whitman. The Soviets did a great deal with Lenin's brain (partly to reassure the citizenry that he had not suffered from neurosyphilis).[45] But, neurologist Kenneth Heilman sums up: "I could find no studies that supported or refuted . . . the hypothesis that creative geniuses in a field might have brain morphology that is different than the general population."[46]

The brains of creatives, however, might have things not visible to the eye of a dissector: more interconnections and larger uninterrupted regions. Bogen and Bogen have suggested that a decrease in the callosal connections between the hemispheres would allow greater specializations, useful in working intensely (convergently) on an idea. Conversely, an increase in callosal connections would allow the linking of widely separated ideas characteristic of the "Eureka" stage.[47] Normals, during creative thinking, showed an increase in the distributed coherence of brain waves (on an EEG) in particular between the electrode sites at the occipital lobe and the pole of the frontal lobe. The experimenters suggest that creativity draws on a stronger involvement of the long fiber systems connecting anterior and posterior cortical areas.[48]

Norbert Jaušovec experimented with the differences in cognitive processes between unusually intelligent ("gifted"), creative, and average individuals while solving complex problems. Highly creative people showed less mental activity than did average people when solving various creative problems. The creative individuals also showed more cooperation between brain areas than did gifted ones (as Winner found). The gifted showed greater *de*coupling of brain areas when solving ill-defined problems.

Jaušovec's results suggest that creativity and intelligence are different abilities with different neurological activity (and most neuropsychologists would agree). In general, creativity seems to draw on greater connectivity between different brain functions.[49] Jaušovec concluded:

> It seems that creative thinking requires a broader cooperation between different brain areas. . . . The idea that during creative problem solving respondents displayed less mental activity is rather appealing, as it can be brought in relation to subconscious processes and defocused attention. The second finding, namely, that creative thinking required a broader cooperation between brain areas—especially cooperation between frontal, parietal, and occipital areas of the left hemisphere—seems also congruent with creative theories which have stressed the importance of conceiving two or more opposites and combining it in a whole—a gestalt.[50]

Martindale likewise speaks of defocused attention: "If one can attend to only two things at the same time, only one possible analogy can be discovered at that time; if one could attend to four things at once, six possible analogies could be discovered, and so on."[51]

Kenneth Heilman comes to a similar, if less arithmetic, conclusion, noting that, today, most neurologists acknowledge that the various forms of intelligence (musical, mathematical, verbal, athletic, and so on) are *modular*. Our brains may consist of anatomically distinct systems that perform specific operations (like, say, picking the phonemes out of a stream of sound). Apparently, these modules are loosely connected in our brains. When creative people bring disparate ideas together, Heilman says, they are using one module to activate another, normally unrelated, module. Like Martindale and Jaušovec, he concludes that the creative person can activate a wider network than the noncreative.[52]

Bruce Miller and his coworkers have explored creativity in patients with frontotemporal dementia, that is, with damage to the frontal lobes or to the anterior temporal lobes or both. Some of the patients Miller examined began painting after their dementia began, and showed, paradoxically, increased artistic talent as a result of that brain damage. But these patients had damage limited to the left temporal lobe, site of the language centers. It is as though the damage to verbal skills released—disinhibited—the skills needed for creativity in visuospatial art found in the right hemisphere. The damage created an imbalance in the brain.[53]

A different form of frontotemporal dementia works in the opposite direction, reducing creativity. Damage to this region may leave victims at the mercy of external stimuli. Put a pencil before them and they will pick it up and begin to use it ("utilization behavior"). The patient is "hooked" to external stimuli and relatively unable therefore to heed internal stimuli (another trade-off). The damage reduces the possibility of the "Aha!" that is the illumination phase of creativity, the sudden internal perception of likeness across different fields,[54] because the individual is too focused on the external.

Even these tentative researches suggest special structural differences in the brains of creative people. Specifically, they say that *for that special "Eureka" moment of illumination, the brain needs to access a lot of regions at once.* Widespread neural connections will enable the thinker to make connections across widely differing fields of intellectual and aesthetic endeavor. *The brain also must reduce its concern with the world external to the creative activity.* Scientists composing a grant application may be being creative at grant-getting, but they are not being creative at science.

Colin Martindale and Nancy Hasenfus compared more creative with less creative people. During an "innovation stage," the creatives had more alpha brain waves (8-12 cycles per second), showing that they were operating at a *lower level of arousal* at moments of inner creativity.[55] "When asked to be original . . . creative people exhibit defocused attention accompanied by low levels of cortical activation."[56] What then diverts attention from the outer world to the inner?

Neurotransmission

Some experiments suggest that creativity involves something special about neurotransmitters. L-dopa is commonly given to sufferers from Parkinson's disease, people who have difficulty initiating movement as a result of dopamine deficiency. This was the drug that produced the dramatic "awakenings" to the world described in Oliver Sacks' book and the movie of that name. The L-dopa becomes transformed in the body to dopamine, and dopamine energizes the SEEKING system. SEEKING energizes us to act, usually on the external world, turning us away from imaginings and inspirations from within. Kischka and his associates administered L-dopa to subjects and found they had become *less* likely to connect distantly related words.[57] Kischka showed that L-dopa *reduced* the spread of activation processes in semantic networks. It reduced, then, the sudden connection of modules associated with an inspirational "Aha!," thereby reducing creativity.

Heilman suggests, however, that the effect does not come from dopamine itself, but from a different neurotransmitter, namely, norepinephrine. Dopamine, he agrees, increases our focus on outer stimuli and decreases our attention to ideation coming from inside our brains. Enzymes in the catecholamine system transform dopamine to norepinephrine. That is why an inspirational moment requires a *de*crease in dopamine and, more generally, all our catecholamines, but especially norepinephrine.

The system that generates norepinephrine affects arousal, attention, and alertness to opportunities in one's environment.[58] Norepinephrine, for example, generates the "fight or flight" response to stress. Norepinephrine decreases the slow alpha waves that, according to Martindale, are the mark of creativity. Conversely, the less norepinephrine, the less arousal.[59] A decrease in norepinephrine is associated with states of dreaming, resting, or relaxing.[60] Since activity toward the outer world interferes with inspiration from within, a decrease in norepinephrine would yield precisely the states of mind needed for "Aha!" thinking and that special moment of "illumination."[61] Reducing the influence of norepinephrine would allow spreading and larger networks—more creativity.[62]

The locus coeruleus, the "blue place" in the brain stem, spritzes norepinephrine widely throughout the brain. The locus coeruleus projects to the limbic system, the thalamus, and the cerebral cortex, and especially to the inferior parietal lobes that are so important in attentional processing. According to Heilman and others, the locus coeruleus probably innervates a greater variety of brain areas than any other single nucleus. High levels of activity in the locus coeruleus make us more alert and favor "bottom-up," stimulus-driven attention to novelty.[63] Heilman speculates that therefore the opposite, low levels of locus coeruleus activity, would lead to less norepinephrine. Less norepinephrine would lead to "top-down" processing, processing driven from within, that would in turn favor the "Aha!" stage of creativity.[64]

But then what controls the locus coeruleus? The frontal lobes. They have the ability to delay response to outer stimuli so as to allow the brain to focus on internal matters. It is the executive function of the frontal lobes that can switch one module so it connects, not to a stimulus from outside, but to another module inside.

In short, when we are motivated to act, we may be effective vis-à-vis the outer world, but we are not in the relaxed state that allows for inner illumination, inspiration, and innovation. Conversely, when we are relaxed and open to inspiration, we are not marketing the novel. And which state we are in depends on how much norepinephrine is coursing through our brains. That in turn depends (via the locus coeruleus) on whether or not the frontal lobes are focused on some action outward and therefore inhibiting the possibly creative or possibly confusing minglings of disparate ideas within. In other words, the norepinephrine hypothesis accords with the finding by other researchers that creativity comes from less focus on purposeful activity.

Heilman sums up several of his group's experiments this way:

> Our results may also explain the 'moment of insight' experiences where a difficult problem is

> repeatedly approached with effort, only to have the solution come later at a moment of rest, such as just before falling asleep. These moments of insight would therefore occur when arousal and noradrenergic activation are . . . at their nadir.[65]

Heilman concludes that *the creative moment, the sudden connection of the unconnected, happens during a period of relaxation after a time of preparation and work.* He instances Friedrich August Kekulé's famous discovery of the benzene ring through dreaming of a snake with its tail in its mouth. Similarly, Dmitri Mendeleev ascribed his discovery of the periodic table of the elements to a dream that showed him where to place the elements. Legend has it that Newton conceived of gravity while sitting under an apple tree, that Buddha had his moment of enlightenment under the bo tree, and that Archimedes achieved his "Eureka!" in the bathtub. These were all moments of relaxation, and all were moments, I would add, when mental or physical action toward the outer world was inhibited. Incidentally, that is something we found essential for "poetic faith" in readers.

There is other, indirect evidence tending to confirm that norepinephrine opposes moments of creative insight. High-functioning autistics have exaggerated talents and cognitive skills, in effect, tightly constricted cognitive networks in a constant state of arousal. Lacking the spreading networks needed for creativity, their talents lead not to creativity, but to compulsive, repetitive, outer-directed demonstrations of skill. And some studies find that autistics have increased norepinephrine.[66]

Another indirect confirmation of Heilman's norepinephrine hypothesis comes from findings linking depression and creativity. Depression is associated with reduced cerebral blood flow to frontal regions that would reduce input to locus coeruleus and therefore reduce cortical norepinephrine. The result would be recruitment of widely distributed rather than focused networks.[67] Depression might bring on the languid state of mind receptive to inner inspiration. Since depression would also sap the energy needed to write, though, one can only conclude that depression might co-occur with creativity, not cause it.

Focusing only on the writer's or artist's mind, however, looks at inner creativity. It leaves out a large part of creativity, namely, creativity as it relates to the outer world.

23 | Outward Creativity

> All in all, the creative act is not performed by the artist alone; the spectator brings the work in contact with the external world by deciphering and interpreting its inner qualifications and thus adds his contribution to the creative act. This becomes even more obvious when posterity gives its final verdict and sometimes rehabilitates forgotten artists.
>
> —Marcel Duchamp, "The Creative Act"

ALL MY TALK of regression, brain organization and structure, interconnected modules, and norepinephrine addresses only one part of creativity, the part I have been calling "inspiration" or "illumination" or "insight." Literary creativity has really two sides. The first is that driven feeling, I have to write!, followed by turning within, then followed (one hopes) by inspiration. That is inner creativity, a state of the artist's mind. There is a second creativity, one that involves turning outward.

Beyond illumination

Howard Gardner defines that second, outward aspect as becoming important in both one's "field" and one's "domain."[1] By "field," Gardner means professional activities like speaking at conferences, getting grants, giving public readings, dealing with publishers, or finding an agent. By "domain," Gardner means an area of knowledge like physics or poetry. To be important in a domain means becoming a "must," someone whose work, be it poetry or physics, a neophyte entering the field must study.

Graham Wallas' four stages of creativity clearly distinguish totally inner-directed illumination from partially inner-directed incubation from totally outer-directed preparation and verification. In short, the magic moment of "Aha!" or "Eureka!"—that is the one on which the brain scientists can say something interesting. The other three stages (preparation, incubation, verification) do not differ from various kinds of everyday thinking. Even so, they matter just as much.

Creativity and value

Creativity as a quality of the mind and brain is necessary but not sufficient for artistic or scientific achievement. We do not award the accolade "creative" to church-bulletin poets or Sunday-afternoon painters. "Creativity," at least in its outward, practical sense, rests on a value judgment. To say a writer is creative, even in the first sense, other people need to feel that the work is "good."

To call a literary work "good" or "great," many people have to be able to re-create their own identities from it, as Duchamp points out in the epigraph. To be good or great, a literary work's audience must find its formal qualities consistent with their own defenses, its "content" open to the projection of their own fantasies. They have to feel emotions, including pleasurable emotions, toward it. They have to be able to make it make sense, and all the other complicated things we have seen in earlier chapters.

Instead, then, of saying creativity is a property of one person's mind, something "in" the writer, we have to think of creativity as including other people alongside the artist. There is inner creativity but also outward creativity. In other words, we should recognize that *art is a process rather than a thing*. Literature and media are, in a word I share with John Dewey, *transactive*. It is a transaction between a story, play, or poem and you, me, and thousands of others. It involves *both* something writers and artists create *and* something the rest of us create from what they create.

A behaviorist view

Robert S. Albert published in 1975 an article called "Toward a Behavioral Definition of Genius."[2]

> A person of genius is anyone who, regardless of other characteristics he may possess or have attributed to him, produces, over a long period of time, a large body of work that has a significant influence on many persons for many years; requiring these people, as well as the individual in question, to come to terms with a different set of attitudes, ideas, viewpoints, or techniques before all can have "peace of mind," that is, a sense of resolution and closure.[3]

This behaviorist account deliberately ignores the genius' inner states. A person does work that others value so highly that they attribute genius to its author. Albert concludes, with typical behaviorist bravado, that, as for genius *per se*, "There is no such thing."[4]

But consider Emily Dickinson. By her death in 1886, she had published only seven poems, and no one paid any particular attention to them. When poetic tastes changed a half century after her death, she was "discovered" and pronounced one of the great geniuses of American literature. No one could have said that in 1886. She lacked creativity in the outer sense then, but it was undoubtedly as true in 1886 as in 1986 that she had creativity in the inner sense.

The point is, inner creativity and outward creativity are *separable.* We can look back at a Chaucer, a Freud, a Napoleon, or a Newton and say they had creative minds. But we cannot *look forward* from today's creative writing class and predict that this student or that will be "creative," whatever poetic prowess the student demonstrates now. *There is no way to predict only from qualities in the individual that that person will succeed in being a "creative writer,"* because we cannot predict the future reactions of thousands of readers yet unborn.[5]

Creativity: a summing-up

At the outset, I urged the common view that the artist's and the scientist's creativity involve the same psychology. Both make connections between disparate ideas that seem to have no connection with one another. Both make something "surprising but right." We commonly observe that writers feel they are compelled to write and to write in a particular style. They do, I suggest, because the medium of words has somehow become embedded in and essential to their core identities. Since life drives us toward identity maintenance, a writer has to write—and has to write in a chosen medium and a certain personal style.

Most theorists of creativity adopt Wallas' four stages: preparation; incubation; illumination; and verification. The preceding chapter focused, though, primarily on illumination, which seems to be a special state of mind. In creating, writers (and other creatives) regress in the service of the ego, in psychoanalytic terms. They become open to some unconscious thrusting up of ideas and wordings. They put aside ordinary problem-solving thinking and engage in "divergent thinking," connecting modules in the brain that are ordinarily unconnected. They achieve this state of mind or brain by focusing on internal ideas, turning away from the outer world. Perhaps, in doing so, their brains draw on greater connectivity, their right hemispheres exerting more than ordinary influence. Perhaps they show more alpha waves, indicating relaxation. Perhaps their brains reduce frontal lobe activity and secrete less dopamine and norepinephrine, neurotransmitters that drive us to act on the outer world.. In an inspirational state, creatives passively let unconscious ideas bubble up to consciousness. Not acting on the outer world, they are like readers in a state of "poetic faith."

The creatives' combination, in "illumination," of regression and compulsion and inner-worldliness suggests a special brain state or a special kind of brain. Also, long lists of writers with psychopathology suggest that perhaps creativity requires a brain more subject than most to depression or bipolar disorder. Psychologists, however, have not found enough evidence to establish a causal link. It may simply be that the qualities needed for "inspiration" or "illumination" (regression and inner-worldliness) co-occur with the qualities that predispose an invididual to depression.

Creativity, however, involves practicalities as well as a magic moment or a special kind of brain. To be fully creative, a writer needs to become a "must" in the domain of literature and needs to succeed in sales and awards and the other accoutrements of literary reputation. For that to happen, readers must attribute value to the writer's creations.

This book deals with two kinds of creativity, the reader's and the writer's. But the two blend. The writer needs readers' re-creations of the work to achieve the practical side of creativity. We have seen that it is important for readers' creation (or re-creation) that they feel they cannot act on the literary work. This may correspond to the relaxation that Heilman found important for the writer's creative moment. When we are inactive, our SEEKING systems are freed from reality-testing. Inhibiting movement turns us away from the outer world and opens us to our inner fantasies. We can project our fantasies into what we are reading (ch. 15). We thus engage in our own form of divergent thinking. As Emerson said, "There is . . . creative reading, as well as creative writing."[6] It is, paradoxically, our ability to create from a writing that makes the writer creative.

The ultimate question

Both the idea of a specially endowed brain and the odd behaviorist account lead us to a peculiar conclusion about creativity. We can agree with the behaviorist that we award that word of praise only to works that seem "great" or "good" to many other people. And we can agree with the psychologists and neuropsychologists that the "illumination" or inspiration or "Eureka!" phase of creativity draws on some special brain state. But what is the connection between that brain state inside and the success of a "great" work in the world outside? How is it that a Milton or a Chaplin or an Arthur Miller or a Henry James out of their deeply different identities can create works through which many other humans can fulfill their equally different identities?

The creative person can make something that I can use to fulfill my identity in a way that satisfies me, and you may be able to use that same something to fulfill your identity in a way that satisfies you. And that can happen with hundreds or thousands or millions of people, all with different identities that must be differently satisfied. Creativity is quite unpredictable and seemingly miraculous. These myriad satisfactions of different identities pose, I think, the ultimate question about creativity. I will not pretend to know an answer, and I think that probably we will never be able to answer it. But the question points us toward another topic, evaluation. Our saying that someone is "creative" includes a value judgment: we must find the work worthwhile.

Having created a literary work or having had a literary experience, we complete that experience by concluding the work is good or bad, and sometimes even great. Virginia Woolf called this, "the second part of reading, to judge, to compare." We do this automatically, forbearing only with effort. "There is always," Woolf goes on, "a demon in us who whispers, 'I hate, I love,' and we cannot silence him."[7] Our brains demand this final step—why?

24 | Evaluating

There is nothing either good or bad, but thinking makes it so.
—William Shakespeare, *Hamlet*, 2.2.

AS PRINCE HAMLET reminds us, when we pronounce a literary work good or bad, that is an act of mind. It is the last stage of a literary experience, a final automatic feeling of, "That was good" or "I don't think that was worth my time." Like any other aspect of literary creation or re-creation, then, we do it with our brains.

Specifically, two things happen in our brains to trigger that automatic evaluation. First, our brains make a rapid, emotional appraisal of any experience of concern to us.[1] Accordingly, we have an involuntary "gut reaction" to the work of art we have been experiencing. Second, because we have primate brains, we assume cognitively, but again, automatically, that others will experience *and appraise* that work the same way we do. Ultimately, their assumed reaction will justify our awarding merit or denying it in a formal way. To be sure, a more sophisticated act of evaluation can override these first, automatic impressions, but the same brain patterns that gave rise to the snap judgment will underlie and bias any subsequent conclusions. Together, the "gut reaction" and the considered opinion become our "taste."

Rather than starting with the brain, however, I think it is helpful to turn to a traditional idea about evaluation. Writing of Shakespeare, Samuel Johnson famously defined the "great" literary work as that which "can please many and please long." Shakespeare pleased the Elizabethans and Jacobeans; he pleased (even when he was rewritten!) Johnson's eighteenth-century spectators; and he pleases today's Broadway and West End audiences. Dr. Johnson's definition makes more sense than any other I know. It too has pleased many and pleased long. And it sets evaluation within response.

Greatness "in" the work

Pleasing, however, is a complicated business, as we have seen in considering enjoyment and creativity. In ordinary parlance, in a newspaper review of a book or movie or play, say, the reviewer finds the goodness or badness of the work *in* the work. Reviewers will point to this or that aspect and say the book is too long or the acting is poor or the language is "forced"—and so on. For centuries, many people, thinking both casually and sophisticatedly about what makes works of art great or good, have tried to explain how some literary works "please many and please long" by things "in" the works.

Most of us when we think offhandedly about literature and media, have a simple, A-B-C causal model in mind. Artists (A) have something called "talent" or "genius" or "creativity" that enables them to make B, a work of art. B in turn has certain properties—call them, for our purposes, "beauty." Then this "beauty" in the object evokes a certain aesthetic appreciation from us, its audience. A causes B which causes C's response, and a reviewer, say, or anyone at the end of this process, will pronounce the work "good" or "great" or "so-so" or whatever. (This is the "text-active model" I countered at the opening of chapter 15.)

There are, as we saw there, problems with this folk picture. Things "in" the work come, really, as a result of our construction of the work. Perhaps that is why, although people have been thinking about literature with this simple A-B-C model at least since Aristotle, it has yielded meager results. We have not been able to settle on those properties in literary works that lead us to call them "great."

One famous formula for value in literature was philosopher Monroe Beardsley's: unity, complexity, intensity.[2] Psychologist Ellen Winner in her thoroughgoing survey of psychological research in the arts suggests three slightly different criteria for artistic merit: repleteness, expression, and composition.[3]

All such criteria, however, the psychologist's entities or the theorist's, are difficult to define, difficult to measure, difficult to isolate, and difficult to replicate. For example, if you use a sonnet to illustrate a valued structure, how do you isolate the effect of that structure from the effect of subject matter? Most important, these qualities ostensibly "in" the work of art itself blur into the way we look at the work of art.

For example, repleteness: Winner adopts this promising idea from the philosopher Nelson Goodman.[4] Consider a zigzag line like the kind you see on stock charts. If we are concerned just with that line as representing stock prices, then we will only be concerned with the numerical values represented by the line. We can, however, look at such a line as a work of art. Indeed, I once saw a show of tapestries by Jan Groth that looked very like white stock market lines on a black background. If we look at such a line as a work of art, we will be concerned with its color, its varying thickness, its size relative to the objects around it, its placement, and so on. "Repleteness," writes Winner, "refers to the fact that in a work of art, relatively more aspects of the symbol 'count' than in a nonart object."[5] But is "counting" really a property of a jagged line? Rather, I think, "counting" is a stance in our minds, and "repleteness" describes the more complex way we look at an object when we think it a work of art. Repleteness is not a property of the object but of our minds.

In a formula like Beardsley's or Winner's, merit equals this quality plus that plus the other. What happens if you turn the criteria around? For example, I can easily create an object that has unity and complexity, for example, by repeatedly copying a stock market chart. I would end up with something unified but complex. I could then make it "replete," perhaps by using different thicknesses of line. Would that be a "good" work of art? Probably not, not without some *je ne sais quoi* that my artist and writer friends can produce, and I cannot. My point is that one can create an object which we agree has these properties: unity, complexity, intensity, repleteness, expression, composition, and so on, but it may very well not please many or please long.

The role of skills

Indeed, some of the experiments with children that Winner herself has carried out with Howard Gardner at Harvard's Project Zero question the whole idea of "effect."[6] That is, does a certain "repleteness" or "complexity" in the work "effect" a certain response in the viewer? No, say Winner and Gardner, when they write about children, not unless the individual is mature or sophisticated enough to recognize and enjoy those features. Not unless the individual has acquired the internal systems necessary to do the perceiving that that work of art requires (through college courses, for example).

There is great variability in our responses from culture to culture. Do you like Chinese opera? Most Westerners don't. That music is not part of our "interpretive community."[7] Picasso's *Guernica* looks unified to us, but it outraged many of the people who first saw the painting. *The Waste Land* provoked consternation and dismay when a reading public was first perplexed by it. Nowadays, we teach it to first-year students.

Even within a given culture, there is great variation. For example, when I collected free responses to stories from five graduate students in English at one university, I was surely exploring a very narrowly defined culture or "interpretive community." Yet even these five showed tremendous variability.[8] For example, here is a sentence from Faulkner's much-anthologized short story, "A Rose for Emily":

> We had long thought of them as a tableau, Miss Emily a slender figure in white in the background, her father a spraddled silhouette in the foreground, his back to her and clutching a horsewhip, the two of them framed by the back-flung front door.

One of these five graduate students read it this way:

> The father was very domineering. One of the most striking images in the book is that of the townsfolk looking through the door as her father stands there with a horsewhip in his hands, feet spread apart and between or through him you see a picture of Emily standing in the background, and that pretty much sums up exactly the kind of relationship they had.

He saw a dominating, tyrannical father. But a second reader read that same sentence this way:

> The father's a spraddled silhouette.' He's no longer stern and erect. He's spraddled across the door.

And he took the image to be one of the father's decline and impotence.[9]

Their readings stemmed ultimately from differences in personality that expressed themselves in different wish-fulfilling fantasies that led to different "content." The first reader wanted to see masculine strength and power. The second feared that superior powers would get from him what he did not want to give. He wanted to see power weakened.

This kind of wide variation in people's readings is not the exception, but the rule. Nor does it have much to do with the amount of training people have in critical reading. These two readers were graduate students in English, and when I collected responses from forty-four professors and graduate students and majors in English, they showed equally various responses even to simple grammatical questions.[10] Collections of critical essays by professors about a given work will show the same kind of variation.

In short, people have styles of reading, just as Ellen (in ch 20) had a personal sense of humor. Just as she found things funny or unfunny in her particular way, anyone's reaction to a literary work depends upon a personal style, ultimately, an identity embodied in that person's brain. *As a result, responses vary tremendously and so therefore does the merit individuals attribute to any given literary work*. (Voltaire and Tolstoy, remember, could downgrade Shakespeare.) This variability gives me a second reason to reject the idea that an artist's creativity puts some quality *in* a work of art which establishes its merit by causing a positive response.

The causal model

Even if we reject the idea that something *in* a work causes goodness or greatness, surely the general direction in which the literary transaction moves is from author to work to audience. When I enjoy a work of art or literature, it certainly *feels* as though something like A-causes-B-and-B-causes-C has taken place (ch. 4). It *feels* as though some "beauty" or "greatness" in the work of art has given me the special pleasure we call "aesthetic." Feeling emotionally that something in a literary work *causes* our response, we think at a cognitive, intellectual level that the causal A-B-C model applies. In fact, we find that idea quite unshakable. We explain our feeling by things "in" the work.

We have two deeply different kinds of literary response, enjoyment and intellection. I think the difference arises from a distinction we learned to draw early in life. The psychologists studying early infancy agree that, very early on, at the age of 27 weeks, they see infants inferring causality (ch. 4). Babies distinguish animate from inanimate objects by whether an object's movements are caused internally or externally. They understand *externally* caused movements through a "naive physics," including an idea of cause-and-effect.[11] They understand *internally* caused movements by a "naive psychology" that leads later to a social intelligence about things like motives, an intelligence that we share with our primate kin, a "theory of mind." Established so early in life, these understandings are, as you would expect, just about impossible to overturn.

I think that when we respond to a literary work, we invoke some combination of these, our deep, early ways of relating to animate and inanimate objects. If we are simply enjoying a work of literature, experiencing it immediately and directly, we are treating the experience, in a way, as like meeting an animate being with feelings and motives. If we are entranced as we read a poem, it seems though the poet is speaking to us. We feel toward the people of a drama on screen or stage as though they were actually "there," and the events were happening (ch. 11). We do the same with a fiction. Its events seem internally caused, and our "naive psychology" leads us to respond emotionally as though what we are reading or watching were animate.

By contrast, someone who is intellectualizing about a literary work, a critic interpreting or evaluating it, for example, takes an analytic stance toward an object "out there," external to the self. The critic or teacher or reviewer treats the literary work as inanimate and thinks in terms of cause-and-effect, our "naive physics."

Philosophers (starting with Alexander Baumgarten and Immanuel Kant in the eighteenth century) have acknowledged these different stances. They have held that when I say, "That is great," I am saying something quite different from "I enjoy that." I am pronouncing an "aesthetic judgment" that diverges, as an act of mind, from the immediacy of "I enjoy." "Aesthetic judgment" (the philosophers point out) involves a contradiction in terms. "Aesthetic" refers to immediate experience, but "judgment" refers to some kind of evaluative thinking that probably happens after the immediate enjoyment; at least it differs from enjoyment. Judgment requires a realistic assessment of reality in the manner of everyday thinking, not the aesthetic experience of being "transported" with a work of art.

Nevertheless, our enjoying has an intellectual component. We have to "make sense" of a text (ch. 21). Philosophers may find this step a contradiction to the immediate sensory experience, but, from a neuropsychological point of view, "making sense" of a sensory experience simply continues that original perception toward its natural end. In "making sense," we complete a SEEKING. We move from wishing or seeking a goal (of coherence, happy ending, a moral to the story, and so on), and we achieve that goal. Understanding a work is part of the enjoying, indeed, a condition for it. Otherwise one feels uncomfortably baffled. And we go on to feel "that was good" or "that was bad."

But that kind of quick understanding and gut reaction is not the same as deliberately evaluating or interpreting.

Critics and criticism

The literary critic's profession enforces that split in response between one's enjoying and thinking about that enjoyment. In an eloquent statement of the value of literature and criticism, the distinguished critic J. Hillis Miller follows thinkers from time immemorial in contrasting these two ways of reading, these two stances that we literary critics and teachers take toward a work of literature.[12] We begin by reading simply for sheer pleasure. We just enjoy, without thinking much about it.[13] Criticism proper, Miller points out, begins when we deliberately, consciously think about the text. The critic does not simply enjoy, but asks, Why am I enjoying? We literature professors hope our students will do both these kinds of things, enjoy literary works and think about their experiences of them.

As a working teacher and critic, I know I tend to swing back and forth between these two stances. I will enjoy and then I will ask myself, Why am I enjoying? And I can, if I wish, point to a turn of phrase, a deepening of character, or an ingenuity of plot that "caused" my enjoyment (or lack of same).

Having enjoyed a literary work, we find a reason why we did. Our brains demand that we seek causes for what we experience (ch. 4). Having felt an emotion, pleasure, we will seek (in Panksepp's sense) reasons for it *and we will find them.* (One might also mention in this context confabulation or Michael Gazzaniga's left-brain "interpreter" that gives reasons for phenomena that only the right hemisphere understands.[14]) A conventional literary critic makes a profession of this explaining. We might find things like the unity, complexity, or repleteness that Beardsley and Winner refer to or, in a postmodern mode, the deconstructions or hegemonies that Derrida or Foucault would allege.

Once, when I was just starting out in academe, a senior professor solemnly informed me that what we critics and professors were supposed to do was evaluate. We were to teach our students to tell the good and the great from the mediocre and the bad. Certainly that was the position taken by F. R. Leavis whose ideas dominated two generations of critics and professors in the United Kingdom. But, as Freud famously said, "One thing only do I know for certain and that is that man's judgements of value follow directly his wishes for happiness—that, accordingly, they are an attempt to support his illusions with arguments."[15]

Nowadays, however, academic critics and teachers don't do much evaluating, leaving that puzzling task to reviewers in the media. Today's critic or teacher is more likely to propound some linguistic contradiction or cultural effect on readers and audiences. Even so, critics are likely to proceed by the A-B-C model like the traditional evaluator. One can find that assumption of language-as-autonomous in the thinking of such critical luminaries of recent decades as Roland Barthes, Jacques Derrida, Umberto Eco, Michel Foucault, or Wolfgang Iser.[16] Today's critics and teachers tend to follow these distinguished predecessors and assume, as they did, that something "in" the text causes (or limits or controls or invites or deconstructs or communicates) some result in the reader or spectator.

Today's critics judge, interrogate, demystify, or interpret as they prepare to write something about the work in question. This planning to act, we have repeatedly seen, puts a stop to the state of being "lost" or "transported" in the work. The work that began its life as something to be enjoyed becomes a thing to be known and explained like other things in a world outside art. Conventionally, critics make the work a part of external reality, separating it from feelings. They are responding intellectually, at most covertly acknowledging the earlier emotional response. We are seeing in this chapter, though, that to do so is to fall for an illusion of causality established very early in our brains.

Having found, through that "naive physics" embodied in the brain since infancy, some cause for enjoyment, the evaluating critic takes a further step. If we wish to award stars, like a movie reviewer, we are likely to say things like, "You'll laugh your head off at that scene." "You'll find the middle section too long." Like all primates, we have an idea of how the minds of our fellow primates work, a "theory of mind," as the neuropsychologists call it. We assume that others' brains will work much as our own do. Social psychologists call this in humans the "false consensus effect," and they have observed it many times over. People tend to "see their own behavioral choices and judgments as relatively common and appropriate to existing circumstances while viewing alternative responses as uncommon, deviant, or inappropriate."[17]

Reviewers and critics typically, then, begin by assuming that their responses are caused by this or that in the work. They then go on to feel (at least, and perhaps decide) that your response will be caused the same way. But these assumptions about literary value do not fit what we know about our brains. Enjoying, we have seen, involves a spontaneous, emotional process, probably stemming from the limbic system and the orbitofrontal cortex. Finding a cause for that enjoyment draws on the cognitive and linguistic processes of the frontal lobes, in particular, probably, the prefrontal cortex. And it is a highly individual process.

Enjoying and admiring

This difference between the brain processes involved in emotional and cognitive evaluating leads to one of the paradoxes that occur in evaluation. Enjoying and admiring differ. I admire as "great" Spenser's *Faerie Queene* and Joyce's *Finnegans Wake* and Bergman's *Persona*, but I cannot honestly say I enjoy any of them. Conversely, I richly enjoy reading Sherlock Holmes' detections or John Mortimer's witty stories about barrister Horace Rumpole, but I would not call either great literature. I can and do separate emotional "I enjoy" from cognitive "That is great," as philosophers Baumgartner and Kant pointed out. Enjoying involves a spontaneous, limbic, emotional brain process, while admiring draws on prefrontal cortex intellection. Admiring also has a superego element of "I *ought* to be enjoying this."

Either way though, enjoying or admiring, we as primates tend to assume that others' minds will work as ours did. If I enjoyed this book or movie or play, than others will, too. If I didn't enjoy it, but admired it, others will admire but not enjoy—or they ought to. If I thought it was awful, others ought to think so, too.

Evaluation, then, proceeds in stages. First, we enjoy or not, an immediate limbic response. Second, we find, cognitively, reasons for our emotion. I may find things to admire, things that *ought* to have made me enjoy the work, but didn't. Third, I assume that others will respond to those features as I did or, as I thought, on reflection I should have responded. This triad makes clear how our brains render aethetic judgment paradoxical.

According to both Dr. Johnson's simple formulation and Kant's weighty "Critique of Aesthetic Judgment," when we admire a work as "great," we are predicting. We are predicting that many others will feel the delight we felt in the work. Or perhaps we are predicting that they will feel the delight I thought I ought to feel in the case of *The Faerie Queen, Persona*, or *Finnegans Wake*. Or perhaps we think that they too will admire without enjoying. In each case, *we tend to assume that they will experience as we have experienced or judge as we have judged.* Literary evaluation thus involves the same paradox as trying to pick a winning stock on the stock market.

Literary value and the stock market

It was Marcel Proust, I believe, who first analogized between the stock market and the rise and fall of various composers and novelists in the lists of our admiration.[18] In fact, I think his analogy between evaluations of literature and the stock market is quite precise.[19]

With stock pricing as with evaluation, there is a traditional, commonsensical, A-causes-B-and-B-causes-C theory. Some property in the stock or its parent company sets the price, some property like the ratio of debt to net worth or price to earnings. Theorists call this "fundamental analysis."[20] Academics who study pricing theory, however, proceed from a simpler principle. A thing is worth as much as it can be sold for.[21] In other words, what determines the price of a stock or anything else, for that matter, your house or your Picasso, is what somebody else will pay you for it.[22] For that reason, it seems to me undeniable, even a tautology, to say that stock prices rest on investors' psychology, that is, their collective state of mind.

The great economist, John Maynard Keynes, himself a highly successful investor, described the stock market as like a newspaper beauty-judging contest—not a beauty contest as such, but a beauty-*judging* contest.[23] Contestants try to select the six prettiest faces out of a hundred photographs, but the prize goes to the person whose selections come closest to those of the rest of the judges. In other words, you don't judge who is the most beautiful. You judge who the other judges will think is the most beautiful. Because stock prices depend on others' evaluations, Keynes is saying, the only way to make money in the stock market is to predict what the other investors will do.

That is precisely what we are trying to do when we try to apply Dr. Johnson's idea, that the great work will please many and please long. Evaluation in the arts means trying to predict how others will respond to the work. When I say that Wallace Stevens is a great poet, I am really saying something like, People will be reading Stevens a hundred or two hundred years from now, students will be assigned him in school, and professors will be writing learned articles about him. This is the same impossible prediction as trying to say how other investors will value a stock one year or ten years from now.

If readers' and critics' judgments are what make up greatness, a change in academic or popular fashion for or against postmodernism or metaphysical wit or projective poetry will change all our professional and popular evaluations of previous literature. In T. S. Eliot's famous epigram, "The past [is] altered by the present as much as the present is directed by the past."[24] The "properties-in-the-work" model for aesthetic value conflicts with Dr. Johnson's test the same way that the brokerage industry's fundamental analysis conflicts with the finance professors' pricing theory. And it seems to me that common sense favors the more psychological model.

From the stock market to life

Notice that this stock market analogy applies to many other phenomena. For example, publishers say a best seller "has legs," that is, it walks right out of the stores. But surely it isn't the book that has legs, but the people who buy it. We are not talking about a property in the book. If we were, writers could all be millionaires. All a writer would have to do is to examine a number of best sellers, find out what quality they have in common, and write a book with that quality. Rather, what happens is that, when enough readers find they can construe a given book to give them satisfaction, then enough people buy the book to make it a best-seller.

So with advertising. People have to accept the ad and buy the product to make the ad "good." The same argument applies to movie stars. Traditionally, we say that someone like Katherine Hepburn "had something" that brought in audiences: "box office" or "star quality" or fine cheekbones. But again, star quality depends on what we are able to do for ourselves with Katherine Hepburn. If enough moviegoers can satisfy their psychological needs with Hepburn, Hepburn, cheekbones and all, becomes a star.

In a political context, "charisma" was once thought a gift from the gods. Today we can see that it comes from what people can do for their own minds with a Roosevelt, a Hitler, a Gandhi, or a Martin Luther King. To learn about charisma, we need to study the citizenry rather than the biography of the leader. To make matters still more troubling, much recent research both in social psychology and neuroscience has shown that we make political decisions largely on emotional grounds so as to minimize conflict with pre-existing opinions.[25]

So too in psychotherapy: meaning is not "in" the symptom, dream, "Freudian slip," or free association. Rather, the patient says something about the symptom, dream, slip, or association, and only then, by an act of interpretation and evaluation, does patient or therapist endow the words about the symptom, dream, slip, or association with meaning.

The reason I have gone from the stock market to literary value to glamour to political charisma to psychotherapy is not that I am scatterbrained, although that is a possibility not to be lost sight of. The reason is that when we try to understand these so very different processes, we begin to recognize that our understanding of literature and the arts and our evaluations in life both rest on one of two fundamentally different ways we think about human beings.[26]

Being human two ways

One assumption says that human beings are relatively passive creatures manipulated by various stimuli ranging from political speeches and cheekbones to the poems of Milton and Shakespeare. The other says that human beings are mostly active creatures who construe advertisements and movie stars and political figures *and literary works* to form and to satisfy their own psychological needs.

I am insisting on this second model, one grounded in today's neuroscience. Any given response to a literary work or a political figure involves a feedback initiated from top-down in our brains' Jacksonian hierarchies and evoking a bottom-up reaction. Our experience involves a dynamic causation that begins from inside and evokes a response from outside that involves further interpretation (as in Figure 15-2). This difference in the models we assume when we evaluate is large; it affects how we think of many human qualities like charm or charisma. So far as literary evaluation is concerned, adopting a model that gives primacy to our own activity instead of an imagined activity by the text transforms the whole enterprise of evaluation. It changes the question we must ask when judging a literary work from, What is good in this?, to, What am I doing with this?

A new aim for evaluation

Writing about outward creativity, I wondered, How can some writers, those we award "greatness" to, create something that enables all kinds of people from many different eras and cultures to fulfill or re-create their identities?

I said that I think the question does not admit of an answer because we cannot predict individual human reactions. And that is why I think criticism cannot really evaluate. A belief that this or that literary work causes some response or other is simply an illusion, a brain illusion like an optical illusion.

Nevertheless, evaluation can be valuable in another way. If we keep in mind that we are animate, not inanimate, that we are governed by our individual psychology, not physics, then we can be trying to understand, ultimately, ourselves. How and why, given our biology and psychology, do many of us feel that certain literary works are "great"? How and why, given *my* biology and my psychology, do *I* feel that this particular literary work is "great"? An inscription at the entrance to the oracle at Delphi enjoined all of us, "Know thyself." By thinking about literature and, in particular, our evaluations of literature, we can do just that.[27]

25 | Is Literature Innate?

Biology gives you a brain. Life turns it into a mind.

—Jeffrey Eugenides, *Middlesex*, "Hermaphroditus."

AN OLD STATISTICAL legend has it that if you give six monkeys typewriters, they will, given enough time, eventually bang out the complete works of Shakespeare. In 2003, some researchers from the University of Plymouth in England gave the theory a try with six Sulawesi crested macaques and one computer.[1] The monkeys produced a truly Elizabethan mess. They bashed the computer with a stone, banged repeatedly on the letter S, and used the computer as a toilet. After a month, the total output was five pages of text consisting primarily of the letter S with a few As, Js, Ls, and Ms. No *Hamlet* there.

Literature is a human thing. Only humans do it, and apparently all humans do it. So far as we know, all human cultures have created and enjoyed some form of art that uses language. Why? Why do we do any kind of art? One answer popular these days among people writing about literature is: we are genetically programmed for art and literature, because the arts enhance our evolutionary chances of surviving and reproducing.[2]

Essentially, this claim has three branches. First, literature is a human universal. All humans do it; therefore we must inherit a propensity for it. Second, it confers advantages in survival and reproduction by letting us try out solutions to life's problems, particularly those with other humans, painlessly. Again, we must therefore inherit a propensity for it. Third, we do literature because it it gives pleasure. Natural selection makes advantageous behaviors pleasurable. Therefore, our very pleasure in literature proves that doing literature confers an evolutionary advantage. Each of these claims reinforces the others, but it is possible to examine them one by one. When we do, we find, I think, that they rest almost entirely on wishful thinking about literature, and, indeed, about evolution itself.[3]

If I look back at the various brain changes when we do literature, I see one overarching principle. *When we are experiencing literature, we turn brain systems on and off in ways that we do not in ordinary life.* In real life, we do not separate the "what" from the "where," we do not stop testing reality, we do not inhibit planning for action, and we do not give free rein to our wish-fulfilling fantasies, except when we are daydreaming. With literature, we take pleasure in something that gives us only imaginary gratifications. In short, when reading and creating literature, we use our brains very differently than when we are simply taking a walk, shopping at the mall, meeting lovers, or any of our daily activities directed to survival and reproduction. How then could reading literature confer an evolutionary advantage for regular life?

Universality

The first claim, that our genetics include a propensity for literature, rests on the fact that all cultures, past and present, make and enjoy some form of art, at least so far as we know. All cultures, past and present, include some form of literature: story-telling, play-acting, words accompanying dance, poetry, and so on. If something occurs universally among humans, if it appears early in life and without deliberate teaching or other environmental cause, then it must be innate in our brains. Where else would it come from?

However, before we can ask, Do we inherit literature?, we face a preliminary question. Do we inherit language itself? Neurolinguists debate this fiercely. Some hold, following Noam Chomsky, that we inherit some special ability that enables us to put words together to form sentences (leading to universal grammar). Others claim that we simply learn to speak sentences as part of our general learning ability embodied in neural networks that function through parallel distributed processing. Others argue that we learn language through social interactions with parents and others. Still others suggest (following Terrence Deacon) that language itself may have evolved from simple to complex along with our brains' evolving.[4]

It is impossible today to answer this much-vexed question, and I want simply to assume that we do acquire language early in life one way or another. Literature, though, is language plus something more. Plus what? What distinguishes literature among all the various uses of language?

Literature = language + ?

Do we have special modules in our brains, perhaps innate modules, that enable us to add something to ordinary language to make it literature? Or is literature just part of some general human ability?

I believe that what literature required was one specific instance of a general ability that cognitive scientists call "metarepresentation."[5] We have a variety of mental states:

desires, percepts, beliefs, memories, knowledge, thoughts, intentions, feelings, and so on. What the meta- adds is that we humans can have *mental states about mental states.* I can think about my desires, percepts, beliefs, and so on. Between myself and one aspect of my mind, I can introduce another aspect of my mind. "I am not sure that what I am seeing is a lion." "I am sorry that I am angry." "I wish I did not wish that."

That ability combines with another, the assumption that we acquire early in life and hold deeply, that others' minds work like our own. Suppose I see a man with red face, heavy breathing, his lips drawn back, teeth bared, and his fists clenched. If I were doing those things, I would be angry. He must therefore be angry, and I had better deal with his state of mind.

The physical signs of emotion serve to communicate among the hominin herd. We infer others' states of mind from their visible state, and that confers a substantial evolutionary advantage. Cognitive scientists call this ability "mentalizing" or "reading minds" or, most frequently, "theory of mind." Literary theorist Lisa Zunshine defines it as "our ability to explain people's behavior in term of their thoughts, feelings, beliefs, and desires," and she regards it as essential to literature and to her own (and presumably our) enjoyment of stories. "I can say that I personally read fiction because it offers a pleasurable and intensive workout for my Theory of Mind."[6]

Various tests administered to children bring out the relation between these two ways of reading others' minds. The "Maxi test" is one of the best known. The film shows a little boy, Maxi, putting his chocolate bar in the kitchen cupboard. Then he goes out to play. Meanwhile his mother moves the chocolate bar from the cupboard to the fridge. Maxi comes back in. Where will he look for his chocolate bar? Up to the age of four or five, children will answer that Maxi will look in the fridge. They are reasoning: I know the chocolate bar is in the fridge. His mind is like mine. Therefore he knows the chocolate bar is in the fridge. After age four or five, children realize that Maxi doesn't know what they know; he still believes the chocolate bar is in the cupboard. They have acquired a more sophisticated version of "theory of mind." They are putting their minds' knowledge of a mind (Maxi's) between themselves and reality. They are able to separate belief from reality.[7]

Interestingly, non-verbal tests of three-year-olds and even 15-month-olds suggest that they know (unconsciously?) that Maxi will look in the cupboard. Chimpanzees, however, never master this task (even when translated into a chimpanzee situation). For a long time, neuroscientists thought chimpanzees had no theory of mind. More recent evidence shows, however, that chimpanzees understand what others do and do not see and what they have or have not recently seen. They understand some things about goal-directed activities, especially in situations of competition.[8] Presumably, then, theory of mind exists in other primates, but in us it evolved into a much more sophisticated form.

We can think of these two different theories of mind, the naive and the sophisticated, and metarepresentations generally as forms of a widespread pattern in the brain. Psychologists speak of the brain as having paired or dual-process systems. One of the pair is rapid-fire, "quick and dirty." It acts willy-nilly and unconsciously in response to stimuli and does not depend on input from its paired system. That system is more analytical, reflective, and regulatory. The "where" or "how" system contrasted with the "what" system for identifying things in the environment (ch. 4) exemplifies these dual process systems. It is some such dual system that creates metarepresentations that can mark a belief (like Maxi's belief that his chocolate is in the cupboard) as hypothetical or mistaken, not corresponding to reality.

The evolutionary advantage

Obviously this ability to "decouple" states of mind from real-world stimuli, to mark the difference between imaginary or hypothetical ideas and ideas that correspond to the real world, has immense value for survival and reproduction. Decoupling enables us to reason deductively, to make decisions about the future, to pretend, to play, to lie, to teach, to do history—and to do literature.[9]

We humans acquire, early in life, this ability to put a mind between our own minds and the world. Instead of being able to say only, "Woolly mammoth coming," we became able to say, "Fred Flintstone think woolly mammoth coming." Instead of being limited to the factual statement, "Cassio had sex with Desdemona," we became able to say, "Iago said that Cassio had sex with Desdemona." And, "Othello believed Iago when he said that Cassio had sex with Desdemona." And even, "Shakespeare wrote that Othello believed Iago when Iago said that Cassio had sex with Desdemona." *We can bracket an action and make a pretense of it or a play* (in both senses). That is the ability we need to make literature and it is, presumably, universal among humans. We can go on to plays of plays: "Laurence Olivier made a film of the play in which Shakespeare wrote that Othello believed Iago when Iago said that Cassio had sex with Desdemona."

This ability to metarepresent, to think about our own and others' mental states, occurs universally among humans, presumably because it confers big advantages in survival and reproduction. And that ability is essential to literature. Is literature, then, universal because our ability to metarepresent, to theorize about other minds, is universal? Does literature confer an evolutionary advantage because theory of mind does?

Inheriting literature

A number of neuroscientific thinkers, coming, in particular, from the perspective of evolutionary psychology, support the idea that literature *per se* confers advantages in survival and reproduction. Therefore humans' doing literature evolved into part of the human genome. Neuroscientist Edmund T. Rolls, for example, writing on emotion, points out that we humans exist in complicated social groups. We therefore need to be able to guess others' emotions in complex situations. That ability takes on considerable evolutionary value. Hence, he suggests, we humans have made emotions and the imagining of others' emotions into the stuff of fiction, drama, poetry, and (recently) movies and televison. He concludes that a capacity for literature therefore has evolutionary value and must be inherited.[10]

In ths vein, Ellen Dissanayake suggests that the arts develop our ability to make something special. When we "do" art, we single one thing out from the stream of experience. Art therefore, she argues, has evolutionary value, and natural selection will favor those who have this proto-artistic ability.[11]

Psychologists John Tooby and Leda Cosmides have put forward the most carefully presented form of the evolutionary position. I hope the table below states their position accurately:

1. The ability to "simulate" situations (to imagine them without acting on them) has great value for humans both in survival and reproduction. This ability to simulate seems to occur innately in the human species. We evolved the "association

cortices" in our large frontal lobes for just this purpose.

2. All cultures create fictional, imagined worlds. We humans find these imagined worlds intrinsically interesting.
3. Responding to imaginary worlds, we engage emotion systems while disengaging action systems (a key point in this book).
4. Humans have *evolved special cognitive systems that enable us to participate in these fictional worlds.* We can, in short, pretend and deceive and imagine, having mental states about mental states.
5. We can separate these fictional worlds from our real life experiences. We can, in a key word, *decouple* them.[12]

These last two points, say Tooby and Cosmides, provide the evolutionary basis for our innate predilection for literature. "This decoupling allows us to solve problems by supposing and by reasoning counterfactually . . . [P]ossible outcomes [can be] evaluated, without the risk that either the counterfactual premise or any conditional downstream inferences will be stored in our encyclopedia of world knowledge as unqualifiedly true."[13]

We humans can use *contingent* information. But this ability creates a problem. We have to decide when a certain piece of information is relevant and when it isn't. We need to understand the boundaries within which a statement of fact applies or doesn't apply. Erroneous or deceptive information could be deadly if taken as true.

Therefore, to decide when information is apropos, Tooby and Cosmides continue, we develop *cognitive firewalls.* We learn to type and categorize information through *metarepresentations* that mark a sentence we are reading as to time, place, and source. We learn a *scope syntax.* We become able to label the statement, "Call me Ishmael," as sometimes a command in the real world and sometimes a sentence in a fictional world in which we need not actually call someone Ishmael. Kant's "disinterestedness" would, I think, include this kind of "cognitive firewall."

Cosmides and Tooby make a powerful argument and an appealing one. They buttress it by pointing to schizophrenia as a test case. Schizophrenics, they say, acquire their delusional beliefs because of a failure in this decoupling system. Schizophrenics lose the ability to make metarepresentations. Schizophrenics, on this theory, have trouble knowing what thoughts apply to what other thoughts.[14]

Cosmides' and Tooby's evolutionary argument says that fictions or, in general, pretense and play allow us to *decouple* the merely thought or imagined from "real" realities. Fictions let us practice simulation, assignments of scope, and decoupling. Fictions, say Tooby and Cosmides, let us try out solutions to problems of living without bringing down harmful consequences. Verbal and other arts therefore aid survival. This small advantage will, over evolutionary time, cause art, music, and literature to occur in all human cultures.[15] The genes in people that favor these activities will in time replace genes that don't.

Certainly play occurs in all humans, indeed in all young mammals, according to Jaak Panksepp. (He suspects that such play is critical to organizing the maturing brain, and he deplores the decline of free play in America's childhoods.[16]) Similarly, the psychoanalysts regard play, creativity, and the arts as part of good mental functioning. Erik Erikson, for example, took Freud's comparing the arts to play further. He insisted that artistic make-believe enhanced the psychological adaptations achieved by play: "The child's play is the infantile form of the human ability to deal with experience by creating model situations and to master reality by experiment and planning."[17] Pediatrician and psychoanalyst D. W. Winnicott famously suggested that creative experiences, either of making or appreciating the arts, take place in a "potential space" between inner and outer worlds. In such a space we recapture our earliest half-merged relationship with a mother. Literature therefore helps us live better, in Winnicott's view, because it allows us to loosen boundaries: between self and not-self; inner and outer; past, present, and future; or using and enjoying (Kant's "disinterestedness"). The arts help us to go back to a time when we were not so rigidly compartmented into our working and playing and loving selves.[18]

Literary pleasure

Logically, metarepresentation, decoupling, and theory of mind are necessary for literature. But are they sufficient? That is, will we inevitably do literature simply because we have the ability to decouple belief from reality or think about the states of others' minds or our own? Or do we need something more?

We need the desire. We may inherit the ability to do literature, but do we inherit the desire?

We read for pleasure. Some evolutionary psychologists argue that pleasure in an action signals that it is evolutionarily advantageous and therefore must be inherited. Why do we have sex? Because, obviously, we enjoy it. But if we didn't enjoy it, we wouldn't do it, and our genes would rapidly disappear and our species along with them. Therefore evolution favors those of us whose genes program them to get pleasure from sex. They come to dominate the gene pool, and the resulting humans enjoy sex. Ultimately, the argument, as applied, for example, by Steven Pinker, leads to the conclusion that if we enjoy anything, we must have a genetic propensity for it. The argument seems plausible when applied to things like sex, play, sweets, and so on, but evolutionary enthusiasts like Pinker extend the claim to just about everything, including literature.[19]

Jerry Fodor, a leading philosopher of mind, cautions, "This kind of inference needs to be handled with great care." "[O]ften enough, where an interest in X would rationalise Y, so too would an interest in P, Q or R. It's reasonable of Jones to carry an umbrella if it's raining and he wants to keep dry. But, likewise, it's reasonable for Jones to carry an umbrella if he has in mind to return it to its owner." "This is, in fact, overwhelmingly the general case: there are, most often, all sorts of interests which would rationalise the kinds of behaviour that a creature is observed to produce." In the case of literature, there are all sorts of reasons besides evolutionary advantage: simple pleasure, self-improvement, curiosity, and so on. Fodor continues:

> [T]the claim [that one reads to gain an evolutionary advantage] affronts a robust, and I should think salubrious, intuition that there are lots and lots of things that we care about simply for themselves. . . . Thus the joke about the lawyer who is offered sex by a beautiful girl. 'Well, I guess so,' he replies, 'but what's in it for me?' Does wanting to have a beautiful woman—or, for that matter, a good read—really require a further motive to explain it?

In other words, isn't our pleasure in reading reason enough? What do we gain by adding that the pleasure evidences an evolutionary advantage?

Ultimately, Fodor dismisses this evolutionary argument as circular (or even tautological). How do we know our genes program us to do literature? Because all cultures in all times enjoy literature. And why do all cultures enjoy literature? Because our genes program us to enjoy literature.[20]

The genetic step in the argument doesn't add a thing.

I believe that our pleasure in literature comes from its duplicating, in a mental way, the pattern of wanting followed by liking that is basic to all our living in the world. We gain pleasure in literature simply for the same reason we gain pleasure from gratifying any SEEKING. What is special about literature? Only that our pleasure is purely mental. We have "poetic faith." We use fictions to allow ourselves to be deceived—where is the evolutionary advantage in that?

Other universals

The claim that literature is genetic because it is universal applies oddly to other universals. As neuroscientist V. S. Ramachandran dryly points out, "Every culture that we know of has some form of cooking, however primitive. (Yes, even the English.) Yet one would never argue from this that there is a cooking module in the brain specified by cooking genes that were honed by natural selection."[21]

So, too, with taking drugs. All human cultures have taken and take mind-altering drugs—so Richard Davenport-Hines' recent book shows.[22] Yet all the available evidence suggests that using recreational drugs to tinker with our neurotransmitters is not a good idea. Does our genome nevertheless insist that we indulge in narcotics? Are we programmed for pot?

So, too, with education. All human cultures, so far as we know, teach their young, as do various animals. Education obviously confers advantages in reproduction and survival. Are we to assume that there are genes for going to school?

To put it bluntly, the claim that literature is genetic because everybody does it is too simple. Patrick Colm Hogan states the bases for literary pleasure more accurately by distinguishing the *function* (enjoying literature) from the particular brain *mechanisms* that that enjoyment uses.

Hogan is one of the rare literary critics who can base an argument from universals on a wide knowledge of non-Western literatures. He points to story universals, although he defines these not as 100% universal, but as motifs that occur across genetically and geographically unrelated literatures more often than would be predicted by chance alone.[23] We have, he points out, universal patterns in human emotions (well-established in the neurological literature and very likely inherited [ch. 9]). Literature plays into these universal emotional patterns and takes advantage of them. The recurring motifs of narrative literature package these patterns in such a way as to give us pleasure. We need not conclude, therefore, that we humans inherit a propensity for literature. Pleasure by itself is enough of a motive. We need only conclude that we inherit certain emotional patterns and brain systems for pleasure, and that we use literature to put these systems through their enjoyable paces.

If so, our pleasure in literature needs no special explanation, because it mimics our pleasures in life. We do not have to invoke any special genetic inheritance other than the general principle that mammals have a limbic system that enables them to guide their behavior by the expectation of rewards. The argument that literature enhances survival or reproduction becomes superfluous. We do literature simply because we enjoy it.

We mammals all have the same brain circuitry to tell us to do things that give us pleasure. I have been calling it (following Jaak Panksepp) the SEEKING system. It is what Wordsworth called, "the grand elementary principle of pleasure, by which [man] knows, and feels, and lives, and moves."[24] Parts of a dopaminergic system light up in a brain image when subjects are given chocolate, are shown a picture of a romantically beloved person, or offered a chance of revenge, all activities that give pleasure.[25] What we have seen is that literature allows us to give ourselves pleasure because it is a self-stimulation system. *If we do literature because we enjoy it, we need no further explanation for its universality*, any more than we need evolutionary explanations for smelling flowers, enjoying a warm soak, or, to use one of Steven Pinker's favorite examples, eating strawberry shortcake.

Advantages from literature?

The second branch of the evolutionary argument, that literature confers various advantages, appeals greatly to literary theorists. We would like to feel that what we do, getting students and others to read or write books, has value. Then there is a practical consideration. We are unprofitable humanities professors who are competing in our universities' budgets with scientists who bring in grant and contract money. What we do sometimes seems to the legislators and trustees who manage our universities, arcane, frivolous, unmanly, or useless. We need some kind of convincer that what we do is worthwhile.

That is perhaps why we read statements like these from distinguished literary theorists who draw on evolutionary psychology:

> I argue that (1) literature, whether encountered in live performance or in textual or electronic recording, can challenge and thus enhance our brains' vital capacities for expression, communication, representation, and signification and that, therefore, (2) the protoliterary experiences of some early humans could, other things being equal, enable them to outdo their less imaginative rivals in the biological competition for becoming the ancestors of later men and women.[26]

And here is another: "Literature . . . in contrast, facilitates changes in perception or in the self in its relationship with others, thus enhancing the survival and reproductive ability of the group."[27] And yet another:

> Imagination in terms of creating worlds in which the rules of nature and society are broken—fantasy—is the most recent form of imagination to have evolved. Evolution had guarded against such ways of thinking . . . . Modern humans, especially those after 50,000 years ago, learned how to overcome those evolutionary constraints by . . . telling stories and performing rituals as a means to . . . provide cognitive anchors for ideas that have no natural home within the evolved mind. In this regard, the modern brain . . . . is linked into the world of human culture.[28]

These theorists downgrade the evidence from biology and paleontology. For example: "The details of an adaptation as it currently exists are often more informative than the fossilized remnants of its earlier forms."[29] We go from *homo neanderthalensis* to H. P. Lovecraft, Philip K. Dick, and Thomas Pynchon in one easy step. The theorist can skip entirely the biological evidence and replace it with indulgent social generalizations.

About literature, Cosmides and Tooby conclude, "With fiction unleashing our reactions to potential lives and realities, we feel more richly and adaptively about what we have not actually experienced. This allows us not only to understand others' choices and inner lives better, but to feel our way more foresightedly to adaptively better choices ourselves."[30]

For those of us who prize literature (and live by it), these large claims make literature a Good Thing. They give it tremendous value and importance. The trouble is, we don't know that any of this super-Darwinian claim is true.

We don't know that literature enhances our brains' vital capacities. We might like to think that literature does all these good things, but do we have any proof?

Tooby and Cosmides conclude their article on beauty by an eloquent statement that works of art "stand on a base of an evolved psychology that uses aesthetic experience throughout the life cycle to guide our minds into becoming more fully realized."[31] Yet we use terms like "bookish" and "the ivory tower" to suggest that those of us who spend our lives reading and writing literature are impractical, unworldly, and poorly adapted for life. If what Tooby and Cosmides claim were true, English departments would be populated by saints and sages. I can only say that, after working for more than fifty years in English departments, that has not been my experience. Now, one could argue that the rampant coupling of English professors with graduate students during the heyday of the "sexual revolution" was spreading the genes of artistic people. True, but was it the combination of literature and genetics that conferred this advantage in reproduction? Or the amatory exuberance of "the Sixties"?

As for beneficial moral effects, critic George Steiner reminds us, "We know that a man can read Goethe or Rilke in the evening, that he can play Bach and Schubert, and go to his day's work at Auschwitz in the morning."[32] And Margaret Atwood slyly says of some women who believed that Culture (with a big C) will make you a better person, "They hadn't yet seen Hitler at the opera house."[33]

In fairness, I should point out that one would not expect to detect the slight evolutionary advantage conferred by a life among great books in some particular English professor or even a whole departmentful. Also, in fairness, neo-Darwinian theorists usually state these propositions conditionally. They are only hypotheses: "can," "could," "may have." But how could one prove these things true or false? We are dealing here with a faith-based theory.

Learning from literature?

Because Tooby and Cosmides emphasize the function of modeling the physical world, they confine their argument to "fictions." They define fiction, though, "in its broadest sense, to refer to any representation to be understood as nonveridical, whether story, drama, film, painting, sculpture, and so on."[34] But when they come to particular examples, they mention only literary works that model life situations, real or imagined. They do not mention lyric poetry, and I wonder how beast fables, creation myths, utopias and dystopias, fantasy, or science fiction would fit in. How about abstract or non-objective art? Music?

Literary theorist Ellen Spolsky has pointed out that deciding what to believe and what not to believe in a fiction is not simply one decision to "uncouple" as Tooby and Cosmides say. She notes that, even "uncoupled," we draw moral instruction from literary texts, giving the obvious instance of Aesop's fables. She points out that more sophisticated authors like George Eliot and Melville offer as asides a great many ideas about human beings and our world.[35] Even mere "entertainments" like detective stories or thrillers give us facts about army equipment, police procedures, brain disorders, neurotoxins—a vast array of subjects. In short, *a fiction is not simply a fiction, but a mix of fictions and statements that claim to be truths.*[36] The latter we do not "uncouple." Just as how-to books or textbooks do, these facts become part of the knowledge we use for living.[37]

Tooby and Cosmides give as an example of literary learning, "How would I feel if I acted in a cowardly fashion, and my community knew it (*Lord Jim*)?" But if we think about Conrad's novel this way, as simply the representation of a thought-provoking series of events, how does the novel differ from a newspaper account? Suppose I read the events of *Lord Jim* in today's *Times*. Would I not think about those events the same way as if I read *Lord Jim*? I don't need Conrad's elaborate narrative scheme and intricate motivations. Indeed, literature may be less helpful than a factual account.

Steven Pinker (in his 1999 book) also makes the claim that we learn life's lessons from, say, *Hamlet*.[38] Philosopher Jerry Fodor extends Pinker's argument to Wagner's *Ring* cycle:

> And here he [Pinker] is on why we like to read fiction: "Fictional narratives supply us with a mental catalogue of the fatal conundrums we might face someday and the outcomes of strategies we could deploy in them. What are the options if I were to suspect that my uncle killed my father, took his position, and married my mother?" Good question. Or what if it turns out that, having just used the ring that I got by kidnapping a dwarf to pay off the giants who built me my new castle, I should discover that it is the very ring that I need in order to continue to be immortal and rule the world? It's important to think out the options betimes, because a thing like that could happen to anyone and you can never have too much insurance.[39]

The idea that we learn how to live from literature claims either too little or too much for literature.

Where are the genetics?

We have considered the three branches of the claim that we have a genetically evolved propensity for making and enjoying literature: universality; evolutionary advantage; pleasure as evolutionary marker. All three, I think, rely on wishful thinking about literature. Further, they do not allow for the complexity of the genetics involved.

Inheriting a behavior involves at least four steps:

There has to be a relevant gene or, more likely, a cluster of genes;

there has to be the particular environment (including intrauterine environment) that makes those genes express their proteins;

the proteins have to cause or at least affect the behavior; and

the behavior must increase the likelihood of survival and/or reproduction.

The claim that literature is "genetic" would get fewer headlines if one claimed that literature comes from a protein.

The genetics for the inheritance of a behavior are incredibly complicated. For example, an important long-term study of depression found that a certain gene, 5-HTT, occurs in two forms (alleles) in humans, a short form and a long form. If someone carries two copies of the long allele, that person is no more likely to become depressed at joblessness, disabling injury, or some other stressor than people who experienced no catastrophe. If, however, someone carries two copies of the short allele, that person is about twice as likely to become depressed under stress as people with the long allele. Experiments showed that the short form of the 5-HTT gene produces less of a protein that helps conduct the neurotransmitter serotonin across synapses and regulates its effect by removing the excess. (Anti-depressant drugs like Prozac act as this protein does.) In short, these researchers produced evidence that *this specific gene is activated by environmental events to produce a protein that has a specific role in predisposing people to this particular behavior.*[40]

Literary theorists who claim an evolutionary function for literature, cannot provide that kind of complex evidence for their claims. Indeed, it is hard to see how such evidence could exist. These theorists usually skip the genetics. Everybody does literature. Reading literature (we know!) is a Good Thing, and it gives pleasure. Therefore there must be a genetic basis for reading and writing literature. But the claim that literature provides "cognitive anchors" or "enhances vital capacities," is speculative. We have no evidence one way or another about such supposed virtues, and I wonder what kind of evidence would be possible. It would be equally difficult to prove that such "anchors" confer enough of an evolutionary advantage for literarily inclined hunter-gatherers to ensure their place in the gene pool. And what protein is involved?

What we do and what we do it with

All these lines of argument from the evolutionary psychologists lead to the conclusion that we inherit an ability to create and to enjoy literature. Surely, we do inherit some forms of intelligence.[41] In the world of music, one can point to the many musically talented members of the Bach family. In the world of letters, one can point to the Waughs, the Huxleys, or the Jameses. Skill with language and metarepresentations may well be an inherited intelligence. Whether that skill expresses itself as writing poetry, though, or writing nasty critical essays or in political speeches or advertising or journalism seems to me wholly a matter of circumstance—of environment. To paraphrase the epigraph, biology may give you a talent, but it is life that turns it into a career.

Literary theorist Patrick Colm Hogan points to what seems to me a useful distinction for thinking about evolu tion and literature. Hogan distinguishes *mechanisms* from *functions*.[42] A mechanism is some fairly precise ability for something the body or brain does: our abilities to grasp or to walk; our auditory system's ability to register slight differences among high frequencies; our separate abilities to perceive motion or colors or to synthesize a world of three dimensions. A single function uses several mechanisms.

In effect, Hogan distinguishes what we do from what we do it with. In general, skills in the arts draw on heritable mechanisms: the artist's eye for relations among shapes and colors or the writer's ability to juxtapose words. Thus reading is a function that combines the abilities of our eyes to saccade across a page, the concentration of visual acuity in the center of the visual field, the ability to perceive edges (hence letters), some sort of visual lexicon in the brain, and many other mechanisms. Writers draw on even more subtle abilities, an ear for words, access to a large vocabulary, and freedom to let unconscious ideas become conscious. Clearly, such mechanisms have evolved, like the concentration of visual acuity. Others have to be learned like the visual lexicon—children have to be taught to read. *It makes sense to say a mechanism evolved. It does not make sense to say a function evolved or is genetic or is an adaptation*, as some evolutionary psychologists do. When we are cooking or reading we are certainly using inherited mechanisms, yet we do not inherit the ability to cook or read.

Hogan is distinguishing between evolved mechanisms (like saccading or recognizing edges) and socially pleasurable or useful functions (like enjoying literature). Surely it does not contradict the biological fact of evolution to distinguish the detailed body *mechanisms* that we clearly do inherit from complicated psychological *functions* like reading a novel or watching a play that we do not inherit. But rejecting the evolutionary explanation leaves us with the very question with which we began this chapter. All human cultures have "done" literature. Why?

26 | Why Literature?

Are we having fun yet?

—Bill Griffith, *Zippy Stories.*

To read without reflecting is like eating without digesting.

—attributed to Edmund Burke.

SURELY THE BIGGEST puzzle about the arts is why we do them at all. They seem useless, yet apparently all cultures in all climes and times do art. The evolutionary answer, we have seen, the idea that art serves some biological purpose, fails. As we have abundantly seen in all the preceding chapters, literature does not engage our brains the same way that life does. We do not, in life, separate "how" from "where," we do not turn off our reality-testing, we do not ignore our environment, and so on. Hence literature cannot train our brains for life.

I suggest a different, simpler answer, Zippy's. We create and re-create literature because we enjoy it. It gives us pleasure. Pleasure that we didn't work for, though, feels somehow illicit. Logan Pearsall Smith, for example, called it, "this polite and unpunished vice" (ch. 19). It needs justification, particularly if it comes from mere imaginings. People thinking about literature like to claim, therefore, that it serves some moral purpose. It has a profound meaning that we must find. Literature is a "higher" pleasure. And it is—provided we bring our brains back from the non-ordinary way they function in enjoying literature to our more everyday ways of coping with reality. *Literature and art, I believe, achieve their "higher" purpose only when we think about them.* Merely reading or going to museums and concerts is not enough. Something more is needed, and that something more is thinking in our ordinary way about the the experience of art or literature we have just had. As Edmund Burke notes in the epigraph, we need to reflect.

We might ask, then, what marks art and literature off from other human activities? Theorist Northrop Frye answered that perennial puzzler this way (in ch. 6): "[W]hether a thing 'is' a work of art or not . . . cannot be settled by appealing to something in the nature of the thing itself . . . . [I]f it now exists for our pleasure it is what we call art."[1] Nothing in the thing itself marks art off from non-art. When we agree to treat a thing as literature and enjoy it as literature that makes it literature. We can make a series of street signs a "found" poem. We read eighteenth-century political speeches for their prose style. These things have served useful purposes, but as literature we simply enjoy them.

What makes literature literature, then, and art art, is not some property of the objects themselves but *us*. When we observe, for example, that the lines of a certain text only go partway across the page, we call it poetry, and we agree to treat it as something that, by its very nature, we cannot alter by our actions. Given a literary work, we agree to approach it with Kant's "disinterestedness." We adopt an "aesthetic stance." We agree just to take pleasure in it.

Literature builds on the convention that we will not change the work by our actions. That fact surely begins an explanation for why all cultures have some kind of verbal art and for why all cultures use this convention. We do it to get pleasure from literary works.

Are we having fun yet?

People do literature because they enjoy it. Isn't that enough? Evolutionary psychologist Steven Pinker (at one time, anyway) cheerfully accepted this position. In his 1999 book, the arts, he wrote, are "biologically frivolous."[2] The arts have no use, and therefore they give us no evolutionary advantage. They offer nothing but pleasure and hence cannot affect survival and the gene pool. The most you can say about the highbrow arts is that they enhance some people's status—according to Pinker in 1999.

He went on to compare our pleasure at the arts (especially lowbrow ones) to taking recreational drugs or eating a strawberry shortcake. We humans concoct certain stimuli that will push our pleasure buttons, things like chess or crossword puzzles, hobbies or philosophical enigmas. These are self-stimulation systems. Literary pleasure, for example, the making sense of a literary work, is just that, a self-stimulation system. We enjoy achieving a consummation after a SEEKING as described by Jaak Panksepp.

Curiously, Pinker's remarks match Freud's:

> [T]he artist makes it possible for other people once more to derive consolation and alleviation from their own sources of pleasure in their unconscious which have become inaccessible to them; he earns their gratitude and admiration and he has thus achieved *through* his phantasy what originally he had

> achieved only *in* his phantasy—honour, power and the love of women.[3]

Over and over again (devoting an entire essay, "Creative Writers and Day-Dreaming," to the idea), Freud wrote that art and literature are like a child's play, a glorified daydream, a mild narcotic, or an illusion offering an escape from reality into fantasy.[4]

Literature, however, is a special pleasure among our many pleasures, because with literature our brains function differently from the way they do in ordinary life. Yet literature is only one experience among many, and, if you believe Pinker or Freud, not one to be taken as seriously as we take life. If so, then, there is no point in proclaiming some high purpose for literature. We don't have to argue that it contributes to our evolutionary success or that it makes us wiser and better people. We get pleasure from seeing a movie or reading a good novel or hearing an edgy poem, and that's enough. We do literature simply because it's fun, the gospel according to Zippy.

That's hardly a verdict likely to satisfy someone like me who has spent his life engaging the verbal arts. Is there no difference between literature and Pinker's strawberry shortcake? Is literature simply frivolous, flattering, or fun? Is that in fact what this long excursion into brain science has shown?

What this book was all about

At the beginning of this book, I wrote, "The point of this book is not to change what we do and feel about literature, but to change how we think about what we do and feel." I said that I would do that by bringing new knowledge from neuroscience to bear on some well-known ideas about the how and why of literature and the arts. I planned to put some flesh (or gray matter) on traditional terms like form, content, style, identification or imagination. I did so by describing brain activity.

At this point, we have seen, I hope, that we enjoy literature by putting our brains through a complex process. We come to a work of literature with two expectations. One, we will not be able to act on it. Two, we expect to take pleasure in the literary work. The form of literature helps us ward off possible unpleasures, and our processing the content enables us to project our own wish-fulfilling fantasies into it. Finally, to enjoy a literary work, we need to make some kind of sense out of it. All of this gives us a sense of mastery. We take pleasure in first passively experiencing, then integrating into our regular mental processing a world that makes as much and maybe more sense than our real one.

This conclusion is odd. We end by taking pleasure in something whose gratifications are only imaginary. And *we achieve all this by using brain systems for gaining pleasure differently than we use those same systems to gain pleasure in daily life*. When we look at the making and enjoying of literature or the media arts from a neuropsychological, neuropsychoanalytic point of view, we find a number of interwoven changes from our regular brain functioning.

1. In the most important move, we accept cognitively that we cannot or will not change the work of art by our actions. This, we have seen, is a cardinal principle in people's thinking about literature, Kant's "disinterestedness." As a result, so far as the work of literature is concerned, we disengage our systems for initiating actions (chs. 6-7).
2. When we turn to literature, we expect to gain pleasure without doing anything to gain it (ch. 12). Hence we can shut off our action systems all the more easily.
3. Because we shut down our action systems in rela-

tion to the literary work, we can become "absorbed" in it. We gain a special trance-like state of mind in which we become unaware of our bodies and our environment (ch. 5-6). We are "transported."

4. Then, too, the brain focuses its attention networks on the work of literature, momentarily salient because the brain is using that text to gain ongoing pleasure. The brain turns away from our bodies and our environment as no longer relevant to its ongoing activity (ch. 6).
5. Because we have disengaged our action systems from the literary work, we also stop testing the reality or probability of the representations in that literary work. In Coleridge's phrase, we have "poetic faith." We are able to accept the most fantastic things that science-fiction or fairy tales or superhero movies can produce (ch. 7).
6. When we shut down our action systems and are "absorbed" in literature, we make the "where" information from our sensory systems independent of the "what" information we derive from the language of a literary work. With a poem or story, we can relate to purely imaginary characters (those with no "where") as if they were real. Conversely, if we are "transported" in watching stage or screen dramas whose characters have a "where," we ignore the "what" fact that the characters are just actors pretending (ch. 11).
7. We humans feel emotions whether we will or no, because emotions begin in the sub-cortical limbic system. If we are presented with a situation that would, in normal primate experience, cause fear or anger or disgust or jealousy or desire, we will feel

those emotions. In life, emotions include impulses to act. (Who ever was enraged at someone without wanting to strike that person?) But if we are transported in relation to a work of literature, we have turned off the relevant action systems. We therefore feel the emotions psychologically but the impulse to act is inhibited or simply not there. This is another reason we can feel real fear or disgust or anger or affection toward literary persons and situations even though (or because!) we know perfectly well that they are not "real" (chs. 9-11).

8. When we enjoy a literary work fully, by being "transported," its form (particularly the omissions) performs some of the functions that our own defenses would normally carry out (ch. 13).
9. When we enjoy a literary work fully, by being "transported," we turn off reality-testing. We are not planning for real actions toward the work. We therefore take the brakes off (disinhibit) our goal-seeking systems. We can project our conscious and unconscious wishes and fantasies freely into the literary work (chs. 14-16).
10. Because we have reduced our reality-testing of the work, we have also reduced our usual constraints on language processing. The right hemisphere is more active than it usually is. Spreading activations in the right hemisphere open us more to puns, jokes, metaphors, ambiguities, and sound-associations. We are, in short, more open to literary language than the left-hemisphere language centers normally permit (ch. 16).
11. We analogize to the literary experience with feelings and memories from our own lives which are disproportionate to the unreal literary events them-

selves (chs. 7, 9, and10). Coleridge said it precisely right when he said, we "transfer from our inward nature a human interest."[5] We can therefore feel toward literary events as though they were "bigger than life."

12. Because we have disinhibited, freed, our wishing systems, we can, as if we were confabulating, attribute personally styled meanings to literary works. We "make sense" of them on our own terms. We fit them into our regular mental processing of experience (chs. 14, 20), making them into sublimations of the fantasies we have wishfully and freely projected into the work.
13. If we succeed in this process, we enjoy literature because we have mimicked the kind of successful achievement of goal-SEEKING that we do in everyday life. A literary work provides us with a self-stimulation system. We feel the pleasure we would feel if we had succeeded in some wish-fulfilling plan or action. And we did so without having to face the obstacles and limits associated with trying to change the real world. On the other hand, the satisfaction is only mental (chs. 19-21).

To sum up, I see one governing principle. *When we are experiencing literature, we turn on and turn off brain systems in ways that we do not in ordinary life.* The brain situations numbered above resemble but differ from things our brains do when we are simply carrying on daily life and, in doing so, ensuring our survival and reproduction.

I somewhat artificially separated our response to literature into: expectation, form, content, and meaning (part III). The combination, if successful, leads to satisfaction. In the literary situation, much more so than in daily life, our expectations reach back from the what-comes-next of what we are reading to earliest infancy: being fed while not acting. Our expectations draw on our experience from the earliest moments of our lives to this moment right now. They span a wider range than, say, my expectations about doing a good job at the office or working out at the gym.

Within that wider expectation, we experience an emotionally charged dialectic between form and content. The form of the literary work takes care of (at least partly) our need to control our imaginings. With reality-testing turned off, we are freer than in daily life to project our wishes and fantasies into what we are perceiving. What we perceive in the literary work provides, as it were, pegs on which we can hang our own deepest and probably unconscious wishes and feelings about mothers, fathers, lovers, children, authorities, government, work, space, love, hate—you name it—everything that populates our dreams. With literature, form adds to our habitual ways of dealing with these issues to control and limit possible anxiety. We can project more freely into content. We can span more and deeper wishes than when we focus on a goal in daily life, and we can feel all right about those wishes.

On the other hand, some aspects of "doing" literature or media or other arts simply carry out the things we do in ordinary life. Thus,

14. All humans live out a pattern of being in which we fulfill and vary an identity theme set in childhood. Writers write and readers read with a style that expresses and confirms that identity theme (ch. 17).
15. Writers have a compulsion to write because language, one particular artistic medium or sensory modality, became part of their identity themes. When this acting-out succeeds, it fulfills identity and is therefore a source of great pleasure. When it fails, it is a source of equally great unpleasure because

identity re-creation has failed. Hence the creative urge acquires its compulsive quality (ch. 22).

16. In life, we necessarily make the assumption, based on a childhood "naive psychology" that others' minds or brains will work as our own would in similar circumstances. In judging literature, then, as writers or readers, we make the same assumption. We automatically think that what pleases us will please others too—will "please many and please long" (ch. 24).

In short, in the special brain states we use with literature, we follow patterns of identity re-creation like those we carry out in everyday life. Thus our brains function with literature partly as they do in ordinary life (identity-re-creation) but partly in a quite different way (inhibited action).

Psychoanalysts have called these likenesses and differences (following Ernst Kris' idea) "regression in the service of the ego."[6] Partly they serve real-world needs, but partly they are childish and unreal. They sublimate.

Today we know some things that Kris could not have known about the brain. Today we can say that, when we experience literature, we alter our brain systems: we inhibit actions. We evolved the ability to turn action systems on and off in ways that even our cousins among the apes cannot. That ability to delay in turn allows us to impose one state of mind upon another, to "metarepresent" our mental states. That ability, though not specifically literary in itself, enables us to create and enjoy literature.

That is what I hope this book has accomplished: saying how systems in our brains function with literature. But this is only a start. Advances in brain science will make it possible to say much more. And I also realize that I have omitted one big thing.

What this book did not do

I have not tried to relate particular literary works to brains, because I do not think that is possible at this stage of neurological knowledge. We experience works of literature through a hierarchy of processes of testing the work against various hypotheses or schemas in our brains. The perceptions will be similar for all of us (as in the Malach and Hasson experiments with films[7]). Some cultural recognitions will be shared by everybody within a given culture. Others will be applied only by certain "interpretive communities." Finally, an individual style of being (identity) drives and shapes all these lower processes of hypothesis and testing (chs. 17-18). We can understand how we share and do not share the same experience of a literary work (chs. 15, 17, and 19).

The individual response is crucial. Nevertheless, not until we can get at individual identities through MRI, optical imaging, diffusion tensor imaging, or technologies yet unknown, do I see brain science being able to say much about the individual experience of individual works of literature. For now we can only approach individual works or individual readers' experiencings psychodynamically. I have done so in a variety of other writings,[8] but this book aims at the brain processes common to us all.

Some evolutionary theorists, however, have forged ahead with readings of particular works. For instance, two enthusiasts begin with this premise, "Characters are believable insofar as they behave in concert with biological expectation." Hence we believe in "such obviously human traits as Romeo and Juliet's hormonally overheated teenage love, Hamlet's intellectualized indecisiveness, Lady Macbeth's ambition as well as her remorse, Falstaff's drunken cavorting, Viola's resourcefulness, Lear's impotent rage, Othello's jealousy, and Puck's well, Puckishness."[9] But wouldn't a simpler explanation be that we believe them simply because we see these traits around us all the time? They are lifelike.

These authors go on to explain the *Aeneid* as reflecting "our shared human biology." Aeneas does not abandon the seductive widow, Queen Dido, to go off and found Rome because Jupiter tells him to. Rather, "Aeneas was following human—that is, biological—impulses, conveniently projected onto the gods." "When the alternative is maximizing your inclusive fitness by founding a dynasty, a sterile dalliance with a middle-aged woman is maladaptive."[10]

This kind of evolutionary explanation seems to me to have three problems. One, it assumes a uniformity of response that the evidence will not support. Biological explanations appeal to the universals of human nature, but what we have seen as crucial to experiencing literature and hard to get at are the individual features. Two, the explanation is circular. Why does Aeneas leave Dido to found Rome? Because his genes tell him to. Why do his genes tell him to? So that he will leave Dido and found Rome. Finally, this kind of evolutionary explanation flattens a rich and complex work. The *Aeneid?* It just acts out our genetic program. Yet, reading the *Aeneid*, I sense great human issues: the glory and brutality of patriotism; our will as opposed to forces beyond us; the splendor and hardness of destiny; the necessary conflicts in what we desire, here, romantic love and valor in the world.

"High" and "low"

Such are the grand themes one seeks and finds in "high" art. We do literature because we get pleasure from it, just as we get pleasure from all our SEEKINGs (at least when they succeed). Yet we draw distinctions. There are different kinds of pleasures: Pinker's strawberry shortcake, Louis Armstrong, Zippy comics, Milton's poetry, orgasm—

all have presumably first energized that dopaminergic, reward-seeking system in our brains and then found consummation. But we also know that they are different, and we rate them differently.

Within the single category of literature, we draw distinctions. No one would claim that the pleasure we get from the current best-selling romance novel or mystery story or soap opera ranks with *Hamlet.* We make value judgments, distinguishing our pleasures both as to kind and what one might call "degree." We translate that degree into judgments of value. We distinguish "highbrow" drama from "lowbrow" soap operas. Critics exclude romances, mysteries, and science-fiction from "The Novel." And we find some agreement among ourselves when we do (ch. 24).

How can we understand, then, what we are feeling when we distinguish literary pleasure from other kinds and a "high" literary pleasure from a "low" one? Most, perhaps all, theories about the value of literature seem to me to proceed from a suspicion of pleasure. Literature must have some higher purpose, because mere passive enjoyment cannot justify fantasizing. How can mere pleasure give a higher purpose to art?

Aut prodesse aut delectare

Most theorists seem to insist that art and literature do two somewhat inconsistent things. Horace in his *De Arte Poetica* put them simply and directly: *prodesse* and *delectare. delectare*: to delight—we turn to literature for enjoyment. Theorists usually translate Horace's other term, *prodesse* as "to instruct" or "to teach" or "to enlighten," and it is what justifies the enjoyment. "A poet should instruct, or please, or both."

But is it the poet or writer or their writings who instruct? Or does enlightenment take more than the literary experience itself. Milton states the problem with special clarity:

Who reads
Incessantly, and to his reading brings not
A spirit and judgment equal or superior,
(And what he brings what need he elsewhere seek?)
Uncertain and unsettled still remains,
Deep versed in books and shallow in himself . . .
As children gathering pebbles on the shore.
(*Paradise Regained*, IV, l).

More succinct is Edmund Burke in the epigraph: "To read without reflecting is like eating without digesting." And Proust goes so far as to find reading "dangerous when . . . truth no longer appears to us as an ideal we can realize only through the intimate progress of our thought and the effort of our heart, but as a material thing . . . which we have only to take the trouble of reaching for on the shelves of libraries and then savoring passively in perfect repose of body and mind."[11]

Just experiencing literature or art is not enough to enlighten (*prodesse*). If it were, the most enlightened people in the world would be those who spend hour after hour and day after day looking at masterpieces, namely, museum guards and copy editors. Merely perceiving great works of art or literature is not enough; something more is needed.

Literature gets us to use our brains in special ways that we rarely or never do in everyday life. It is hard, then, to see what use there is in just reading great books and using our brains oddly. Merely enjoying art cannot by itself meet the ethicists' demand for *prodesse*. Milton, Burke, and Proust insist that we do something ourselves, something from our own spirit or judgment.

A lesson from the critics

We can learn more about that second step, that *prodesse*, from those who make enlightenment from literary works their professional concern, literary critics and professors of literature. The distinguished critic and theorist, J. Hillis Miller, contrasts two ways of experiencing literature. We can simply enjoy. We can respond emotionally, *un*critically. Alternatively, we cogitate. We think in a purely intellectual way about a literary work.[12]

That duality should reassure the legislators and trustees of universities who wonder about the function of the humanities in an age dominated by science. Historically, our universities stumbled into thinking about literature instead of just reading it. In the 1930s, colleges and universities began to put in humanities requirements. Previously students and professors addressed the humanities through a Germanic scientism. Studying literature meant philology, bibliography, and literary history: facts about literature, not the experience of literature. Gradually, professors of literature began to read and to ask their students to read for reading's sake. But they did not ask students just to read stories, poems or plays. As Northrop Frye put it decades ago, "It is impossible to teach or learn literature: what one teaches or learns is criticism."[13] The professors asked students to read *and then to think and write and talk about what they had read.* And surely it is good for the young to think and write and talk. We need no evolutionary explanation for that. And that is what we professors, theorists, and critics do as well.

The Victorian critic Walter Pater described exactly the process I am suggesting:

> What is this song or picture, this engaging personality presented in life or in a book, to *me?* What effect does it really produce on me? Does it give me pleasure? and if so, what sort or degree of pleasure? How is my nature modified by its presence, and under its influence? The answers to these questions

> are the original facts with which the aesthetic critic has to do . . . .[14]

We begin by enjoying, but then we are to ask why, and seek the answer *in ourselves.* That is the job of the "aesthetic critic," the student, the professor, and the theorist. It is our task to bring what Proust called "the intimate progress of our thought and the effort of our heart" to literary works.

We have already seen three critics trying to do just that: Bate, Fiedler, and Holland (ch. 21). We three have all thought and written about literature in our several individual ways. We all have said what we believed to be useful things about literature. We have produced *prodesse* in Horace's sense.

When, however, we critics insist that we are talking about Keats' poetry or *Huckleberry Finn* or a Kafka story, we succumb to an illusion. *Necessarily, we are talking about those things "out there" as we perceive and respond to them "in here."* In Pater's words, that "in here" is "the original [fact] with which the aesthetic critic has to do." As a 1960s slogan had it, "Who you are is how it is." The essays we write say as much about who we are as about the literary works we address. More precisely, they talk about those works refracted through the lenses of our personal identities.

Ideally, understanding and enjoying literature would go on together. Surely the occasions when that happens are the most exalted moments of literary experience. But they are rare. The thinking parts of our brains (frontal and cortical) are separate from the enjoying (sub-cortical) parts. To be sure, they work together, but thinking about an experience is almost never the same as enjoying it. Enjoying requires only a minimal "making sense" of the text. Bringing spirit and judgment in Milton's sense requires much more frontal brain activity. Reading criticism can help. The art gives us the experience, but criticism can give us some understanding of the experience.

Mostly, students, professors, and critics do as Pater does in the epigraph. We enjoy and then we deliberately and separately think about what we have enjoyed. When we do, we are understanding something about the work *as we perceive and understand it in relation to ourselves.* That is surely what matters to us, as Pater points out. We are finding what parts stand out for us, what aspects we find most enjoyable, or what parts we feel most moved by, and why, in terms of our individual and particular styles of being, ultimately our identities and the individual brains that embody them.

Enlightenment

To enjoy a literary work fully, we "make sense" of it. At the most rudimentary level, we fit literary works into our everyday mental processing. The sitcom ends, we find the ending satisfactory, we turn off the television, and we go to bed. But this is the least of "making sense." If we are experiencing literature wholly, we reflect. We need to let our minds float, as it were, somewhere above that literal level. We do not take away simple lessons, like what to do if your uncle murders your father and marries your mother. Reading *Hamlet*, I come face to face, as the Prince does, with a task too large for me, that complicated play itself. How will I respond? Will I feel crazy? Betrayed? Will I, as he does, write a play of my own? Will I, as he does, dither and dilly-dally and finally give up and say, "Let Providence take care of it" ?

In short, when we make a literary work mean, when we make it make *more* sense than mere coherence, we confront the strange perplexities of life itself. Instead of answers, we find questioning. Experiencing those questions seems to me precisely Horace's *prodesse*. This, I think, is what Milton meant when he asked that readers bring "a spirit and judgment equal or superior" to what they are reading. "And what he brings what need he elsewhere seek?"

The play may tell of a Danish prince with troubles that one could find in a soap opera. But what we mean by "high" or "great" literature is literature that allows us a larger and different range of activity in our brain systems. Great literature can become an intense experience of informing pleasure, different from other kinds of pleasure, mental and emotional, not physical, yet somehow larger, more enriching, more enlightening, more questioning—and more delighting. And we assume that others can and will share that pleasure and, then, that brain activity. We respond individually, though, as well as collectively. Our individual responses are natural and inevitable, to be worked with, not ignored in the interests of coming to a consensus or a tidy conclusion.

What this book has shown, I hope, is how, when our brains work in special ways to create or re-create a literary work, we can freshly sense our selves and our world, relish our language, and confront our feelings toward one another. Fully engaged with and thinking through works of literature and the arts, we uncover our own individuality. We open ourselves to the largest truth of who we are, who we have been, and who finally we will be. In the last analysis, understanding a literary work means understanding our own humanity. That was the foremost command of the Oracle at Delphi: Know thyself. That is the wonder and joy we get from literature—and the thoughtfulness—that our brains create.

Acknowledgments

Many friends and colleagues, both literary and neurological, have read or discussed parts of this book with me and shared their considerable knowledge and given invaluable advice and help. To Jeffrey Berman, James Engell, Andrew Gordon, Kenneth Heilman, Patrick Hogan, John Kuldau, Christiana Leonard, Howard Mancing, Lois Oppenheim, Jaak Panksepp, Alonso Riestra, Louis Ritz, Murray Schwartz, Robert Sikes, Mark Solms, Oliver Turnbull, and Anne and Bertram Wyatt-Brown, I offer my profound gratitude. And, although they have long since passed away, I still benefit from the psychoanalytic wisdom of G. Henry Katz and Elizabeth Zetzel.

I have enjoyed lunching and listening and learning at the weekly sessions of the Center for Neuropsychological Studies directed by Kenneth Heilman. I have also learned much from the lively and friendly discussions at the Group for Applied Psychoanalysis at the University of Florida, at the International Conference in Literature-and-Psychology, and in the online discussion group PSYART. These organizations and this book would not have happened without the support I have been given by the University of Florida in the Marston-Milbauer Eminent Scholar's chair (pun intended).

I am particularly grateful to Bernard Paris for counsel, encouragement, friendship, and professional midwifery throughout this book's long gestation. My heart warms especially when I think of all the things my wife Jane has contributed. I have tried to list them in the dedication, but there are always more.

Appendix | About the Brain

> Not Chaos, not
> The darkest pit of lowest Erebus,
> Nor ought of blinder vacancy, scooped out
> By help of dreams—can breed such fear and awe
> As fall upon us when we look
> Into our Minds, into the Mind of Man . . .
> —William Wordsworth, *The Recluse*, Prospectus.

IN THIS BOOK, I try to bring out what the growing body of knowledge about the brain can say to some of the questions we traditionally ask about literature. How do readers read and enjoy—what is the psychology of that? Why do we feel real emotions toward imaginary people? How is literature made? What goes on in our brains when we call something "great"?

In this appendix, I am providing a small introduction to the physical brain for literary readers who are new to neurology, neuroscience, neuropsychology, and neuropsychoanalysis. If you are well acquainted with the pars triangularis, if you have delved into the mysteries of the

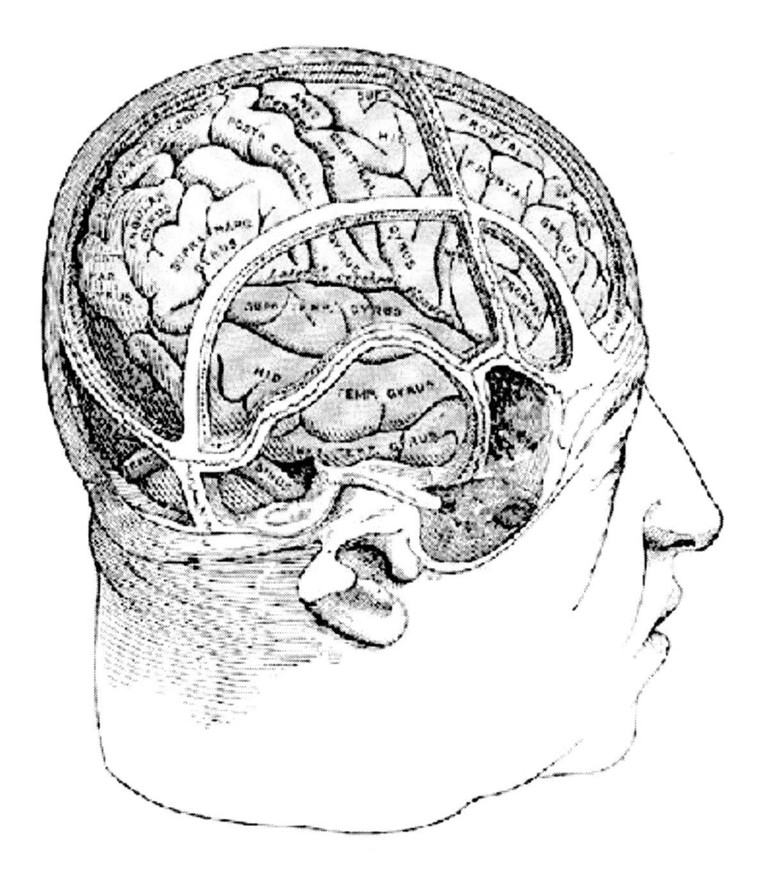

Figure A-1. The brain in the skull.

nucleus reticularis thalami, you will probably want to skip this appendix.[1] For thinking about literature, we do not need to know all the things neuroscientists know. We do not have to concern ourselves with diseases of the brain, for example, or the brain's arterial network. But for reading the various chapters of *Literature and the Brain*, it is good to have some idea of the brain's functioning.

We will be interested primarily in the branch of neuroscience called "neuropsychology." It connects functions like writing and reading to *systems* within the brain—never to a single locus! (That would be the nineteenth-century fallacy of *localization.*) With functions, we are always dealing with a distributed system that typically spreads widely in the brain. That is why, when neuropsychologists talk about this or that part of the brain, they say over and over that such-and-such a region "is involved in," "is essential to," and other phrases to keep us mindful that *locations* in the brain are parts of *systems*.

The brain

A normal human brain weighs approximately three and a half pounds or 1.6 kilograms. (See Figure A-1 and Animation 1 at *http://web.clas.ufl.edu/users/nnh/sem04/lobefr.mov*.) The outer layer, the *cerebrum*, is convoluted into furrows and protrusions. If one were to spread the cerebrum out flat, this folded cortical surface (which is 4 mm. or about 1/6 of an inch thick) would be about the size of a large bandanna. As we grew during our embryonic and foetal stages, our brains became compressed within our skulls and folded to make bulges and grooves. A bulge produced by this squeeze of a flat surface is called a *gyrus*, and the groove, if deep, a *fissure*, if less deep, a *sulcus* (pronounced |sulkus|; the plurals are *gyri*, *sulci*.

Neurologists speak of our brains as divided into two hemispheres (left and right) and four lobes. These lobes are formed by the outer layers of the brain, the gray tissue called the cerebrum or *cerebral cortex*. The *longitudinal fissure* divides the brain left and right, and the *central sulcus* divides the cerebrum front and back, with sensory regions toward the back and motor regions toward the front. (See Figure A-2.) The *occipital lobe* is at the back of the brain, and the *frontal lobe*, logically enough, at the front, that is, in front of the central sulcus. The *parietal lobe* lies behind the central sulcus and forms the roof and side walls of the brain. The

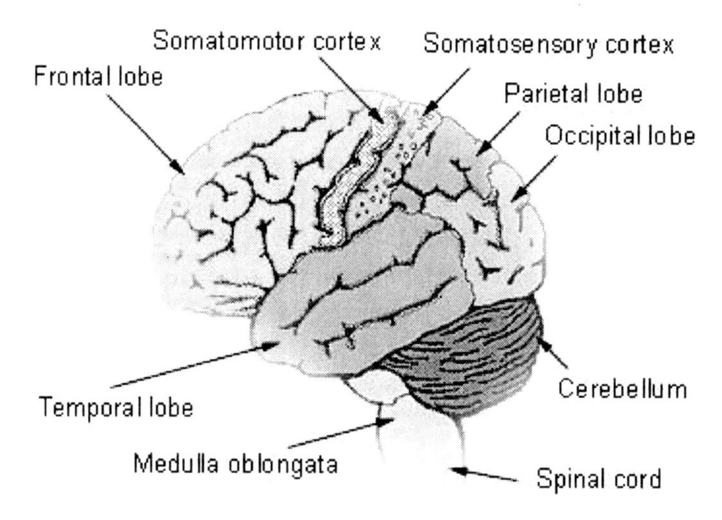

Figure A-2. Lobes of the brain

temporal lobe is at the bottom of the cerebrum, inside our temples, divided from the frontal and parietal lobes by the *Sylvian* or *lateral fissure*. It is associated with hearing and identifying objects. The cerebellum, associated with coordinating movements, lies beneath the occipital lobe. The brain stem (which includes the pons and medulla) runs downward from the center of the brain, into the top of the spinal cord that conveys information up and down between our arms, legs, and torso and our brains. (See Animation 2, which gives a view from underneath the brain: *http://web.clas.ufl.edu/users/nnh/sem04/lobelat.mov*.)

The neuron

Like other organs, the brain is composed of several different kinds of cells. For our purposes, we can focus on one kind of cell, the *neuron*. In a space the size of a pinhead there can be six million interconnected neurons. The brain as a whole contains about 100 billion neurons. In any space big enough for us to specify, there are simply too many neurons involved to be sure they have only one function. That fact greatly complicates life for neuroscientists.

Figure A-3 shows in a schematic way one kind of neuron. (There are several different shapes of neurons but they function like the one shown.) A neuron consists of the cell body or *soma* where small elements within the cell body supply energy for the cell's activities and keep the chemicals in the cell balanced. The *nucleus* of the cell contains the genetic material (DNA) that determines what proteins will be synthesized in the rest of the cell body. Outward from the soma, several *dendrites* radiate from the cell body like a

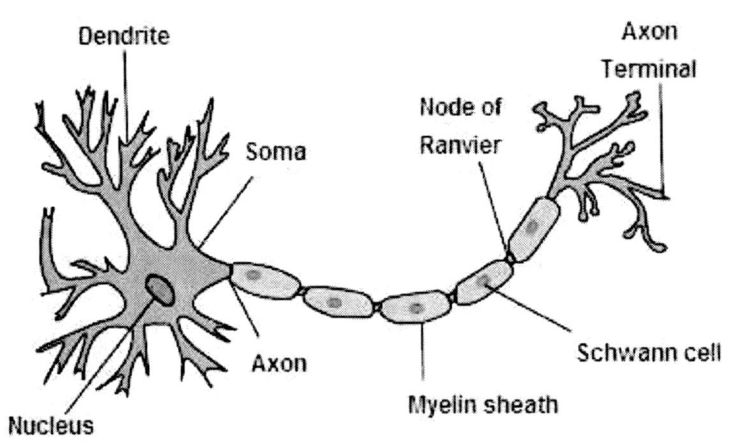

Figure A-3. A typical neuron.

series of twigs branching out in all directions. A single *axon*, a thin but quite long fiber, exits the cell body at a specialized region called the axon hillock. The axon reaches out until the *axon terminal* forms a *synapse* where it touches another cell, usually at the tip of a dendrite.

A very few neurons communicate by purely electrical connections ("gap junctions"). The great majority use chemical neurotransmission (as shown in Figure A-4). Information—that is, whether the sending neuron is

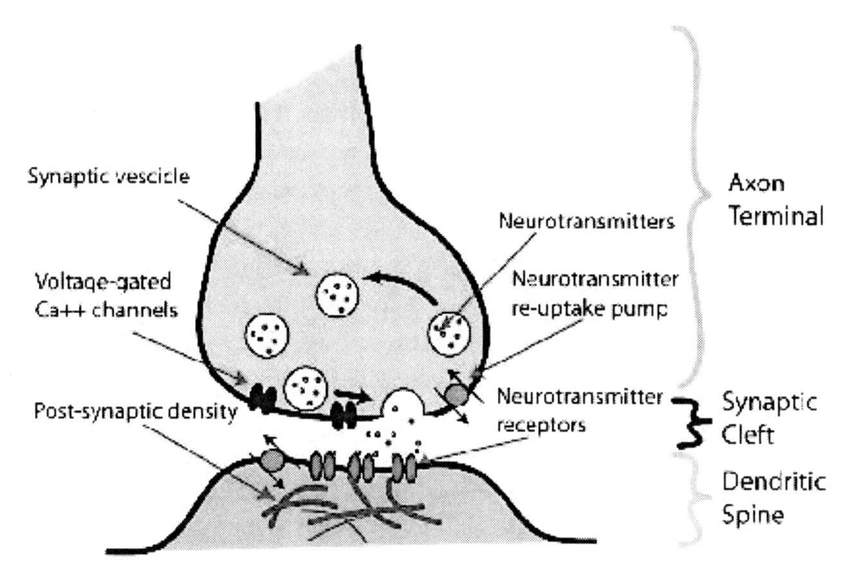

Figure A-4. Neurotransmission.

"firing" or not—passes from one neuron to another neuron in the form of complex chemicals called *neurotransmitters*. The dendritic spines on the receiving (or *post-synaptic*) neuron get signals from the many axons touching them. Some excite and some inhibit the receiving neuron. If the net effect is excitatory and big enough, the neuron opens channels on its membrane through which positive ions travel. These reduce the normally negative charge inside the cell, creating a momentary blip of less negative, i.e., relatively positive, voltage.

If this blip is large enough, it triggers the cell body to generate an *action potential*, a millisecond change of voltage toward the positive. This action potential then flows out along the long tube of the axon. A neuron constantly creates inside itself tiny, microscopic balloons or bubbles (*vesicles*) containing the particular neurotransmitters that that cell generates. The electrical pulse causes these vesicles to migrate toward the little bulge at the tip of the axon (the *axon terminal*). The vesicles fuse with the cell membrane, open, and dump their neurotransitter molecules into the tiny synaptic gap or "cleft" between the tip of the axon and the receiving cell. In this way, they activate receptors on the receiving cell. The excess neurotransmitter either gets destroyed by enzymes in the post- and pre-synaptic membranes, returned to the pre-synaptic neuron for recycling, or diffused into the salty fluid between the cells.

The process begins again when the receiving cell becomes a sending or pre-synaptic cell. The transmission proceeds from cell to cell this way, branching, adding, inhibiting, in links so complex that neurologists can trace only the largest paths of transmission.

Any given neuron may have 1,000 to 10,000 synaptic connections, and they may run from an axon to a dendrite, a cell body, another axon, or even the same axon. Thus information can be transmitted, changed (modulated), or suppressed at 10-100 trillion, 10-100,000,000,000,000, synapses (give or take many billion). Some say the human brain is the single most complicated object in the universe. Even allowing for human conceit, I can believe it.

Estimates are that there are as many as two hundred different neurotransmitters, and neurochemists have investigated only fifty or so closely. To make matters still more complicated, some neurotransmitters stimulate, some inhibit, and a single neurotransmitter may behave differently with different *receptors* at different points in the brain.

The action potential, the voltage pulse, traveling along the long tube of the axon could leak out into the conductive solution surrounding the axon. To prevent that, in fetal development and all through childhood and adolescence, neurons grow a fatty sheath, *myelin*, that serves, roughly, like the insulation on an electrical wire (with small openings, the *nodes of Ranvier*, where the voltage is reinforced). (See Figure

A-3.) This fatty myelinization is what gives whiteness to the "white matter" toward the center of the brain (where the neurons cover some distance). In the "gray matter" on the outer surface of the brain, cell bodies are closely packed together and therefore not myelinated.

Growing and ungrowing brain

Our neurons myelinate and our brains develop synapses over many years. In a newborn infant's brain, little myelinization has taken place, and consequently its motions and other actions governed by long axons are, as we say, "infantile," that is, erratic and uncontrolled. Only during early childhood does the human brain begin to function like a human brain as more and more synapses are developed and more and more myelinization takes place. And our brains do not complete this development until early adulthood, say, age 25.

Learning takes place by creating and strengthening the synaptic connections between neurons (a principle put forward by Donald Hebb in the 1940s). Steven Pinker is easy to quote: "Neurons that fire together, wire together. Neurons that don't synch, don't link."[2] These links are the way the brain stores information: *not in the cells, but in the patterns of linkage between cells.* These constitute *long-term potentiation* (LTP) or its opposite, *long-term depression* (LTD), in which what is learned is to inhibit the neuron rather than to activate it. Huge patterns of LTP and LTD make up the things we call knowledge and memory and mood and all the rest of the brain's "contents." Most importantly, these connections grow if we use them or "ungrow" if we don't. Hence, as we grow up, our experiences and habits get written into our brains and become our personality or (the term I use) "identity."

In the first year of life, the metabolic rate of a baby's brain is about two-thirds that of an adult brain. By the age of two, the rate equals the adult's. During those two years, the neurons have been branching and interconnecting at a furious rate. Indeed, during the first year of life, "dendritic and synaptic elaboration" increases by a factor of 20. Then, by age three or four, the metabolic rate becomes twice that of an adult's. By the age of six or seven, a child's brain equals in weight and volume an adult's, but it uses twice as much energy, and it has twice the number of synaptic connections. The brain stays "supercharged" until early adolescence. Then, from eleven to fourteen (because of those famous hormones?), the metabolic rate begins to fall until it subsides to the adult level. Similarly, there are twice as many synaptic connections in the cortex of a child's brain as in an adult's. Then that number falls by half in early adolescence.[3]

One can think of nature, Sandra Blakeslee suggests, as sculpting the brain. First, to an armature provided by genetics, nature applies clay (neurons), roughly the shape desired but more than is needed. Then nature pulls the unused excess away until the adult brain appears.[4] The bigger the animal and the longer it takes to develop from infant to adult, the greater this growth and ungrowth relative to the rest of the brain. All higher mammals that have been studied show this brain growth and ungrowth, and humans do not vary the rule.[5]

Nature first grows and then prunes away vast numbers of neurons, axons, and synapses in the course of bringing humans (and other mammals) from infancy to adulthood. Moreover, this growth and ungrowth results from activity—from early experience. Neural circuits that get lots of use generate "nerve growth factors" that help them to survive.[6] Neural circuits that get little or no use are sacrificed, probably in the interests of stabilizing the brain itself and reducing the energy consumption that the supercharged childhood brain had required.[7] In effect, to survive, nerves compete for a limited supply of such things as "nerve growth factor," and since those nerve cells and brain cells that survive are those we use the most, we grow nerves and brains suited to the environment in which the whole human organism has to survive. In this mechanism lies the extraordinary ability of the human being to thrive in locations as different as an ice floe, a rain forest, Manhattan, or the Saharan desert.[8]

In the nature-nurture, heredity-environment debate, then, research establishes not just a psychological but a *physiological* role for nurture alongside nature's. In the older view, the genes set the physical layout of the brain and the routes of synaptic contact. In fact, there are not enough genes in the human complement to account for 10^{14} synapses. Genes determine overall aspects of brain architecture and wiring patterns, but factors outside the genome change details in the basic organization. Evidently, then, *intrauterine and childhood experience is the outside factor that shapes the final architecture of the individual brain.* Brains are a genetic "given," but experiences change them, and experiences in turn depend, after infancy, on how an the individual chooses among the various activities his or her environment offers or demands.

Studying the brain

Neuroscientists have two fundamental ways of learning about brains. The classic method dates back to the nineteenth century. A patient suffers damage to the brain, from a stroke, say, an accident, or a tumor. Post-mortem, the neurologist compares the resulting changes in behavior to the anatomical changes in the brain and tries to derive the system, the multiple structures and neurochemical pathways, involved in that behavior. Today's neuropsychologists might hypothesize a set of connected but independent *modules.* They would then, on the basis of psychological experiments, try to trace the connections among these modules in the kind of complicated block diagram that computer scientists use.

In the early 1970s, neuroscientists became able to computerize X-rays and measurements of voltage, oxygen flow, and other things to generate detailed pictures of the brain. They had had EEGs (electroencephalograms) for a long time, measuring voltage changes near the surface of the brain. Now they acquired techniques like computed tomography (CT); positron emission tomography (PET); MRI (magnetic resonance imaging), diffusion tensor imaging (DTI), and others.

These techniques have different strengths and weaknesses. Some can pick out spatial details of a millimeter or so. Some respond to blood flow (and hence react slowly), others to electrical voltages (and react quickly). DTI reveals white matter connections deep in the brain. One can even picture the brain (particularly its outer regions) as it functions (hence fMRI). Powerful as these techniques are, no one method serves all purposes well. Because they generate such vivid pictures, though, the media have tended to over-state results from MRIs and PET scans.[9]

Brain structures

Within the brain, there are a variety of different textures. Some neurons occur in a clearly distinguishable mass or *nucleus* (plural, *nuclei*). Others occur in a thin sheet or *cortex* (plural, *cortices*). And so on through a variety of the mouth-filling Greek and Latin names that have come down to us from medieval medicine. (It is claimed they ensure precision, but, despite the claim, neuroscientists often use several different terms for the same thing.)

In the early twentieth century, the German neuroanatomist Korbinian Brodmann created a "cytoarchitectural map" of the brain (*cyto-* meaning cellular). He created

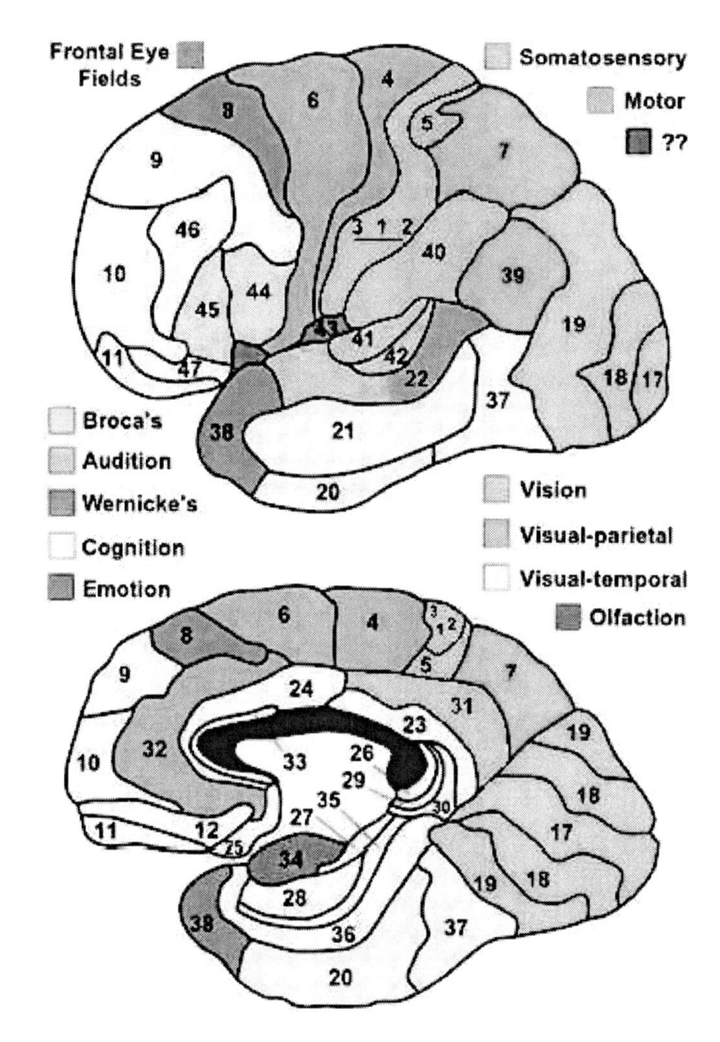

Figure A-5. A simplified Brodmann map, relating functions to regions (courtesy of Mark Dubin).

detailed maps of the different areas of the brain based on differences in the microscopic texture. His map and numbers remain standard to this day, although the numbers do not mean anything—they simply record the order in which he studied the different areas. The original presents a formdable picture to the layperson with its crowded little triangles and squares. (In Figure A-5, I have provided a simplified version of the Brodmann map, created by Professor Mark Dubin at the University of Colorado. For a colored version and other helpful materials on Brodmann's diagram by Mark Dubin, see *http://tinyurl.com/qhdd5* or *http://spot.colorado.edu /~dubin/talks/brodmann/brodmann.htm.*) Neuroscientists (and I) will sometimes refer to, for example, Brodmann Area 17 (or simply "BA 17" or "area 17") and know that they are referring to the primary visual cortex V1 at the back of the brain. Brodmann's numbers will prove useful in pointing to various functional areas referred to in the body of this book.

By and large . . .

For our purposes, we can make some "by and large" generalizations about our brains. The statements that follow, please remember, are very "by and large," useful but rough guidelines, not careful, absolute distinctions.

"By and large," we can say that a brain has one purpose and one purpose only. It serves to maximize an organism's chances for evolutionary success through survival and reproduction by moving that organism's body through the environment. That is the sole purpose of a brain, moving a body. Plants do very well without brains.

"By and large," we can say that, in the human brain, the back part, behind the central sulcus, has to do with sensory perception. The front part, in front of the central sulcus, the frontal lobe, has to do with executing and planning for motor activity. "By and large," we can say that the more frontal the area in the frontal lobe, the more removed the thinking from immediate motor action. That is, we use the most frontal part of the frontal lobes (called the *prefrontal cortex*) when we inhibit motor actions and plan far into the future. (The "prefrontal" cortex should really be called just the frontal cortex, but an early misnomer stuck.) It is these far forward, last-developing parts of the brain that allow us to think abstractly about politics, ethics, cosmology—and literature.

"Front" and "back" are lay terms. Neurologists use more latinate navigational terms:

anterior	forward	*posterior*	backward
inferior	lower	*superior*	higher
lateral	on the side	*medial*	on the midline
caudal	toward the nose	*rostral*	toward the spine

Dorsal and *ventral* are a little tricky. Within the spinal cord, the terms follow their Latin roots: *dorsal* means toward the back, hence posterior; *ventral* points toward the belly, hence anterior. But the human brain tilts forward at roughly a right angle to the spinal cord. In order to be consistent with other mammals (think of a dog's head), within the human brain, *dorsal* means toward the crown of the head, and *ventral*, toward the chin.

Caudal means, in animals, toward the tail, in humans, toward the spinal column. *Rostral* means toward the nose or beak. These terms are useful for linear parts of the nervous system, like the curvy spinal cord or the brain stem, that are not truly vertical or horizontal.

"By and large," we can parcel out our three major sensory modalities, sight, hearing, and "touch," among the three pairs of lobes behind the central sulcus. The occipital lobe has to do with vision. Hearing takes place through the temporal lobe. "Touch," although one thing in ordinary speech, includes a variety of different sensations with different peripheral, spinal, and brain processors: vibration, temperature, light touch, and pain. We deal with limb position or "sensorimotor" information in our parietal lobes.

Like the lobes, the hemispheres specialize. "By and large," most humans (more than 90%) deal with language primarily in the left hemisphere and non-verbal information (including "visuospatial") information in the right hemisphere. In infancy, our right hemispheres "come online" some years before the left. That is why it takes humans some years before we have memories that we can speak of ("conscious" memories, in Freud's sense).

"By and large," the left hemisphere deals with sequential and the right with holistic information. "By and large," the left hemisphere deals with logic and the right with emotion. But even this is specialized. "By and large," the left hemisphere generates positive emotions, and the right, negative emotions.

Perhaps the most important of the "by and large" statements we can make is one that neuropsychoanalysts emphasize. The brain is the organ in all mammals that combines input from the world outside our bodies with input from the world inside our bodies. The brain combines what we perceive "out there," like colors, shapes, sounds, or smells with feelings "in here," physiological ones like thirst or hunger and emotional ones like desire, anger, or fear.

By and large, that second, outer knowledge comes from the three posterior lobes involved with perception. The inner knowledge comes from the body's hormonal pathways and neural pathways feeding up from the spinal cord or the nerves in the head into *sub-cortical* structures. Of these, the *limbic system* is important for our purposes because it is essential to generating emotional responses. Within the limbic system, the *amygdala* (near the tip or *pole* of the temporal lobe) plays a key role in many emotions, espeically the "fight or flight" reactions of anger and fear. The *hypothalamus* links the brain, through hormones, to the endocrine system; it generates our physical responses (like heart rate or blood pressure) to emotional stimuli.

Kinds of neurotransmission

Broadly speaking, then, we can distinguish two kinds of neural transmission. One takes specific pieces of information from one neuron to the next and to the next and so on. A particular cell in the retina will send information to a particular neuron in the visual cortex all the way at the back of the brain. These pathways are quite narrow, and the rest of the brain remains untouched by this transmission. The other kind of transmission involves widespread effects through large areas of the brain. We can distinguish these two kinds of transmission; one is "channel" transmission, the other "state" transmission (in M.-M. Mesulam's terms). Perhaps we could even borrow a couple of literary terms and speak of "content" and "style."

Channel transmission uses three main neurotransmitters. Glutamate and aspartate are the two chief exciters of neuron activity. GABA (gamma-aminobutyric acid) is the main inhibitor, involved in sedation, sleep, and diminished emotional reaction.

In state transmission, cells clustered together in nuclei in the brain stem send their axons along divergent pathways to many different areas in the higher centers of the brain causing widespread global change. More than one neurochemical may affect any given neuron.

These chemicals from the brain stem exert global effects, "states," modulating the activities of other systems, by such things as mood, attention, arousal, or sleep-and-waking. Because their names come up in discussions of psychological (hence, literary) functions, we do well to become familiar with four of them:

acetylcholine, acting through "cholinergic" neurons, affects arousal, attention, learning, mood, and sleep, waking, dream, and muscle action.

serotonin influences appetite, sexual activity, aggression, body temperature, sleep, mood and distractibility.

norepinephrine (abbreviated NE) or, in the U.K., noradrenaline (NA) is involved in pain reduction, attention and motivation; it regulates blood pressure and prompts extreme arousal and the "fight or flight" response.

dopamine (abbreviated DA), concerned in various appetites, an important part of the brain's "reward" system, causing feelings of wellbeing.

The *peptides*, many and various, are associated with pain, emotions, and mood. These are longer-lasting states because peptides act relatively slowly. The body as well as the brain produces peptides. They include the opioids associated with feelings of pleasure ("highs"). At sites far from the brain, the body produces still other chemicals that act on the brain as a whole, sexual and stress hormones, for example. Estimates are that there are as many as two hundred different neurotransmitters and other chemicals that affect the brain. Neuroscientists have closely investigated only fifty or so.

Emotions

Thanks to intense study by neuropharmacologists and animal researchers, though, we can trace some pathways useful for thinking about emotions and hence, about literature. Here I am going to draw on the work of Jaak Panksepp, who has produced much evidence that there are distinct emotional pathways for the basic emotions.[10] He derives these discrete emotions from animal experiments and the fact that various neurochemicals or lesions can knock out single emotions, say, sadness, leaving others like anger, untouched.[11] These emotional pathways all connect one way or another with the brain stem.

The most basic of these systems, Panksepp calls the SEEKING system. (Panksepp uses capitals to indicate that he is using the term in a technical sense, although, clearly, he also wants the connotations of our ordinary usage.) SEEKING includes our basic impulses to search, investigate, and make sense of the environment; an earlier term was "foraging/expectancy." These dopamine circuits make us feel that something good will happen to us if we interact with the environment, leading us actively to explore and seek out satisfactions.

Physiologically, we have need-detecting mechanisms in the hypothalamus (the part of the brain that "reads" the state of the body), and somehow these need detectors activate the SEEKING system. We can also be stimulated by outer-world perceptions like, say, the sight of a hot fudge sundae. When we turn to literature and the arts for pleasure or understanding, we are evidently responding to this SEEKING system. SEEKING is what keeps us reading *War and Peace* all the way to the end. Some neuropsychoanalysts identify this system with Freud's concept of libido, others with his idea of "drive."

Closely related to the SEEKING system is the LUST (or consummatory) system. This system takes over in the brain from the sites where the SEEKING system stops; it feeds *backward* onto the brain stem. The LUST system replaces the appetitive behaviors of SEEKING with consummatory behaviors. For example, in rats, the male stops sniffing around and mounts the female, and the female arches her back. The system leads ultimately to orgasm. Outside perceptions can trigger the system's internal chemical changes, and erotic literature and pornography take lucrative advantage of this possibility. In general, enjoying literature involves a series of SEEKINGs as we read or listen, followed by consummations as we get successive gratifications, for example, as a story resolves suspense or the final rhyme of a limerick completes that pattern.

Neuroscientists distinguish among types of aggression. The RAGE system has to do with the "hot" aggression we feel at frustration. (The "cold" aggression of predatory behavior, the leopard prowling for its next meal, lacks the feelings of rage and relates to the SEEKING system.) RAGE modifies heart rate and body temperature and sends extra blood to the muscles, shutting down digestive processes (your mouth goes dry). These are, obviously, useful responses for survival and for sexual rivalry. In a way, the RAGE system is the opposite of the SEEKING sytem. The one looks for a reward, with neurotransmitters acting upward toward cognitive systems; the other comes into being when a reward is denied and neurotransmitters act downward on the brain stem. Audiences feel RAGE (frustration anger) when a work of art is interrupted, as when the sound track fails in a movie theater or the last pages of a mystery novel are missing. Good-guys-bad-guys propaganda can arouse a RAGE response, and I can feel rage toward Iago and Claudius (although Shakespeare, being Shakespeare, complicates the feeling).

As with aggression, neuroscientists distinguish kinds of anxiety: fear-anxiety and panic-anxiety, according to the medications that reduce them. The FEAR system generates feelings of extreme anxiety and terror and impulses toward flight (or, in milder situations, "freezing"). It is also responsible for neurotic anxiety, a general sense of dread without any apparent cause. FEAR generates body responses like those of RAGE: more blood for the muscles and less for the digestive system.

In the FEAR system, projections going from the amygdala arouse the sensation or feelings of fear. The amygdala (Joseph LeDoux has shown[12]) has two kinds of output. One process is rapid-response. It goes directly to the hypothalamus (to reset the body) and then on to the brain stem and spinal cord to move the body. In the dark of night, I see a shadowy stranger in the living room. I jump back. A fraction of a second later, I realize my heart is pounding. Another fraction of a second later I realize that it is my reflection in a mirror. This later process is more cognitive. The signal has gone more slowly from the amygdala to the frontal lobes, which evaluate the stimulus and the reaction. One can easily see the evolutionary advantage in having a self-preservative system that reacts very, very fast and only evaluates the threat later. Better I should jump back and it not be a burglar than I wait to decide if I am seeing a burglar and get murdered. Obviously, a lot of literature uses the FEAR system: ghost and mystery stories like those of Poe or Lovecraft, adventure movies and stories, and the horror movies so popular for teen-age dates (leading perhaps to SEEKING and LUST). An important fact: the brain has other such dual systems, one "quick and dirty," the other slower and more cognitve.

The PANIC system shows another kind of negative emotion, perhaps best described as sorrow or grief, the feelings that go with loneliness or separation, the opposite of the good feelings associated with attachment and belonging. What the neuroscientists are studying is, like LUST, a social emotion. The PANIC system follows pathways profoundly involved with our feelings of pleasure and unpleasure. The ventral (lower) periaqueductal gray gives rise to pleasurable sensations, the dorsal (upper) to pleasurable. The neurochemistry of this system rests on the the brain's self-generated opioids, but also on some of the peptides associated with maternal behavior. The opioids inhibit the system; if the system is activated (by reducing the sense, originally associated with a mother, of belonging or reward and so reducing the brain's self-generated opioids), we feel unpleasure.

As Freud pointed out, we are deeply motivated to try to avoid unpleasure. In animals, stimulating this PANIC system leads to what are ponderously called in the literature, "distress vocalizations," i.e., crying. In humans, stimulation can lead to panic attacks. Psychoananalysts associate this system with the human infant's cries at separation from its mother. In animals, stimulating the PANIC system over a period of time leads to withdrawal from the environment (no more SEEKING) and behavior that looks like depression.

Much literature plays on the PANIC system, our feelings of grief at separation and loss. Quite irrationally, we cry at movies or stories: the death of a beloved character, an unhappy ending, boy-loses-girl, the "weepie" or the "three-handkerchief movie."

Among the positive emotions, Panksepp points to a CARE system, the basis for maternal nurturing and, more generally, affection. This bonding is rooted in neuropeptides such as oxytocin and prolactin as well as endogenous opioids like the endorphins.[13] Crucial to sexual and social relations in the larger world, we also feel affection and care for various literary characters although we know they are not real people.

Finally, we can conceptualize a PLAY system. All young mammals, including humans, need a certain amount of PLAY. PLAY may be necessary for juveniles to learn how to get along. That is, PLAY may program various cortical functions needed for social behavior. PLAY has several kinds, exploratory, functional, building, symbolic-dramatic, and games-with-rules play. In particular, though, young male mammals all seem to require rough-and-tumble play, something young humans often miss in today's environment. (Hence we have Ritalin.)

Panksepp concludes that the PLAY system serves the organism by allowing the exercise of emotional operating systems (fear, anger, separation distress, sexuality) in the safety of one's home environment. In general, as long as PLAY seems fun, we feel joy, and we (and other primates) laugh. If true negative emotional states intervene (FEAR or RAGE, for example), the playful mood will subside, and the organism begins to address these feelings more realistically. We have all seen a child run home in tears because the play got cruel. Play can evoke laughter and another important emotion, JOY.[14] Incidentally, laughter (like crying) involves pre-programmed motor systems in the brain that can be released by certain chemicals and disorders as well as by jokes (which are, for me, a form of literature). Both play and laughter serve the purpose of social bonding (ch. 20).

PLAY, obviously, is close to literature. We call a drama a "play," as do the Germans (*eine Spiel*). (And, in French, one of the meanings of "to play," *jouer*, is "to act" in a play or movie.) PLAY may also be connected to dreaming. For the professional critic, though, literature is not play, any more than sports are PLAY for the professional for whom they are a realistic business proposition.

Language

Plays and other literature depend on language, a different kind of brain function from emotion. Sometime in the distant past—the best guess is 80-120,000 years ago—we humans became the modern human species, *homo sapiens sapiens*, as opposed to *homo sapiens neanderthalis* and other hominins. Sometime in the past—the best guess is 40-100,000 years ago—we developed language.

In this book, I will use the neuroscientists' convention

and speak of language as in the left hemisphere. It is for 96% of right-handers, but for some left-handers, too, it is in the left hemisphere, for some left-handers in the right, and for some distributed between both. In sum, the language system occurs in the left hemisphere for about 93% of humans.

Chimpanzees have the slight swelling in the left hemisphere of the brain that marks, in humans, the language centers and sytems. But chimpanzees and other primates lack language, and the results from efforts to teach them demonstrate nothing like the complex grammars all human children acquire without being taught.[15] By grammar, I mean simply our procedures for forming legitimate sentences. Something happened to give us a universal grammar shared by all humans within which we grow up with one specific language. No one knows what.

Again, sometime in the remote past, we developed art. By 40,000 years ago, humans were burying their dead with ceremony and making beads, pendants, and figurines of female bodies Recently, even earlier evidence turned up in South Africa an incised piece of red ocher, about 77,000 years old.[16] This piece of criss-crossed clay tells us that we had learned decoration by that time. *We had gained the ability to use our advanced brains for non-utilitarian purposes.* (Is this Kant's aesthetic "disinterestedness" [ch. 7]?) Presumably, we learned to use speech the same non-utilitarian way, and literature was born. Because literature consists of language, one particular part of the cerebrum plays a key role.

The temporal lobes

"By and large," the temporal lobes deal with auditory perception. (See Figure A-6.) Also, in most humans, the *left temporal lobe* is specialized for understanding language. We can think of this lobe as divided into four gyri, called, logically enough, superior, middle, inferior, and, underneath the

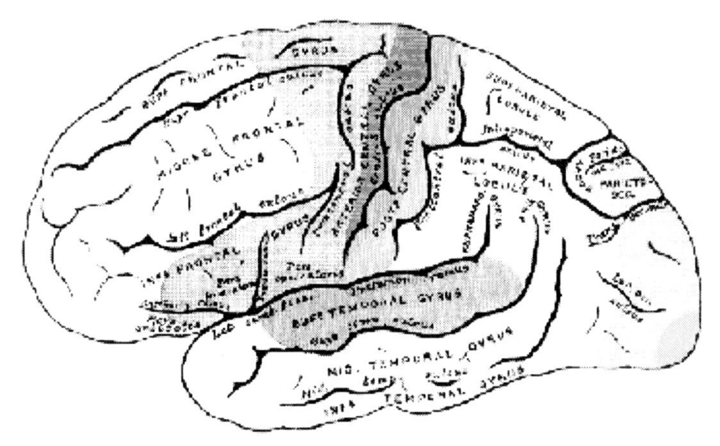

Figure A-6. The left hemisphere (lateral view).

brain and inside it, the fusiform gyrus or fourth or occipito-temporal gyrus. We can take them from the top down.

The anterior portion of the superior temporal gyrus has to do with the preliminary processing of information from our auditory nerves—our ears. It is here that we establish the directions and distances of sounds, for example. As we move posteriorly along the lobe into the region where the parietal and occipital and temporal lobes intersect, we come to Wernicke's area (the posterior section of the superior temporal gyrus, in Brodmann area 22). This region was discovered in the 1880s to be crucial for understanding and, in part, generating speech that makes sense. (See Animation 3 at *http://web.clas.ufl.edu/users/nnh/sem04/language.mov.*)

When we speak to one another, the sounds we make vary tremendously. The waveforms of the separate phonemes (that constitute the smallest units of speech) like the *b* in "bat" and the *b* in "but" look different. The *t*s likewise. The waveform of each phoneme varies depending on the adjacent phonemes. Similarly, when I say a word and you say a word, the pitch, speed, and intonation will all differ. Yet neither of us has any trouble recognizing the word or name no matter who speaks it. Somehow we pick out individual phonemes and recognize particular words despite these confounds. Some system in our superior left temporal region involving Wernicke's area has done an amazing job of decoding. This has to happen quite early in the processing of language, but just how neuroscientists do not yet know.

The middle temporal gyrus also plays a role in language understanding, and it is particularly important for reading. That is, it seems to be specialized for the "visual lexicon," our stored memory for connecting written letters and words to meanings. These reading networks get established by age six or seven in normal children. In one fascinating study, the researchers contrasted brain activity while looking at pictures of famous persons and buildings with nonfamous. "Famous" they define as "having a name for." If the person or building was famous, in addition to the appropriate brain areas elsewhere lighting up, in the middle temporal gyrus words came automatically with the perception. The subjects automatically named in their brains the famous person or building.[17]

The posterior portion of the occipito-temporal gyrus (Brodmann area 37) is involved in recognizing the objects we perceive in the world. It has strong connections to the visual system. In general, this ventral temporal area seems to contribute to our ability to place things in categories, to see a robin and recognize that it is a "bird."

Damage to the brain can produce strikingly limited symptoms: patients can name things you can manipulate (tools, for example), but not edibles or animals. Or they can give proper names but not common nouns. Thus, some stroke victims can say only "bird" and not "robin"; others can say "robin" but not "bird."[18] Apparently, and, to me, quite remarkably, certain categories are mapped into our brain anatomy (innately? through learning?).

Above the Sylvian fissure that separates the temporal lobe from the frontal lobe are two regions, the *pars triangularis* and the *pars opercularis* (Brodmann areas 44 and 45, in the "inf. frontal gyrus" of Figure A-6). These constitute *Broca's area*, discovered in the 1860s to be essential for fluent speech. It abuts the section of the motor cortex that governs the mouth and tongue. A band of neurons called the *arcuate fasciculus* (green in Animation 3) connects Broca's area with Wernicke's to complete the language apparatus. "By and large," Wernicke's area seems to deal with our ability to put words together into coherent statements, while Broca's area deals with our muscular ability to form phonemes, syllables, and words.

In sum

Even this brief survey should have made clear that doing literature, like any other human cognitive act, uses a brain and brain processes of extraordinary complexity. Yet many people who think about literature, from movie reviewers in the daily newspapers to the most sophisticated of professorial literary theorists, often ignore the crucial role that our brains play.

We literary types value words. Movie reviewers value movies. They are what we like to talk and write about. We like to think that these things have power and can impose meanings and emotions on a relatively passive brain. But even this sketch of the brain's complexity shows that such a picture is topsy-turvy. We "do" literature with our brains. We *perform* a literary work. But all of us tend to think that literature does something to us, not we to literature. Why do we think that? Because it feels that way. And why does it feel that way? That is one of the many questions about literature that I try to answer in this book.

Notes

Part I. The Questions

Chapter 1. About This Book

[1] Holland 1968; 1973; 1975; 2000.
[2] Holland 1998; 2002.

Chapter 2. The Alp of Mind

[1] Turner 1991.
[2] Chomsky 1981.
[3] Heilman and Valenstein, eds. 2003, 6.
[4] Kandel 1998, 505.
[5] *http://www.clas.ufl.edu/ipsa/journal/2004_holland08.shtml.* Accessed March 10, 2008. For a summary of the online article, Crews' reply, my response to Crews, and a commentary by psychiatrist Peter Barglow, see *Scientific Review of Alternative Medicine* 10 (2006): 21-35.

Chapter 3. Neuropsychoanalysis

[1] Solms and Turnbull 2002.
[2] Posner and Raichle 1994.
[3] Sacks 1984, 164.
[4] Solms and Turnbull 2002, 307-8.
[5] I take heart and hope from the fine book by Semir Zeki on

the visual arts that proceeds the same way. Zeki points to aspects of the visual arts—line, color, shape, motion, representation, abstractness—and relates them to different modules of the visual system in the brain, V1, V2, and so on (Zeki 1999).

Part II. Being Transported

Chapter 4. Where is a Text?

[1] Bownds 1999, 183-84.
[2] Bach-y-Rita 1969, 1970. Kaczmarek et al., 1991.
[3] Feinberg 2001, 165n13.
[4] Fauconnier 1999, 99-100.
[5] Ungerleider and Mishkin 1982. Mishkin and Ungerleider 1982. Mishkin, Ungerleider, and Macko 1983.
[6] Goodale et al 1991. Carnahan and Marteniuk 1993. Goodale and Milner 1992.
[7] Brungart and Rabinowitz 1999. Brungart, Durlach, and Rabinowitz 1999.
[8] Weeks et al. 1999
[9] Freud 1940a, 196.
[10] Solms and Turnbull 2002, 155.
[11] Crick and Koch 2000, 10.
[12] Freeman 1997, 67-70.
[13] Mesulam 1998, 1013.
[14] Freeman 1997, 67-70.
[15] Griffiths 2000.
[16] Freud 1940a, 196.

Chapter 5. Four Brain Changes

[1] Niesz and Holland 1984.
[2] Iser 1978. Hogan 2003b, ch. 5.
[3] *Love's Labor's Lost* 4.2.24-26.
[4] Nell 1988, ch. 6.
[5] Fenichel 1953, 376.
[6] Trevarthen 1979.
[7] Baars 1996, 102-08.

Chapter 6. Being Transported

[1] Shiffrin 1997.

[2] Rainer, Rao, and Miller 1999.
[3] Stein, Wallace and Meredith 1995. Stein, Wallace and Stanford 1999.
[4] Kalat 2001, 383-4.
[5] Csikszentmihalyi and Robinson 1990, 114.
[6] Austin 1998, 264.
[7] Austin 1998, 502-04.
[8] Nell 1988, ch. 4,
[9] Frye 1971, 345.
[10] Hospers 1967, 1: 37.
[11] "Aesthetics." Encyclopædia Britannica Online. 2003.
[12] Gerrig 1998 [1993].
[13] Nell 1988, 75.
[14] Kant 1790, Part I, bk. 1.2.
[15] Fuster 1999, 193.
[16] Bear, Connors and Paradiso 1996, 613, 390, 630.
[17] Rizzolatti et al. 2006, 142-143, citing Baldissera et al., 2001.
[18] Storey 1996, 115.
[19] Nell 1988, 77.

Chapter 7. Why Don't We Doubt

[1] Leslie 1995. Spelke, Phillips and Woodward 1995.
[2] Coleridge 1817, ch. xiv.
[3] By "willing," I understand simply my willingness to pick up a book, to buy a ticket, or to sit in the theater seat or my armchair. I am "willing" to participate in some literary transaction. In participating, I may from time to time suspend disbelief, but I cannot deliberately "will" that state of mind.
[4] Gilbert 1991a and b.
[5] Gilbert 1991a, 114; Gilbert 1991b. Gerrig 1998 [1993], ch. 6.
[6] Angier 2008. See,for example, Ekman and O'Sullivan 1991.
[7] Prentice and Gerrig 1999, 512.
[8] Gerrig 1998 [1993], 240.
[9] Ladowsky-Brooks and Alcock 2007.
[10] Gerrig 1989.
[11] Gerrig 1998 [1993], 201-2.
[12] Tooby and Cosmides 2001, 13.
[13] Kelly and Keil 1985.
[14] Hobson 1995, ch. 6. Chelazzi et al. 1998.

[15] Clark 1997, 51.
[16] Llinás 2001, 58-59.
[17] Knight and Grabowecky 1995.
[18] Knight and Grabowecky 1995. Kahneman and Miller 1986.
[19] Rolls 1995.
[20] Fuster 1999, 192-3.
[21] Knight and Grabowecky 1995. Knight, Grabowecky, and Scabini 1995. Kenneth Heilman has told me in conversation that patients he has seen with frontal lobe damage become more and less involved in movies depending on the region of damage. Damage to the orbitofrontal region leads to an inability to inhibit responses to a movie. The patient reacts too much. Damage to dorsolateral cricuitry decreases interest and response. Personal communication, May 20, 2005.
[22] Young and Saver 2001, esp. 76-77.
[23] Moscovitch 1989, 137. Johnson 1991. Bauer, Grande, and Valenstein 2003, 540.
[24] The confabulator described by Solms (2001; Solms and Yovell 2003) neatly fits this pattern.
[25] Schnider, von Daniken, and Gutbrod 1996.
[26] Lesser 1957, 200, 203–4, 210, 242–47.
[27] Gerrig 1996; 1998[1993], ch. 3.
[28] Csikszentmihalyi 1988.

Chapter 8. Metafictions

[1] Jonze 2002.
[2] Scott 2002.
[3] Berns, Cohen, and Mintun 1997.

Chapter 9. About Emotions

[1] Oatley and Johnson-Laird 1996.
[2] Kalat 2001, 338.
[3] Ledoux 1998, 126.
[4] Brothers 1997, 145.
[5] Panksepp 2003, 210.
[6] See also Oatley and Johnson-Laird 1996.
[7] Springer and Deutsch 1998, 233-4.
[8] Kalat 2001, 338-39. Heilman, Blonder et al. 2002b, 456-464.
[9] Davidson 1992.

[10] Oatley and Johnson-Laird 1996. Adolphs 2002. Ekman 2003. Panksepp 1998. Damasio 1999, 50-51, 340-41n9.

[11] Ekman and Friesen 1971. Ekman 2003.

[12] Dimberg and Thunberg 1998. Dimberg, Thunberg, and Elmehed 2000.

[13] Jenkins, Oatley, and Stein 1998a; 1998b, 8-9, 71.

[14] Hogan 2003a.

[15] Ekman 1999.

[16] Keats, Letter of 14 February to 3 May 1819 to George and Georgiana Keats (Rollins, ed., 2.80).

[17]Panksepp 1998, 144–63. I think it of interest that the right hemisphere is important both for reading the minds of others and for social interactions (Brownell and Martino 1998). One can speculate, then, that one could relate Freud's pleasure-seeking drive to the object-seeking drive posited by psychoanalytic object-relations theorists through a common brain system.

[18] Italics mine. In these quotations and those that follow, I am drawing on Panksepp 1998, 144-146 and ch. 8 generally. Alcaroa, Huber, and Panksepp 2007 provides a detailed description of the neurophysiology and neurochemistry of the SEEKING system.

[19] Robinson and Berridge 1993.

[20] Alcoroa, Huber, and Pansepp 2007.

Chapter 10. Why Do We Care?

[1] Darwin 1890, quoted in Jenkins, Oatley, and Stein 1998, 19.

[2] Ledoux 1998.

[3] Lang, Greenwald, Bradley, et al. 1993. Lang, Bradley and Cuthbert 1998.

[4] Hogan 2003b, ch. 6.

[5] Lesser 1957, 200, 210, 242-47. Oatley 1999, 114.

[6] Brothers 1997, 98-99.

[7] Smith 1976 [1759], sect. 1, ch. 1.

[8] Hogan 2003b, ch. 6. Tan 1996.

[9] In what follows I am drawing on V. S. Ramachandran's account of this work (1995; 2000) and Marco Iacoboni's recent book (2008). For a review article on mirror neurons, see Iacoboni and Dapretto 2006.

[10] Iacoboni et al. 2001.

[11] Iacoboni et al. 2005.

[12] Buckner and Carroll 2007.
[13] Buccino et al. 2005. Tettamanti et al. 2005.
[14] Baldissera et al. 2001. Rizzolatti et al. 2006, 142. Marco Iacoboni suggests that "super mirror neurons" perform this inhibition (Iacoboni 2008, 201-203).
[15] de Gelder et al. 2004
[16] Bargh and Chartrand 1999.
[17] Goleman 1996.
[18] Keen 2006.
[19] Feldman and Narayanan n.d.
[20] Gallese and Lakoff 2005
[21] Aziz-Zadeh and Damasio 2008, 38.
[22] Lang, Greenwald, Bradley, et al. 1993.
[23] Phillips 2002.
[24] Fuster 1999, 191-93.
[25] Iacoboni 2008b, 201-203. See also Iacoboni 2008a.
[26] Aron et al. 2007.
[27] Stanford University provides a basic tutorial on the limbic system (and other brain systems) at http://tinyurl.com/yprmwe or http://www.stanford.edu/group/hopes/basics/braintut/ab5.html. Accessed Dec. 4, 2008.
[28] Watt 2001.
[29] Kövecses 2000.
[30] Miall 1989a. Miall and Kuiken 1994.
[31] Jenkins, Oatley, and Stein 1998, 143.
[32] Tooby and Cosmides 2001, 8.
[33] Hogan 2003b, 185.
[34] Panksepp 2003a, 8.
[35] Skolnick and Bloom 2005.
[36] Aristotle, *Poetics*, ch. 4. McKeon 1947, 627.

Chapter 11. Characters and People

[1] Bortolussi and Dixon 2003, 164.
[2] Morgann 1777, 171-2.
[3] Bradley 1905.
[4] Jones 1949 [1910], 20.
[5] See, for example, Krims 2002.
[6] Paris 2008, 8-9.
[7] See, for example, Knight 1930.
[8] Holland 1992.
[9] Poe 1902 [1845], 12: 225

[10] Forster 1927, 98.
[11] Proust 1971[1905], 25.
[12] Matisse 1939, 14.
[13] Heider and Simmel 1944.
[14] Premack and Premack 1995, 210-11.
[15] Leslie 1987; 1995. Spelke, Phillips and Woodward 1995.
[16] Lang 1993.
[17] I am grateful for help in this section to my colleague in linguistics, D. Gary Miller.
[18] Kelly and Keil 1985.
[19] Mishkin and Ungerleider 1982. Ungerleider and Mishkin 1982. Mishkin, Ungerleider, and Macko 1983. See also Mesulam 1998. Bownds 1999, 196-97. Bear 1996, 266-69. Zillmer 2001, 129-130.
[20] Holland 2002.
[21] Schnider and Ptak 1999. Eichenbaum and Bodkin 2000.
[22] Goodale et al. 1992. Goodale and Milner 1993. Carnahan and Marteniuk 1993.
[23] Kinzer 2004. The play was Michael Murphy's *Sin: A Cardinal Deposed.*
[24] Boxer 2001.
[25] "Aesthetics" 2003.

Part III. Enjoying

Chapter 12. Expectations

[1] Solms and Turnbull 2002, 155.
[2] Zeman 2002, 191.
[3] Solms and Turnbull 2002, 139-180.
[4] Pinker 2002, 92.
[5] Solms and Turnbull 2002, 142–46.
[6] Suzuki and Eichenbaum 2000.
[7] *http://www.wikipedia.org*, s.v. hippocampus, provides several illustrations of this structure.
[8] Hafting et al. 2005. Sargolini et al. 2006.
[9] Solms and Turnbull 2002, 163.
[10] Markowitsch 2000, 267.
[11] Chekhov actually said, "One can't put a loaded gun on the stage if no one plans to fire it" From a letter to Lazarev-Gruzinsky, [1 November] 1889. Quoted in Bitsilli 1983. My thanks to Daniel Rancour-Laferriere and Bob Rothstein for

this source.

[12] Heilman 2002, 155-159. Markowitsch 2000. Llinás 2001, 151.

[13] Llinás 2001, 152.

[14] Damasio, Tranel, and Damasio 1991, 217-229.

[15] Damasio 1994, ch. 9.

[16] Solms and Turnbull 2002, 176-80.

[17] Solms and Turnbull 2002, 169.

[18] Grigsby and Stevens 2000.

[19] Holland (1975) offers five detailed examples of different readers' expectations as they read three short stories, expectations (and other aspects of their readings) revealed by open-ended questions leading to free associations.

[20] Holland and Schwartz 2008.

[21] Nell 1988, 212.

[22] Luria 1973, 267-68.

[23] Miall 1995.

Chapter 13. Form and Control

[1] Lane 2008, 88.

[2] Hayes 1953, 3.

[3] Bordwell 1997. Bordwell and Thompson 2008. Carroll 2003.

[4] Hasson et al. 2004.

[5] Leone 1966.

[6] Hasson et al. 2008.

[7] Holland 1968, chs. 4 and 5.

[8] Mesulam 2000, 185–86.

[9] Shklovskii 1988 [1917], paragraphs 13 and 15.

[10] Coleridge 1817, ch. 4.

[11] Shelley 1821 [1840], 83.

[12] Chesterton 1902, 60.

[13] Miall 1989b; 1995. Miall and Kuiken 1994.

[14] Laughlin 1979, 6.

[15] Freud 1937c, 237, 240.

[16] Bibring 1961.

[17] Laughlin 1979, 7.

[18] For a longer comparison of literary forms to defenses, see Holland 1968, chs. 4-5.

[19] Freud 1937c, 236.

[20] Lacan n.d. [1956], 169.

[21] Freud 1926d, 92, 94. See also Damasio 1994, ch. 9.

Strachey 1959, 83.
[22] Pally 2000, 58–59.
[23] Grigsby and Stevens 2000, 316-17.
[24] Gergely 1992; Gergely and Watson 1996.
[25] Grigsby and Stevens 2000, 316.
[26] Freud 1937c, 23: 237.
[27] Freud 1937c, 23: 238.
[28] Rizzolatti, Fadiga, Gallese, and Fogassi 1996.
[29] Brothers 1997. Brothers posits "ensembles" that simultaneously encode sensory aspects of social situations and set the relevant responses in motion. She sees these ensembles physiologically as involving amygdala, orbitofrontal cortex, and anterior cingulate (Brothers 1995).
[30] In this connection, the visual arts present an interesting variation. Literature is sequential, but we see a painting or a sculpture very nearly all at once. We ourselves focus our attention here or there, but the work of art ordinarily cannot control the process the way literary works do. Nancy Aiken has offered a solution. We begin with stimuli, she says, that evoke a faint touch of fear, Freud's unpleasure signal: a sharp, jagged line, for example. That signal mobilizes defenses in our brains and in the work of art to manage that fear toward an "aesthetic response." In other words, she is saying that certain shapes produce for the visual arts what I am saying sequence and constant novelty produce for literature (Aiken 1998, chs. 5-7).
[31] Holland 1975. Bleich 1975; 1978. Steig 1989. Berman 1994. Holland and Schwartz 1975; 2008. Holland 2000c.

Chapter 14. Endings

[1] Stanley 2004.
[2] Forster 1927, 139-131.
[3] Kermode 1967, 45, 43.
[4] Oatley 1992. Oatley and Johnson-Laird 1996.
[5] Tan 1996.
[6] Hogan 2003b, 182-185.
[7] Ledoux 1998.
[8] Hasson and Malach 2006. Hasson et al. 2008.
[9] Tan 1996.
[10] In these quotations and those that follow, I am drawing on Panksepp 1998, 144-146 and ch. 8 generally.

[11] Robinson and Berridge 1993.
[12] My quotations are from Panksepp 1998, 145-146.
[13] Erikson 1963, 247-252.
[14] Panksepp 1998, 145.

Chapter 15. The "Content" Fallacy

[1] Nashe 1592, fol. 26, sig. H2.
[2] See, for example, van Oostendorp and Goldman 1999; Goldman, Graesser and van den Broek 1999; Britton and Graesser 1996; Weaver, Mannes and Fletcher 1995.
[3] Reddy 1979.
[4] Lakoff and Johnson 1980, 101–2; Lakoff 1987.
[5] Fish 1980.
[6] For a review of this line of research with movies, see Hasson et al. 2008.
[7] Hasson and Malach 2006, 1638.
[8] See, for example, Robeck and Wallace 1990, ch. 6.
[9] Nell 1988, 80-82.
[10] Hogan 2003b, ch. 5. Bordwell 1985.
[11] Hogan 2003b, 115.
[12] Yarkoni et al. 2008.
[13] Gerrig 1998 [1993], 13. Ryan 1980.
[14] Nell 1988, 217-218.
[15] Schank & Abelson 1977. Rumelhart 1980. Anderson 1977. Laberge and Samuels 1977.
[16] Martindale 1990; 1988.
[17] Cp. Arbib and Erdi 2000 with Morasso and Sanguinetti 1997.

Chapter 16. Literary Language

[1] See, for example, the journal *Discourse & Communication* or the *Concise Encyclopedia of Pragmatics* 1998.
[2] Solms 2002; 2003. Solms and Yovell 2003.
[3] Solms 2002, 140-41.
[4] See also Moscovitch 1989 and Moscovitch and Melo 1997.
[5] Fotopoulou et al. 2004; 2007. See also Burgess and McNeil 1999 and Burgess and Shallice 1996.
[6] Panksepp 1998, 162. One study suggests that, whereas the medial frontal lobe is important for suppressing internally-generated thoughts, the lateral frontal lobe is important in

generating and maintaining these thoughts (Burgess et al. 2003).

[7] Whiter 1794, 68. For commentary see Whiter 1967.

[8] Spurgeon 1935. Armstrong 1946.

[9] Holland 1968, ch. 2.

[10] Rycroft 1979, 150-151.

[11] Maher et al. 1987.

[12] Greenhouse 2003.

[13] Holland 1968, ch. 1.

[14] Freud 1923 [1922], 238.

[15] Bollas 2002, 15-16.

[16] Menand 2004, 104.

[17] Panksepp 2008, 50, citing Callan et al. 2006.

[18] Chiarello 1991. Burgess and Chiarello 1996. See in general, Beeman and Chiarello 1998.

[19] Aziz-Zadeh and Damasio 2008, 4. I have omitted the extensive citations in this passage to work by Rachel Giora, Nira Mashal, Miriam Faust, and others.

[20] That would be a sentence like, "The horse raced round the barn—dropped dead." When you come to the word "dropped," you realize you have to go back to the beginning and re-interpret the sentence. You have been "led down the garden path."

[21] Faust 1998. Chiarello 1998.

[22] Maher 2003.

[23] Brownell and Martino 1998.

[24] Brownell et al. 1983. Bihrle et al. 1986. Brownell and Martino 1998.

[25] Kane 2004.

[26] Heilman 2002, 58-69. Bauer and Demery 2003, 269. Heilman et al. 2003, 451-452, 453, 455-464.

[27] Borod, Bloom and Haywood 1998.

[28] Georges Ghacibeh and Kenneth Heilman describe a sad case. This woman's language was normal. But, because she was suffering from right-hemisphere lesions, she could understand emotions, yet was no longer able to express them. She became incomprehensible to normal people expecting tonal and facial indications of the interpersonal significance of what she was saying. As a result, she could not work, her husband was convinced she had stopped loving him, and her doctors could not understand even her

simplest requests (Ghacibeh and Heilman 2003).
[29] Panksepp 1998, 144-163.
[30] Solms and Turnbull 2002, 119.
[31] Freud 1900a, 555-66.
[32] Bownds 1999, 205.
[33] Panksepp 1998, 162.
[34] Freud 1985 [1887-1904], 272. For a strenuous critique of Freud's evidence and reasoning, see Armstrong 1999.

Chapter 17. Individual Styles

[1] Proust 1971 [1905], 55.
[2] Holland 1992, part 1.
[3] Sacks 1990.
[4] Sacks 1974, 239n.
[5] Freud 1900a, 565-66.
[6] Freud 1920g, chs. ii-iii.
[7] Freud 1920g, ch. vii.
[8] Ferenczi 1925, 393.
[9] Fenichel 1945, 523, 467.
[10] Lichtenstein 1961; 1977.
[11] Holland 1989.
[12] John and Srivistava 1999.
[13] Lichtenstein 1961, 252.
[14] Varela 1979. Maturana and Varela, 1980.
[15] Varela 1979, 17.
[16] Maturana and Varela 1980, xxvii, xxv.
[17] Damasio 2003, 30.
[18] Spinoza, *Ethics*, propositions 6, 7, and 8, discussed in Damasio 2003, 36.
[19] Modell 1993, 153.
[20] Lichtenstein 1970; 1977.
[21] Hebb 1949.
[22] Pinker 2002, 92.
[23] Deacon 1997, 202–3.
[24] For time-lapse videos of this process, the brain gaining and losing gray matter from age five to twenty, see: http://www.loni.ucla.edu/~thompson/DEVEL/dynamic.html or http://tinyurl.com/bn9v2m.
[25] Grigsby and Stevens 2000. See also Grigsby and Hartlaub 1994.
[26] Sacks 1974, 239n.

[27] Grigsby and Stevens 2000, 91-95.
[28] Grigsby and Stevens 2000, 310.
[29] Grigsby and Stevens 2000, 311.
[30] Grigsby and Stevens 2000, 321.
[31]Grigsby and Stevens cleverly propose chaos theory for mathematicizing our characteristic defenses. According to chaos theory, one can describe a chaotic system (like the weather or our everyday behaviors) as a myriad of energy states, some requiring high energy, some low. Graphed on a plane, they appear as a surface with high points, hills, and low points, valleys between the hills. The system will tend to gravitate to the valleys. Hence they are called "attractors" and sometimes "strange attractors." We can think of our character, including our defenses, as a configuration of such attractors. That is, we will tend to respond to the ever-changing and random demands of reality (chaos) in ways that involve the least expenditure of energy. We will, therefore, tend to repeat the valley patterns of behavior. Notice that this theory has much in common with Freud's concept of a repetition compulsion (Grigsby and Stevens 2000, 317).
[32] Schore 1994.
[33] Schore 1999, 51.
[34] Trevarthen 1979; 1993.
[35] Schore 1994, 69–196.
[36] Schore 1994, 197–282.
[37] Schore 2003, 206-207, quoting Westen 1997, 542.
[38] Modell 1993, 201–202.
[39]Rafael Malach and his associates have found overlapping extrinsic and intrinsic systems, corresponding to external perceptions and inner-directed thinking, during viewing of natural scenes (Golland et al. 2007).
[40] Edelman 1989, 94.
[41] Holland 1975, 67-112; 1982, 143-171; 1988; 1989.

Chapter 18. Cultural Styles

[1] Jackson 1958 [1881-87].
[2] Kelly 1955.
[3] Fish 1980.
[4] Hirsch 1987.
[5] For a review of this line of research with movies, see Has-

son et al. 2008.
[6] Hasson et al. 2004, 1638.
[7] Henry 1972.

Chapter 19. Pleasure Principles

[1] See Heilman, Watson, and Valenstein 2002, Figs. 13-8 and 13-9.
[2] Dulawa et al. 1999.
[3] Nell 1988, 240.
[4] Tan 1996, 98. Hogan 2003b,149.
[5] Panksepp 1998, 148.
[6] Solms and Turnbull 2002, 119.
[7] Panksepp 1998, 148.
[8] Panksepp 1998, 148-9.
[9] Forster 1927, 98.
[10] Lane 2002, 153.
[11] Taylor 1990, 384-386.
[12] Menand 2003.
[13] Emerson 1869.
[14] Frost 1949.
[15] I have surprised myself a little in writing this section by not including, in "literary" language, metaphors as I now understand them through "cognitive linguistics." George Lakoff, Mark Johnson, Mark Turner, Gilles Fauconnier, and others have analyzed metaphor as a mapping from an easily understood "source" to something more difficult that one wants to understand, the "target" (Lakoff and Johnson 1980). These theorists have shown, however—it is their most important point—that *source-to-target metaphor is not just literary; it is a basic way that we humans think*. We use metaphor in ordinary speech and writing all the time. Hence metaphor by itself does not make language "literary."

Chapter 20. Enjoying the Ugly

[1] Leslie 1843, 308.
[2] *Poetics*, ch. 4. McKeon 1947, 627.
[3] Riestra et al. 2002.
[4] Alcaro, Huber, and Panksepp 2007, 285-286, 294.
[5] Freud 1905d, 203-204.
[6] La Rochefoucauld 2002 [1665], maximes 583 and 19.

[7] Swift 1742.
[8] Johnson 2003.
[9] Panksepp 2000.
[10] Holland 1982, 107.
[11] Provine 2000.
[12] Ramachandran 1998, 352.
[13] For a longer version of this discussion, see Holland 1982; Holland 2007.
[14] In earlier books I have written extensively, from a psychoanalytic point of view, about this process (then called "DEFT") for defense, expectation, fantasy, transformation): Holland 1973b; 1975; 1985; 1988; 1992.

Chapter 21. Making Meaning

[1] Frost 1940, vii.
[2] Fish 1981, 7.
[3] Gazzaniga 1988; 1992.
[4] Gazzaniga 1992, 124-33.
[5] Gazzaniga 1970, 105-106.
[6] Freud 1940a, 164, 198.
[7] Panksepp 1998, 145.
[8] Holland 1975.
[9] Hasson and Malach 2006. Hasson et al. 2004.
[10] Holland 2000c; 1973; 1975.
[11] Panksepp 1998, 145.
[12] Oz 1999 [1996], 114.
[13] Csikszentmihalyi 1990.
[14] See, for example, Bate 1963; 1975.
[15] See, for example, Fiedler 1960; 1978.
[16] See, for example, Holland 1958; 1964.
[17] See, for example, Holland 1988; 1992.
[18] Gadamer 1975.
[19] Habermas 1984; 1987.

Part IV. The Big Questions

Chapter 22. Inner Creativity

[1] Kubie 1970 [1958], 93-96.
[2] Heilman 2005.
[3] Heilman 2002; 2005. Beardsley 1958.

[4] Martindale 1999, 137, 148.
[5] James 1880.
[6] Wallas 1926.
[7] Quoted by Winner 1982, 16.
[8] Anchell 2007.
[9] Winokur 1986, 23.
[10] Plath 2000, 404-5.
[11] Rushdie 2007, 21.
[12] Chekhov, *The Sea Gull*, Act II.
[13] Flaherty 2003. See also Brand 1989.
[14] Winner 1982, 16-17.
[15] Winner 1982, 16.
[16] Gardner 1983; 1988; 1993a.
[17] Holland 1985, 56-67.
[18] Moore et al. 2003.
[19] Lightman 2003.
[20] Kubie 1970 [1958]. Rothenberg 1979.
[21] Andreasen 1987. Jamison 1989; 1993. Kaufman and Baer 2002. There are many others.
[22] Weisberg 2006, 385.
[23] Freud (1916-1917 [1915-1917]), Lectures XXIII and XVI. Freud 1910, 136.
[24] The quotations are from: Freud 1916-1917 [1915-1917], 375-377; 1910, 136; 1919, 261.
[25] Kris 1952, 177 and *passim.*
[26] Menand 2004, 104.
[27] Davies 1987.
[28] Quoted in Livingstone 2002, 200-201.
[29] Haddon 2003.
[30] Miller and Hou 2004. Niedowski 2004.
[31] Wolff and Lundberg 2002.
[32] Winner 2000.
[33] James 1880.
[34] Martindale 1999, 138 and references there cited.
[35] James 1880.
[36] Schore 1994.
[37] Weinstein and Graves 2002.
[38] Winner 2000.
[39] Martindale 1999, 146.
[40] Kleiner-Fisman, Black, and Lang 2003.
[41] Dimond and Beaumont 1974.

[42] Atchley, Burgess, and Keeney 1999.
[43] Atchley, Keeney, and Burgess 1999.
[44] Lewis 1979.
[45] Bernstein 2003.
[46] Heilman 2005, ch. 6.
[47] Bogen and Bogen 1988.
[48] Petsche 1996. Jaušovec and Jaušovec 2000.
[49] Jaušovec 2000. Jaušovec and Jaušovec 2000.
[50] Jaušovec 2002, 205-206.
[51] Martindale 1999, 139.
[52] Heilman 2005, ch. 6.
[53] Miller et al. 2000. Miller et al. 1998.
[54] Kenneth Heilman describes such a patient in Heilman 2005, ch. 8.
[55] Martindale and Hasenfus 1978.
[56] Martindale 1999, 141-142.
[57] Kischka et al. 1996.
[58] Heilman 2005, ch. 8. Waterhouse and Woodward 1980. Servan-Schreiber et al. 1990. Hasselmo et al. 1997.
[59] Cape and Jones 1998.
[60] McCarley 1982.
[61] Martindale 1999, 149.
[62] Faigel 1991.
[63] Heilman 2005, ch. 8. Morrison and Foote 1986. Foote et al. 1991.
[64] Heilman 2005, ch. 8. Aston-Jones et al. 1991.
[65] Beversdorf et al. 1999. See also Heilman, Nadeau, et al. 2003.
[66] Heilman 2005, ch. 8. Gillberg and Svennerholm 1987. Frankhauser et al. 1992.
[67] Liotti and Mayberg 2001.

Chapter 23. Outward Creativity

[1] Gardner 1982; 1988; 1993b.
[2] Albert 1975.
[3] Albert 1975, 143-144.
[4] Albert 1975, 146.
[5] Holland 2000a; 2000c.
[6] Emerson 1869.
[7] Woolf 1932.

Chapter 24. Evaluating

[1] Frijda 1988.
[2] Beardsley 1958, chs. 10-11.
[3] Winner 1982, 7-8.
[4] Goodman 1976; 1977.
[5] Winner 1982, 170.
[6] Gardner, 1982.
[7] Fish 1980.
[8] Holland 1975.
[9] Holland 1975, ch. 6.
[10] Holland 1986.
[11] Premack and Premack 1995. Leslie and & Keeble 1987.
[12] Miller 2002.
[13] Schafer 1968, 101, 109-110.
[14] Gazzaniga 1992.
[15] Freud 1930 [1929], 145. For a modern neuropsychoanalytic corroboration, see Schore 2003, ch. 7.
[16] Holland 1992.
[17] Ross, Greene, and House 1977, 280. Marks and Miller 1987.
[18] Proust 1981 (1913-1927), 2: 844.
[19] Holland 2000a. Holland 2000c.
[20] Graham and Dodd 1934.
[21] Granger and Morgenstern 1970.
[22] For a readable summary of these competing points of view, see Cassidy 2003.
[23] Quoted by Malkiel 2000, 23-24, a particularly engaging and readable account of these theories. See also Brealey 1983; Cootner, ed. 1967; Cragg and Malkiel 1982.
[24] Eliot 1919, 5.
[25] Shermer 2006. Westen, Blagov, Herenski, et al. 2006. Kaplan, Freedman, and Iacoboni 2007. Westen 2007.
[26] Holland 1985.
[27] Holland and Schwartz 2008.

Chapter 25. Is Literature Innate?

[1] "No Words," BBC News, 9 May 2003.
[2] Hsu 2008 gives examples.
[3] For a vigorous critique of this kind of thinking, see Buller 2009. Although the article says it addresses "pop" evolu-

tionary psychology, it gives as examples of same, writings by Tooby, Cosmides, and Pinker.

[4] See the journal *Language Acquisition: A Journal of Developmental Linguistics* for continuing argument.

[5] See, for example, Sperber, ed. 2000.

[6] Zunshine 2006, 6, 164.

[7] Frith and Frith 2005.

[8] Tomasello, Call, and Hare 2003.

[9] Stanovich 2004.

[10] Rolls 1999, 283-4.

[11] Dissanayake 1992; 2001.

[12] For literary purposes, the two key essays are Tooby and Cosmides 2001 and Cosmides and Tooby 2000.

[13] Tooby and Cosmides 2001, 20.

[14] Cosmides and Tooby 2000, 101-104.

[15] Cosmides and Toooby 2000. Tooby and Cosmides 2001.

[16] Panksepp 1981. Panksepp, Siviy, and Normansell 1984.

[17] Erikson 1963, 222.

[18] Winnicott 1971. Schwartz 1975.

[19] Pinker 1999.

[20] Fodor 1997.

[21] Ramachandran and Blakeslee 1998, 184.

[22] Davenport-Hines 2002.

[23] Hogan 2003a, 19; 2003b, 133-135.

[24] Wordsworth, "Observations Prefixed to 'Lyrical Ballads,'" 508.

[25] de Quervain et al. 2004. Small et al. 2001. Fisher et al. 2002.

[26] Hernadi 2001, 56.

[27] Miall 2001, 417.

[28] Mithen 2001, 51.

[29] Miller 2000, 25. See also Miall 2001, 417.

[30] Tooby and Cosmides 2001, 23.

[31] Tooby and Cosmides 2001, 25.

[32] Steiner 1967, preface.

[33] Atwood 2000, 59.

[34] Tooby and Cosmides 2001, 7.

[35] Spolsky 2001b.

[36] Spolsky 2001b; 2001a.

[37] Prentice and Gerrig 1999.

[38] Pinker 1999, 538-545.

[39] Fodor 1997.
[40] Caspi et al. 2003.
[41] Gardner 1999.dir
[42] Hogan 2003b, 216-217.

Chapter 26. Why Literature?

[1] Frye (1971 [1957]), 345.
[2] Pinker 1999, 521.
[3] Freud 1916-1917 [1915-1917], 16: 376-377.
[4] Freud 1908e; 1930 [1929], 79-81; 1920g, 17.
[5] Coleridge 1817, ch. xiv.
[6] Kris 1952, 177 and *passim.*
[7] Hasson et al. 2004.
[8] See, for example, Holland 1975; 1988; 1992; 2000 or Holland and Schwartz 2008.
[9] Barash and Barash 2002.
[10] Barash and Barash 2002.
[11] Proust 1971 [1905], 43.
[12] Miller 2002. See also Schafer 1968, 101, 109-110.
[13] Frye 1970, 75. Graff 1987. Turner 1991.
[14] Pater 1899, x.

Appendix | About Your Brain

[1] Here are books, some directed to lay readers (including textbooks), that you might use to supplement this introduction to the brain: Bear, Connors, and Paradiso 1996; Bownds 1999; Damasio 1999; Gazanniga 1988, 1992; Heilman 2002; Heilman and Valenstein 2003; Kalat 2001; Kaplan-Solms and Solms 2000; Mesulam 2000; Pally 2000; Panksepp 1998; Passingham 1993; Solms and Turnbull 2002. The sections on neurology and the brain in the online encyclopedia Wikipedia.com are usually reliable and particularly helpful, and I am grateful to be able to obtain public domain illustrations from the Wikipedia site. I am also exceedingly grateful to Dr. Robert Sikes of Northeastern University and Dr. Alonso Riestra, formerly of the University of Florida and now of the Instituto Mexicano de Neurociencias. They have both checked this appendix in detail and rescued me from many an error. Those that remain are my very own creation.

[2] Pinker 2002, 92

[3] Cole and Cole 1996, 189, 160-61, 223-4, 358-9, 483-4. Purves and Lichtman 1985. Blakeslee 1986. For MRI videos of these changes from age 5 to age 20, see http://www.loni. ucla.edu/~thompson/DEVEL /dynamic.html or http://tinyurl.com/bn9v2m. Accessed March 5, 2009.

[4] Blakeslee 1986.

[5] Purves and Hadley 1985.

[6] Henderson et al. 1986, 68.

[7] Barnes 1986.

[8] S. S. Easter, Jr., et al., "The Changing View of Neural Specificity," *Science* 230 (1 Nov. 1985): 507-511. A highly readable account of this and other discoveries about brain development is Richard M. Restak's *The Infant Mind* (Garden City NY: Doubleday, 1986).

[9] Shermer 2008.

[10] Panksepp 2000; 2006.

[11] Adolphs, Tranel, and Damasio 2003.

[12] Ledoux 1998.

[13] Panksepp 1998, ch. 13. Lim and Young 2006.

[14] Panksepp 2007.

[15] Wynne 2004, ch. 5.

[16] Wilford 2002.

[17] Gorno-Tempini and Price 2001.

[18] Mesulam, ed. 2000, 338.

References

Adolphs, Ralph. 2002. "Neural Systems for Recognizing Emotion." *Current Opinion in Neurobiology* 12 (2, April): 169-77.

Adolphs, Ralph, Daniel Tranel, and Antonio R. Damasio. 2003. "Dissociable Neural Systems for Recognizing Emotions." *Brain and Cognition* 52 (1, June): 61-69.

"Aesthetics: The Ontology of Art." 2009. In *Encyclopædia Britannica Online*. Retrieved 28 Jan. 2009. http://www.search.eb.com/eb/article-11707.

Aiken, Nancy E. 1998. *The Biological Origins of Art*. Human evolution, behavior, and intelligence. Westport CT; London: Praeger.

Albert, Robert S. 1975. "Toward a Behavioral Definition of Genius." *American Psychologist* 30:140-51.

Alcaro, Antonio, Robert Huber, and Jaak Panksepp. 2007. "Behavioral Functions of the Mesolimbic Dopaminergic System: An Affective Neuroethological Perspective." *Brain Research Reviews* 56 (2, December): 283-321.

Anchell, Steve. 2007. "Maggie Taylor." In *Profiles*. Retrieved 28 Jan. 2009. http://www.steveanchell.com/index.php?option=com_content&task=view&id=64&Itemid=98.

Anderson, Richard C. 1977. "The Notion of Schemata and the Educational Enterprise: General Discussion of the Conference." In *Schooling and the Acquisition of Knowledge*. Ed. Richard C. Anderson, Rand J. Spiro, and William E. Montague. Hillsdale NJ: Lawrence Erlbaum. 415-31.

Andreasen, Nancy C. 1987. "Creativity and Mental Illness: Prevalence Rates in Writers and Their First-Degree Relatives." *American Journal of Psychiatry* 144(10): 1288-92.

Angier, Natalie. 2008. "A Highly Evolved Propensity for Deceit." *The New York Times*, 23 December.

Arbib, Michael A., and Peter Erdi. 2000. "Precis of Neural Organization: Structure, Function, and Dynamics." *Behavior and Brain Science* 23 (4, August): 513-33.

Armstrong, Edward A. 1946. *Shakespeare's Imagination*. London: Lindsay Drummond.

Armstrong, Richard. 1999. "Oedipus as Evidence: The Theatrical Background to Freud's Oedipus Complex." In *PsyArt: An Online Journal for the Psychological Study of the Arts*. Retrieved 28 Jan. 2009. http://www. clas.ufl.edu/ipsa/journal/articles psyart1999/oedipus armstr01.htm or http://tinyurl.com/4ohhz.

Aron, Adam R., et al. 2007. "Triangulating a Cognitive Control Network Using Diffusion-Weighted Magnetic Resonance Imaging (MRI) and Functional MRI." *Journal of Neuroscience* 27 (14, 4 April): 3473-52.

Aston-Jones, G., C. Chiang, and T. Alexinsky. 1991. "Discharge of Noradrenergic Locus Coeruleus Neurons in Behaving Rats and Monkeys Suggests a Role in Vigilance." *Progress in Brain Research* 88: 501-20.

Atchley, R. A., C. Burgess, and M. Keeney. 1999. "The Effect of Time Course and Context on the Facilitation of Semantic Features in the Cerebral Hemispheres." *Neuropsychology* 13 (3, July): 389-403.

———, M. Keeney, and C. Burgess. 1999. "Cerebral Hemispheric Mechanisms Linking Ambiguous Word Meaning Retrieval and Creativity." *Brain and Cognition* 40 (3, August): 479-99.

Atwood, Margaret. 2000. *The Blind Assassin*. New York: Random House / Anchor.

Austin, James H. 1998. *Zen and the Brain: Toward an Understanding of Meditation and Consciousness*. Cambridge MA: MIT Press.

Aziz-Zadeh, Lisa, and Antonio Damasio. 2008. "Embodied Semantics for Actions: Findings from Functional Brain Imaging." *Journal of Physiology - Paris* 102:35-39.

Baars, Bernard J. 1996. *In the Theater of Consciousness: The Workspace of the Mind.* New York: Oxford University Press.

Bach-y-Rita, Paul. 1969. "A Tactile Vision Substitution System." *American Journal of Optometry & Archives of American Academy of Optometry* 46 (2): 109-11.

———. 1970, 9. "Neurophysiological Basis of a Tactile Vision-Substitution System." *IEEE Transactions: Man-Machine Systems* 11 (1): 108-10.

Baldissera, Fausto, Paolo Cavallari, Laila Craighero, and Luciano Fadiga. 2001. "Modulation of Spinal Excitability During Observation of Hand Actions in Humans." *European Journal of Neuroscience* 13 (1): 190-94.

Barash, David P., and Nanelle Barash. 2002. "Evolution and Literary Criticism." *Chronicle of Higher Education* 49 (8, 18 October): B7.

Bargh, John A., and Tanya L. Chartrand. 1999. "The Unbearable Automaticity of Being." *American Psychologist* 54 (7, July): 462-79.

Barnes, Deborah M. 1986. "Research News. Brain Architecture Beyond Genes." *Science* 233 n.s. (4760, 11 July): 155-56.

Bate, Walter Jackson. 1963. *John Keats.* New York: Oxford University Press.

———. 1975. *Samuel Johnson.* New York and London: Harcourt, Brace, Jovanovich.

Bauer, Russell M., and Jason A. Demery. 2003. "Agnosia." In *Clinical Neuropsychology.* 4th ed.. Ed. Kenneth Heilman and Edward Valenstein. New York: Oxford University Press. 236-95.

Bear, Mark F., Barry W. Connors, and Michael A. Paradiso. 2006. *Neuroscience: Exploring the Brain.* 3rd ed. Baltimore MD: Lippincott Williams & Wilkins.

Beardsley, Monroe. 1958. *Aesthetics.* New York: Harcourt Brace.

Bechara, Antoine, Hanna Damasio, Daniel Tranel, and Antonio Damasio. 1997. "Deciding Advantageously Before Knowing the Advantageous Strategy." *Science* 275 (5304): 1293-95.

Beeman, Mark, and Christine Chiarello, eds. 1998. *Right Hemisphere Language Comprehension: Perspectives from Cognitive Neuroscience.* Mahwah NJ: Erlbaum.

Berman, Jeffrey. 1994. *Diaries to an English Professor: Pain and Growth in the Classroom.* Amherst MA: University of Massachusetts Press.

Berns, Gregory S., Jonathan D. Cohen, and Mark A. Mintun. 1997. "Brain Regions Responsive to Novelty in the Absence of Awareness." *Science* 276 (23 May):1272-75.

Bernstein, Hans-Gert. 2003. "Dissecting Einstein's Brain." In *IQ Magazine*, July.

Beversdorf, D. Q., et al. 1999. "Noradrenergic Modulation of Cognitive Flexibility in Problem Solving." *NeuroReport* 10:2763-67.

Bibring, Grete. 1961. "A Study of Pregnancy." Appendix B, Glossary of Defenses. *The Psychoanalytic Study of the Child* 14:57-72.

Bihrle, A. M., Hiram H. Brownell, J. A. Powelson, and Howard Gardner. 1986. "Comprehension of Humorous and Non-Humorous Materials by Left and Right Brain-Damaged Patients." *Brain and Cognition* 5 (4, October): 399-411.

Bitsilli, P. M. 1983. *Chekhov's Art, a Stylistic Analysis.* Trans. Toby W. Clyman and Edwina Jannie Cruise. Ann Arbor: Ardis.

Blakeslee, Sandra. 1986. "Rapid Changes Seen in Young Brain." *The New York Times*, 24 June.

Bleich, David. 1975. *Readings and Feelings: An Introduction to Subjective Criticism.* Urbana IL: National Council of Teachers of English.

———. 1978. *Subjective Criticism.* Baltimore: Johns Hopkins University Press.

Bogen, Joseph E., and Glenda M. Bogen. 1988. "Creativity and the Corpus Callosum." *Psychiatric Clinics of North America* 11 (3, September): 293-301.

Bollas, Christopher. 2002. *Free Association.* Ideas in Psychoanalysis. London: Icon Books.

Bordwell, David. 1985. *Narration in the Fiction Film.* Madison, WI: University of Wisconsin Press.

———. 1997. *On the History of Film Style.* Cambridge, Mass.: Harvard University Press.

———, and Kristin Thompson. 2008. *Film Art: An Introduction.* Boston: McGraw-Hill.

Borod, Joan C., Ronald L. Bloom, and Cornelia Santschi Haywood. 1998. "Verbal Aspects of Emotional Communication." In *Right Hemisphere Language Comprehension*. Ed. Mark Beeman and Christine Chiarello. Mahwah, NJ: Erlbaum. 285-307.

Bortolussi, Marisa, and Peter Dixon. 2003. *Psychonarratology: Foundations for the Empirical Study of Literary Response*. Cambridge and New York: Cambridge University Press.

Bownds, M. Deric. 1999. *The Biology of Mind: Origins and Structures of Mind, Brain, and Consciousness*. Bethesda MD: Fitzgerald Science Press.

Boxer, Saraveh. 2001. "Therapists Go Crazy for One in 'Sopranos'." *New York Times*, 2001, 29 December.

Bradley, A. C. 1905. *Shakespearean Tragedy: Lectures on Hamlet, Othello, King Lear, Macbeth*. London: Macmillan.

Brand, Alice. 1989. *The Psychology of Writing: The Affective Experience*. New York: Greenwood.

Brealey, Richard A. 1983. *An Introduction to Risk and Return from Common Stocks*. 2d ed. Cambridge MA: MIT Press.

Britton, Bruce K., and Arthur C. Graesser, eds. 1996. *Models of Understanding Text*. Hillsdale NJ: Erlbaum.

Brothers, Leslie. 1995. "Neurophysiology of the Perception of Intentions by Primates." In *The Cognitive Neurosciences*. Ed. Michael S. Gazzaniga. Cambridge MA: MIT Press. 1107-15.

———. 1997. *Friday's Footprint: How Society Shapes the Human Mind*. New York: Oxford University Press.

Brownell, Hiram, and Gail Martino. 1998. "Deficits in Inference and Social Cognition: The Effects of Right Hemisphere Brain Damage on Discourse." In *Right Hemisphere Language Comprehension*. Ed. Mark Beeman and Christine Chiarello. Mahwah NJ: Erlbaum. 309-28.

———, D. Michel, J. A. Powelson, and Howard Gardner. 1983. "Surprise but not Coherence: Sensitivity to Verbal Humor in Right-Hemisphere Patients." *Brain and Language* 18:20-27.

Brungart, D. S., and W. M. Rabinowitz. 1999. "Auditory Localization of Nearby Sources: Head-Related Transfer Functions." *Journal of the Acoustical Society of America* 106 (3-1, September): 1465-79.

———, N. I. Durlach, and W. M. Rabinowitz. 1999. "Auditory Localization of Nearby Sources: II. Localization of a Broadband Course." *Journal of the Acoustical Society of America* 106 (4-1, October): 1956-68.

Buccino, Giovanni, et al. 2005. "Listening to Action-Related Sentences Modulates the Activity of the Motor System: A Combined TMS and Behavioral Study." *Cognitive Brain Research* 24: 355-63.

Buckner, Randy L., and Daniel C. Carroll. 2007. "Self-Projection and the Brain." *Trends in Cognitive Science* 11 (2): 49-57.

Burgess, Curt, and Christine Chiarello. 1996. "Neurocognitive Mechanisms Underlying Metaphor Comprehension and Other Figurative Language." *Metaphor & Symbol* 11 (1): 1967-84.

Burgess, P. W., and J. E. McNeil. 1999. "Content-Specific Confabulation." *Cortex* 35 (2, April): 163-82.

———, and T. Shallice. 1996. "Confabulation and the Control of Recollection." *Memory* 4 (4, July): 359-411.

———, S. K. Scott, and C. D. Frith. 2003. "The Role of the Rostral Frontal Cortex (Area 10) in Prospective Memory: A Lateral Versus Medial Dissociation." *Neuropsychologia* 41 (8): 906-18.

Callan, Daniel. E, et al. 2006. "Song and Speech: Brain Regions Involved with Perception and Covert Production." *Neuroimage* 31 (3, July): 1327–1342.

Cape, E. G., and E. B. Jones. 1998. "Differential Modulation of High-Frequency Gamma-Electroencephalogram activity and Sleep-Wake State by Noradrenaline and Serotonin Microinjections into the Region of Cholinergic Basalis Neurons." *Journal of Neuroscience* 18 (7): 2653-56.

Carnahan, Heather, and Ronald G. Marteniuk. 1993. "Grasping Versus Pointing and the Differential Use of Visual Feedback." *Human Movement Science* 12 (3, May): 219-34.

Carroll, Noël. 2003. *Engaging the Moving Image*. Yale Series in the Philosophy and Theory of Art. New Haven: Yale University Press.

Caspi, Avshalom, et al. 2003. "Influence of Life Stress on Depression: Moderation by a Polymorphism in the 5-HTT Gene." *Science* 301 (5631, 18 July): 386-89.

Cassidy, John. 2003. "Smart Money: Two Wall Street Classics Appear in New Editions." *The New Yorker*, 6 October.

Chekhov, Anton. 1951. *The Sea Gull.* Trans. Elizaveta Fen. New York: Penguin.

Chelazzi, Leonardo, John Duncan, Earl K. Miller, and Robert Desimone. 1998. "Responses of Neurons in Inferior Temporal Cortex During Memory-Guided Visual Search." *Journal of Neurophysiology* 80 (6): 2918-40.

Chesterton, G. K. 1902. "A Defence of China Shepherdesses." In *The Defendant.* New York: Dodd, Mead. 59-65.

Chiarello, Christine. 1991. "Interpretation of Word Meanings by the Cerebral Hemispheres: One is not Enough." In *The Psychology of Word Meanings.* Ed. Paula J. Schwanenflugel. Hillsdale NJ: Erlbaum. 251-78.

———. 1998. "On Codes of Meaning and the Meaning of Codes: Semantic Access and Retrieval Within and Between Hemispheres." In *Right Hemisphere Language Comprehension: Perspectives from Cognitive Neuroscience.* Ed. Mark Beeman and Christine Chiarello. Mahwah NJ: Erlbaum. 141-160.

Chomsky, Noam. 1981. "Principles and Parameters in Syntactic Theory." In *Explanation in Linguistics: The Logical Problem of Language Acquisition.* Ed. N. Hornstein and D. Lightfoot. London: Longman. 32-75.

Clark, Andy. 1997. *Being There: Putting Brain, Body, and World Together Again.* Cambridge MA: MIT Press.

Cole, Michael, and Sheila R. Cole. 1996. *The Development of Children.* 3rd edn. New York: W. H. Freeman.

Coleridge, Samuel Taylor. 1907 [1817]. *Biographia Literaria.* 2 vols. Ed. J. Shawcross. Oxford: Clarendon Press.

Concise Encyclopedia of Pragmatics. 1998. Ed. Jacob L. Mey, cons. ed R. E. Ahser. Amsterdam and New York: Elsevier.

Cootner, Paul H., ed. 1967. *The Random Character of Stock Market Prices.* Rev. ed. Cambridge MA: MIT Press.

Cosmides, Leda, and John Tooby. 2000. "Consider the Source: The Evolution of Adaptations for Decoupling and Metarepresentation." In *Metarepresentations: A Multidisciplinary Perspective.* Vancouver Studies in Cognitive Science. Ed. Dan Sperber. New York: Oxford University Press. 53-116.

Cragg, John G., and Burton Malkiel. 1982. *Expectations and the Structure of Share Prices.* Chicago: University of Chicago Press.

Csikszentmihalyi, Mihaly. 1988. "Society, Culture, and Person: A Systems View of Creativity." In *The Nature of Creativity: Contemporary Psychological Perspectives*. Ed. Robert J. Sternberg. Cambridge: Cambridge University Press. 325-339.

———. 1990. *Flow: The Psychology of Optimal Experience*. New York: Harper and Row.

———, and Rick E. Robinson. 1990. *The Art of Seeing: An Interpretation of the Aesthetic Encounter.* Malibu CA: J. Paul Getty Trust.

Damasio, Antonio R. 1994. *Descartes' Error: Emotion, Reason, and the Human Brain*. New York: Grosset/Putnam.

———. 1996. "The Somatic Marker Hypothesis and the Possible Functions of the Prefrontal Cortex." *Philosophical Transactions of the Royal Society of London: B Biological Sciences* 351 (1346, 29 October): 1413-20.

———. 1999. *The Feeling of What Happens: Body and Emotion in the Making of Consciousness*. New York: Harcourt Brace.

———. 2003. *Looking for Spinoza: Joy, Sorrow, and the Feeling Brain.* New York: Harvest/ Harcourt.

———, Daniel Tranel, and Hanna C. Damasio. 1991. "Somatic Markers and the Guidance of Behavior: Theory and Preliminary Testing." In *Frontal Lobe Function and Dysfunction.* Ed. H. S. Levin, H. M. Eisenberg, and A. L. Benton. New York: Oxford University Press. 217-229.

Darwin, Charles. 1890. *The Expression of the Emotions in Man and Animals*. 2d. Ed. Francis Darwin. London: John Murray.

Davenport-Hines, Richard. 2002. *The Pursuit of Oblivion: A Global History of Narcotics*. New York: Norton.

Davidson, Richie, J. 1992. "Emotion and Affective Style: Hemispheric Substrates." *Psychological Science* 3: Get Norm Holland39-43.

Davies, Robertson. 1987. "We Must Sing with the Voices God Gave Us." *Toronto Star*, 19 September.

de Gelder, Beatrice, et al. 2004. "Fear Fosters Flight: A Mechanism for Fear Contagion When Perceiving Emotion Expressed by a Whole Body." *Proceedings of the National Academy of Science* 101 (47, 23 November): 16701-06.

de Quervain, Dominique J.-F., et al. 2004. "The Neural Basis of Altruistic Punishmen." *Science* 305 (5688, 27 August):1254-8.

Deacon, Terrence. 1997. *The Symbolic Species: The Co-Evolution of Language and the Brain.* New York: Norton.

Dimberg, Ulf, and Monika Thunberg. 1998. "Rapid Facial Reactions to Emotional Facial Expressions." *Scandinavian Journal of Psychology* 39: 39-45.

———, Monika Thunberg, and K. Elmehed. 2000. "Unconscious Facial Reactions to Emotional Facial Expressions." *Psychological Science* 11 (1, January): 86-89.

Dimond, S., and J. G. Beaumont. 1974. "Experimental Studies of the Hemisphere Function in the Human Brain." In *Hemisphere Function in the Human Brain.* Ed. S. Dimond and J. G. Beaumont. New York: Halsted. 48-88.

Dissanayake, Ellen. 1992. *Homo Aestheticus: Where Art Comes from and Why.* Seattle WA: University of Washington Press.

———. 2001. "Becoming *Homo Aestheticus*: Sources of Aesthetic Imagination in Mother-Infant Interaction." *SubStance* 94/95: 85-103. Special issue, H. Porter Abbot <ed>.

Dulawa, S. C., et al. 1999. "Dopamine D4 Receptor-Knock-Out Mice Exhibit Reduced Exploration of Novel Stimuli." *Journal of Neuroscience* 19 (21, 1 November): 9550-6.

Easter, S. S., Jr., Dale Purves, Patricia Rakic, and N. C. Spitzer. 1985. "The Changing View of Neural Specificity." *Science* 230 (4725, 1 November): 507-11.

Edelman, Gerald M. 1989. *The Remembered Present: A Biological Theory of Consciousness.* New York: Basic Books.

Eichenbaum, Howard, and J. Alexander Bodkin. 2000. "Belief and Knowledge as Distinct Forms of Memory." In *Memory, Brain, and Belief.* Ed. Daniel L. Schacter and Elaine Scarry. Cambridge MA: Harvard University Press. 176–207.

Ekman, Paul. 1999. "Basic Emotions." In *Handbook of Cognition and Emotion.* Ed. Tim Dalgleish and Mick J. Power. Chichester: JohnWiley and Sons. 45-60.

———. 2003. *Emotions Revealed: Recognizing Faces and Feelings to Improve Communication and Emotional Life.* New York: Times Books.

———, and Maureen O'Sullivan. 1991. "Who Can Catch a Liar?" *American Psychologist* 46 (9, September): 913-20.

———, and W. V. Friesen. 1971. "Constants Across Cultures in the Face and Emotion." *Journal of Personalty and Social Psychology* 17:124-29.

Eliot, T. S. 1950. "Tradition and the Individual Talent." 1919. In *Selected Essays*. New ed. New York: Harcourt Brace. 3–11.

Emerson, Ralph Waldo. 1909-14. "Good Writing." Oct.-Nov. 1869. In *Journals of Ralph Waldo Emerson*. 10 vols.. Ed. Edward Waldo Emerson and Waldo Emerson Forbes. Boston: Houghton Mifflin.

———. 1837. *An Oration Delivered Before the Phi Beta Kappa Society, at Cambridge, August 31, 1837*. Boston.

Erikson, Erik H. 1963. *Childhood and Society*. 2d ed. New York: Norton.

Faigel, H. C. 1991. "The Effect of Beta Blockade on Stress-Induced Cognitive Dysfunction in Adolescents." *Clinical Pediatrics* 30 (7, July): 446-48.

Faust, Miriam. 1998. "Obtaining Evidence of Language Comprehension." In *Right Hemisphere Language Comprehension*. Ed. Mark Beeman and Christine Chiarello. Mahwah, NJ: Erlbaum. 161-85.

Feinberg, Todd E. 2001. *Altered Egos: How the Brain Creates the Self.* New York: Oxford University Press.

Feldman, Jerome, and Srinivas Narayanan. n.d. "Embodied Meaning in a Neural Theory of Language." Retrieved 26 Jan. 2009. http://www.icsi.berkeley.edu/NTL/papers/B+L.doc.

Fenichel, Otto. 1945. *The Psychoanalytic Theory of Neurosis*. New York: Norton.

———. 1953. "The Scoptophilic Instinct and Identification." 1935. In *Collected Papers of Otto Fenichel: First Series*. New York: W. W. Norton. 373-97.

Ferenczi, Sándor. 1925. "Psycho-Analysis of Sexual Habits." *International Journal of Psycho-Analysis* 6:372-404.

Fiedler, Leslie A. 1960. *Love and Death in the American Novel.* New York: Criterion Books.

———. 1978. *Freaks: Myths and Images of the Secret Self.* New York: Simon and Schuster, Touchstone.

Fish, Stanley. 1980. *Is There a Text in This Class? The Authority of Interpretive Communities*. Cambridge MA: Harvard University Press.

———. 1981. "Why no One's Afraid of Wolfgang Iser." *Diacritics* 11: 2-13.

Fisher, Helen E., et al. 2002. "Defining the Brain Systems of Lust, Romantic Attraction, and Attachment." *Archives of Sexual Behavior* 31 (5, October): 413-19.

Flaherty, Alice W. 2003. "Writing Like Crazy: A Word on the Brain." *Chronicle of Higher Education* 50 (13, 21 November).

Fodor, Jerry. 1997. "The Trouble with Psychological Darwinism." Rev. of *How the Mind Works* by Steven Pinker and *Evolution in Mind* by Henry Plotkin. In *London Review of Books* 20 (2). Retrieved 28 Jan. 2009. http://www.lrb.co.uk/v20/n02/fodo01_.html.

Foote, S. L., C. W. Berridge, L. M. Adams, and J. A. Pineda. 1991. "Electrophysiological Evidence for the Involvement of the Locus Coeruleus in Alerting, Orienting, and Attending." *Progress in Brain Research* 88:521-32.

Forster, E. M. 1927. *Aspects of the Novel.* New York: Harcourt, Brace & company.

Fotopoulou, Akaterina, et al. 2007. "Self-Enhancing Confabulation: Revisiting the Motivational Hypothesis." *Neurocase* 13 (1, Febraury): 6-15.

———, Mark Solms, and Oliver Turnbull. 2004. "Wishful Reality Distortions in Confabulation: A Case Report." *Neuropsychologia* 42 (6): 727-44.

Frankhauser, M. P., et al. 1992. "A Double-Blind, Placebo-Controlled Study of the Efficacy of Transdermal Clonidine in Autism." *Journal of Clinical Psychiatry* 53 (3, March): 77-82.

Freud, Sigmund. 1900a. *The Interpretation of Dreams. Std. Edn.* 4-5: 1-627.

———. 1905d. *Three Essays on the Theory of Sexuality. Std. Edn.* 7: 125-243.

———. 1908e. "Creative Writers and Day Dreaming." *Std. Edn.* 9: 142-153.

———. 1910c. *Leonardo da Vinci and a Memory of His Childhood. Std. Edn.* 11: 17-137.

———. 1916-17 [1915-1917]. *Introductory Lectures on Psycho-Analysis. Std. Edn.* 15-16: 16-476.

———. 1919g. "Preface to Reik's *Ritual: Psycho-Analytic Studies.*" *Std. Edn.* 17: 257-265.

———. 1920g. *Beyond the Pleasure Principle. Std. Edn.* 18: 7-64.

———. 1923a [1922]. "Two Encyclopaedia Articles: Psycho-Analysis." *Std. Edn.* 18: 233-59.

———. 1926d. *Inhibitions, Symptoms, and Anxiety*. *Std. Edn.* 20.
———. 1930a [1929]. *Civilization and its Discontents*. *Std. Edn.* 21: 59-145.
———. 1937c. "Analysis Terminable and Interminable." *Std. Edn.* 23: 209-253.
———. 1940a. *An Outline of Psycho-Analysis*. *Std. Edn.* 23: 139-207.
———. 1985. *The Complete Letters of Sigmund Freud to Wilhelm Fliess, 1887- 1904*. Ed. and trans. Jeffrey Moussaieff Masson. Cambridge, Massachusetts: Harvard University Press, Belknap Press.
Frijda, Nico H. 1986. *The Emotions*. Cambridge: Maison des Sciences de l'Homme and Cambridge University Press.
———. 1988. "The Laws of Emotion." *American Psychologist* 43: 349-58.
———. 2007. *The Laws of Emotion*. Mahwah, NJ: Lawrence Erlbaum Associates Publishers.
Frith, Chris, and Uta Frith. 2005. "Theory of Mind." *Current Biology* 15 (17, September): R644-R645.
Frost, Robert. 1949. "The Figure a Poem Makes." In *Complete Poems*. New York: Henry Holt. v-viii.
Frye, Northrop. 1970. *The Stubborn Structure: Essays on Criticism and Society*. Ithaca: Cornell University Press.
———. *Anatomy of Criticism: Four Essays*. 1957. Princeton: Princeton University Press.
Fuster, Joaquin M. 1999. "Cognitive Functions of the Frontal Lobes." In *The Human Frontal Lobes: Functions and Disorders*, eds Bruce L. Miller and Jeffrey L. Cummings. New York: Guilford Press. 187-95.
Gadamer, Hans-Georg. 1975. *Truth and Method*. Trans. Garret Barden and John Cumming. New York: Seabury Press, Continuum.
Gallese, Vittorio, and George Lakoff. 2005. "The Brain's Concepts: The Role of the Sensory-Motor System in Conceptual Knowledge." *Cognitive Neuropsychology* 22 (3-4, May-June): 455-79.
Gardner, Howard. 1982. *Art, Mind, and Brain: A Cognitive Approach to Creativity*. New York: Basic Books.
———. 1983. *Frames of Mind: The Theory of Multiple Intelligences*. New York: Basic Books.

———. 1988. "Creative Lives and Creative Works: A Synthetic Scientific Approach." In *The Nature of Creativity: Contemporary Psychological Perspectives*. Ed. Robert J. Sternberg. Cambridge: Cambridge University Press. 298-321.

———. 1993a. *Creating Minds: An Anatomy of Creativity Seen Through the Lives of Freud, Einstein, Picasso, Stravinsky, Eliot, Graham, and Gandhi*. New York: Basic Books.

———. 1993b. *Multiple Intelligences: The Theory in Practice*. New York: Basic Books.

———. 1999. *Intelligence Reframed: Multiple Intelligences for the 21st Century*. New York: Basic Books.

Gazzaniga, Michael S. 1970. *Bisected Brain*. New York: Appleton-Century-Crofts.

———. 1988. *Mind Matters: How Mind and Brain Interact to Create Our Conscious Lives*. Bradford Books. Boston: Houghton Mifflin Co.

———. 1992. *Nature's Mind: The Biological Roots of Thinking, Emotions, Sexuality, Language, and Intelligence*. New York: Basic Books.

Gergely, György. 1992. "Developmental Reconstructions: Infancy from the Point of View of Psychoanalysis and Developmental Psychology." *Psychoanalysis and Contemporary Thought* 15: 3-55.

———, and John S. Watson. 1996. "The Social Biofeedback Theory of Parental Affect-Mirroring." *International Journal of Psycho-Analysis* 77: 181-212.

Gerrig, Richard J. 1996. "Participatory Aspects of Narrative Understanding." In *Empirical Approaches to Literature and Aesthetics*. Ed. Roger J. Kreuz and Mary Sue MacNealy. Norwood NJ: Ablex publishing. 127-42.

———. 1998. *Experiencing Narrative Worlds: On the Psychological Activities of Reading*. New Haven: Westview Press, Yale University Press.

Ghacibeh, Georges A., and Kenneth M. Heilman. 2003. "Progressive Affective Aprosodia and Prosoplegia." *Neurology* 60 (7, April): 1192-94.

Gilbert, Daniel T. 1991a. "How Mental Systems Believe." *American Psychologist* 46 (2, February): 107-19.

———. 1991b. "How Mental Systems Believe: Reply." *American Psychologist* 47 (5, May): 670-71.

Gillberg, Christopher, and Lars Svennerholm. 1987. "CSF Monoamines in Autistic Syndromes and Other Pervasive Developmental Disorders of Early Childhood." *British Journal of Psychiatry* 151 (July): 89-94.

Goldman, Susan R., Arthur C. Graesser, and Paul van den Broek, eds. 1999. *Narrative Comprehension, Causality and Coherence: Essays in Honor of Tom Trabasso.* Mahwah NJ: Erlbaum.

Goleman, Daniel. 1996. *Emotional Intelligence: Why It Can Matter More Than IQ.* New York: Bantam Books.

Golland, Yulia, et al. 2007. "Extrinsic and Intrinsic Systems in the Posterior Cortex of the Human Brain Revealed During Natural Sensory Stimulation." *Cerebral Cortex* 17 (4, April): 766-77.

Goodale, Melvyn A., and A. David Milner. 1992. "Separate Visual Pathways for Perception and Action." *Trends in Neuroscience* 15 (1, January): 20-25.

———, et al. 1991. "A Neurological Dissociation Between Perceiving Objects and Grasping Them." *Nature* 349 (6305, January): 154-56.

Goodman, Nelson. 1976. *Languages of Art.* 2d ed. Indianapolis: Hackett.

———. 1977. "When is Art?" In *The Arts and Cognition.* Ed. David Perkins and Barbara Leondar. Baltimore: Johns Hopkins University Press. 11–19.

Gorno-Tempini, M. L., and C. J. Price. 2001. "Identification of Famous Faces and Buildings: A Functional Neuroimaging Study of Semantically Unique Items." *Brain* 124: 2087-97.

Graff, Gerald. 1987. *Professing Literature: An Institutional History.* Chicago: University of Chicago Press.

Graham, Benjamin, and David Dodd. 1934. *Security Analysis.* 1st ed. New York: McGraw-Hill.

Granger, Clive W. J., and Oskar Morgenstern. 1970. *Predictability of Stock Market Prices.* Lexington MA: D. C. Heath.

Greenhouse, Linda. 2003. "Court Appears Ready to Reverse Sodomy Law." *The New York Times*, 27 March.

Griffiths, Timothy D., et al. 2000. "Human Brain Areas Involved in the Analysis of Auditory Movement." *Human Brain Mapping* 9 (2): 72-80.

Grigsby, Jim, and G. Hartlaub. 1994. "Procedural Learning and the Development and Stability of Character." *Perceptual and Motor Skills* 79:355-70.

———, and David Stevens. 2000. *Neurodynamics of Personality*. New York: Guilford Press.

Habermas, Jürgen. 1984. *Reason and the Rationalization of Society*. Vol. 1 of *Theory of Communicative Action*. Trans. Thomas McCarthy. Boston: Beacon Press.

———. 1987. *Lifeworld and System: A Critique of Functionalist Reason*. Vol. 2 of *The Theory of Communicative Action*. Trans. Thomas McCarthy. Boston: Beacon Press.

Haddon, Mark. 2003. *The Curious Incident of the Dog in the Night-Time*. New York: Doubleday.

Hafting, Torkel, et al. 2005. "Microstructure of a Spatial Map in the Entorhinal Cortex." *Nature* 436 (11 August):801-06.

Hasselmo, Michael E., et al. 1997. "Noradrenergic Suppression of Synaptic Transmission May Influence Cortical Signal-to-Noise Ratio." *Journal of Neurophysiology* 77 (6, June): 3326-39.

Hasson, Uri, et al. 2004. "Intersubject Synchronization of Cortical Activity During Natural Vision." *Science* 303 (12 March): 1634-40.

———, et al. 2008. "Neurocinematics: The Neuroscience of Film." *Projections: The Journal for Movies and Mind* 2 (1, Summer): 1-23.

——— and Rafael Malach. 2006. "Human Brain Activation During Viewing of Dynamic Natural Scenes." in *Percept, Decision, Action: Bridging the Gaps*, Novartis Foundation Symposium 270. Chichester: Wiley. 203-16.

Hayes, John Michael. *Rear Window*. 1953. Final white script. Based on a short story by Cornell Woolrich. Retrieved 28 Jan. 2009. http://www.imsdb.com/scripts/Rear-Window.html.

Hebb, Donald O. 1949. *The Organization of Behavior: A Neuropsychological Theory*. New York: Wiley.

Heider, Fritz, and Marianne Simmel. 1944. "An Experimental Study of Apparent Behavior." *American Journal of Psychology* 57: 243-59.

Heilman, Kenneth M. 2002a. "Defining Creativity." Lecture, McKnight Brain Institute at the University of Florida, 1 October.

———. 2002b. *Matter of Mind: A Neurologist's View of Brain-Behavior Relationships*. New York: Oxford University Press.

———. 2005. *Creativity and the Brain*. New York: Psychology Press.

———, and Edward Valenstein, eds. 2003. *Clinical Neuropsychology*. 4th ed. New York: Oxford University Press.

———, Dawn Bowers, and Edward Valenstein. 1993. "Emotional Disorders Associated with Neurological Diseases." In *Clinical Neuropsychology*. 3rd ed.. Ed. Kenneth M. Heilman and Edward Valenstein. New York: Oxford University Press. 461-97.

———, Lee X. Blonder, Dawn Bowers, and Edward Valenstein. 2003. "Emotional Disorders Associated with Neurological Disease." In *Clinical Neuropsychology*. 4th ed.. Ed. Kenneth Heilman and Edward Valenstein. New York: Oxford University Press. 447-78.

———, Robert T. Watson, and Edward Valenstein. 2002. "Neglect and Related Disorders." In *Clinical Neuropsychology*. 4th ed.. Ed. Kenneth M. Heilman and Edward Valenstein. New York: Oxford University Press. 296-346.

———, Stephen E. Nadeau, and David O. Beversdorf. 2003. "Creative Innovation: Possible Brain Mechanisms." *Neurocase* 9:369-79.

Henderson, Christopher E., et al. 1986. "Increase of Neurite-Promoting activity for Spinal Neurons in Muscles of 'Paralysé' Mice and Tenotomised Rats." *Brain Research* 390 (1, February): 65-70.

Henry, Jules. 1965. *Pathways to Madness*. New York: Random House.

Hernadi, Paul. 2001. "Literature and Evolution." *SubStance* 94/95: 55-71. Special issue, H. Porter Abbot, ed.

Hirsch, E. D., Jr. 1987. *Cultural Literacy: What Every American Needs to Know*. Boston: Houghton Mifflin.

Hobson, J. Allan. 1995. *The Chemistry of Conscious States: How the Brain Changes its Mind*. Boston: Little, Brown.

Hogan, Patrick Colm. 2003a. *The Mind and its Stories: Narrative Universals and Human Feeling*. Cambridge UK: Cambridge University Press.

———. 2003b. *Cognitive Science, Literature, and the Arts: A Guide for Humanists*. New York and London: Routledge.

Holland, Norman N. 1958. "Kafka's 'Metamorphosis': Realism and Unrealism." *Modern Fiction Studies* 4: 143-50.

———. 1964. "The Puzzling Movies: Three Analyses and a Guess at Their Appeal." *Journal of Social Issues* 20: 71-96.

———. 1968. *The Dynamics of Literary Response.* New York: Oxford University Press.

———. 1973. *Poems in Persons: An Introduction to the Psychoanalysis of Literature.* New York: Norton.

———. 1975. *5 Readers Reading.* New Haven: Yale University Press.

———. 1982. *Laughing: A Psychology of Humor.* Ithaca NY: Cornell University Press.

———. 1985. *The I.* New Haven and London: Yale University Press. Retrieved January 29, 2009. http://www.clas.ufl.edu/users/nnh/ theihome.htm.

———. 1986c. "The Miller's Wife and the Professors: Questions About the Transactive Theory of Reading." *New Literary History* 17:423-47.

———. 1988. *The Brain of Robert Frost.* New York and London: Routledge.

———. 1989. "The L-Shaped Mind of Ronald Reagan: A Psychoanalytic Study." *Psychohistory Review* 17 (2): 183-214.

———. 1992. *The Critical I.* New York: Columbia University Press.

———. 2000a. "Creativity and the Stock Market." *Bulletin of Psychology and the Arts* 1 (2): 62-64.

———. 2000b. *Poems in Persons: A Psychology of the Literary Process.* Rev. ed. Christchurch, N.Z.: Cybereditions.

———. 2000c. "Creativity and the Stock Market." Article 000825. *PsyArt: An Online Journal for the Psychology of the Arts.* Retrieved January 29, 2009. http://www.clas.ufl.edu/ipsa/journal/2000_holland02.shtml.

———. 2002. "Where is a Text? A Neurological View." *New Literary History* 33 (1, Winter): 21-38.

———. 2004. "Psychoanalysis as Science." Article 040522. *PsyArt: An Online Journal for the Psychological Study of the Arts* 8.

———, and Murray M. Schwartz. 1975. "The Delphi Seminar." *College English* 36:789-800.

———, and Murray M. Schwartz. 2008. *Know Thyself: Delphi Seminars*. Gainesville FL: The PsyArt Foundation. Retrieved January 29, 2009. http://www.know thyselfdelphiseminars.com .

Hsu, Jeremy. 2008. "The Secrets of Storytelling." *Scientific American Mind* 19.4 (August/September):46-51.

Iacoboni, Marco, et al. 2001. "Reafferent Copies of Imitated Actions in the Right Superior Temporal Cortex." *PNAS (Proceedings of the National Academy of Sciences)* 98 (24, 20 November): 13995-99.

———, et al. 2005. "Grasping the Intentions of Others with One's Own Mirror Neuron System." *PLoS Biology* 3 (3, March): e79.

———, 2008a. "Mesial Frontal Cortex and Super Mirror Neurons." *Behavioral and Brain Sciences* 31 (1): 30.

———, 2008b. *Mirroring People.* New York: Farrar Straus and Giroux.

Iser, Wolfgang. 1974. *The Implied Reader: Patterns of Communication in Prose Fiction from Bunyan to Beckett.* Baltimore: Johns Hopkins University Press.

Jackson, J. Hughlings. 1958 [1881-87]. *Selected Writings of John Hughlings Jackson: Vol.2* . . . Ed. J. Taylor. London: Staples Press.

James, William. 1880. "Great Men, Great Thoughts, and the Environment." *Atlantic Monthly* 46 (276, October): 441-59.

Jamison, Kay Redfield. 1989. "Mood Disorders and Patterns of Creativity in British Writers and Artists." *Psychiatry* 52: 125-34.

———. 1993. *Touched with Fire: Manic-Depressive Illness and the Artistic Temperament.* New York: Free Press.

Jaušovec, Norbert. 2000. "Differences in Cognitive Processes Between Gifted, Intelligent, Creative, and Average Individuals While Solving Complex Problems: An EEG Study." *Intelligence* 28 (3): 213-37.

———. 2002. "Neuropsychological Bases of Creativity." In *Advances in Psychology Research, Vol. 15.* Ed. Serge P. Shohov. New York: Nova Science. 193-219.

———, and Ksenija Jaušovec. 2000. "EEG activity During the Performance of Complex Mental Problems." *International Journal of Psychophysiology* 36 (1, April): 73-88.

Jenkins, Jennifer M., Keith Oatley, and Nancy J. Stein. 1998. "The Development of the Emotions in Infancy, the Development of Children's Understanding of Emotions, and Individual Differences in Emotionality." In *Human Emotions: A Reader*. Ed. Jennifer M. Jenkins, Keith Oatley, and Nancy J. Stein. Oxford: Blackwell Publishers. 139-45.

John, O. P., and S. Srivastava. 1999. "The Big-Five Trait Taxonomy: History, Measurement, and Theoretical Perspectives." In *Handbook of Personality Theory and Research*. Vol. 2. Ed. L. A. Pervin and O. P. John. New York: Guilford Press. 102-38.

Johnson, Marcia K. 1991. "Reality Monitoring: Evidence from Confabulation in Organic Brain Disease Patients." In *Awareness of Deficit After Brain Injury: Clinical and Theoretical Issues*, eds George Prigatano and Daniel L. Schacter. New York: Oxford University Press. 176-97.

Johnson, Steven. 2003. "Emotions and the Brain: Laughter." *Discover* 24.4 (April):62-69.

Jones, Ernest. 1949 [1910]. *Hamlet and Oedipus*. New York: Norton.

Jonze, Spike, dir. 2002. *Adaptation*. Meryl Streep and Nicolas Cage. Columbia Pictures.

Kaczmarek, K. A., J. G. Webster, Paul Bach-y-Rita, and W. J. Tompkins. 1991. "Electrotactile and Vibrotactile Displays for Sensory Substitution Systems." *IEEE Transactions: Biomedical Engineering* 38 (1, January): 1-16.

Kahneman, D., and D. T. Miller. 1986. "Norm Theory: Comparing Reality to its Alternatives." *Psychological Review* 93 (2): 136-53.

Kalat, James W. 2001. *Biological Psychology*. Belmont CA: Wadsworth/Thomson Learning.

Kandel, Eric R. 1998. "A New Intellectual Framework for Psychiatry." *American Journal of Psychiatry* 155 (4, April): 457-69.

Kant, Immanuel. 2000 [1790]. *Critique of the Power of Judgment*. Trans. and ed. Paul Guyer and Eric Matthews. The Cambridge Edition of the Works of Immanuel Kant. Cambridge, UK ; New York: Cambridge University Press.

Kaplan, Jonas T., Joshua Freedman, and Marco Iacoboni. 2007. "Us Versus Them: Political Attitudes and Party Affiliation Influence Neural Response to Faces of Presidential Candidates." *Neuropsychologia* 45 (1): 55-64.

Kaplan-Solms, Karen, and Mark Solms. 2000. *Clinical Studies in Neuropsychoanalysis: Introduction to a Depth Neuropsychology.* London: Karnac Books.

Kaufman, James C., and John Baer. 2002. "I Bask in Dreams of Suicide: Mental Illness, Poetry, and Women." *Review of General Psychology* 6 (3): 271-86.

Keats, John. 1958 [1819]. Letter of 14 February to 3 May to George and Georgiana Keats. *The Letters of John Keats.* 2 vols. Ed. Hyder E. Rollins. Cambridge MA: Harvard University Press.

Keen, Suzanne. 2006. "A Theory of Narrative Empathy." *Narrative* 14 (3, October): 209-36.

Kelly, George A. 1955. *The Psychology of Personal Constructs.* 2 vols. New York: W. W. Norton.

Kelly, Michael, and Frank Keil. 1985. "The More Things Change . . . ; Metamorphoses and Conceptual Structure." *Cognitive Science* 9:403-16.

Kermode, Frank. 1967. *The Sense of an Ending.* Oxford: Oxford University Press.

Kinzer, Stephen. 2004. "Priests and Sexual Abuse Ignite a Stage in Chicago." *The New York Times*, 9 March.

Kischka, U., et al. 1996. "Dopaminergic Modulation of Semantic Network Activation." *Neuropsychologia* 34 (11): 1107-13.

Kleiner-Fisman, Galit, Sandra E. Black, and Anthony E. Lang. 2003. "Neurodegenerative Disease and the Evolution of Art: The Effects of Presumed Corticobasal Degeneration in a Professional Artist." *Movement Disorders* 18 (3, March): 294-302.

Knight, G. Wilson. 1930. *The Wheel of Fire.* Oxford: Oxford University Press.

Knight, Robert T., and Marcia Grabowecky. 1995. "Escape from Linear Time: Prefrontal Cortex and Conscious Experience." In *The Cognitive Neurosciences.* Ed. Michael S. Gazzaniga. Cambridge MA: MIT Press. 1357-71.

———, Marcia Grabowecky, and Donatella Scabini. 1995a. "Role of Human Prefrontal Cortex in Attention Control." In *Epilepsy and the Functional Anatomy of the Frontal Lobe.* Ed. Jasper. H. H., S. Riggio, and P. S. Goldman-Rakic. New York: Raven Press. 1357-71.

Kövecses, Zoltán. 2000. *Metaphor and Emotion: Language, Culture and Body in Human Feeling.* Cambridge UK: Cambridge University Press.

Krims, Marvin. 2006. *The Mind According to Shakespeare: Psychoanalysis in the Bard's Writing.* Westport CT: Praeger Publishers.

Kris, Ernst. 1952. *Psychoanalytic Explorations in Art.* New York: International Universities Press.

Kubie, Lawrence S. 1970 [1958]. *Neurotic Distortion of the Creative Process.* New York: Noonday/Farrar, Straus and Giroux.

La Rochefoucauld, François, duc de. 2002 [1665]. *Réflexions Ou Sentences et Maximes Morales et Réflexions Diverses.* 3me éd. Éd. Laurence Plazenet. Paris: Honoré Champion.

Laberge, David, and S. Jay Samuels, eds. 1977. *Basic Processes in Reading: Perception and Comprehension.* New York: Lawrence Erlbaum.

Lacan, Jacques. n.d.[1977]. "The Agency of the Letter in the Unconscious or Reason Since Freud." In *Écrits: A Selection,* trans. Alan Sheridan. New York: Norton. 146-78.

Ladowsky-Brooks, Ricki, and James E. Alcock. 2007. "Semantic-Episodic Interactions in the Neuropsychology of Disbelief." *Cognitive Neuropsychiatry* 12 (2): 97-111.

Lakoff, George. 1987. *Women, Fire, and Dangerous Things: What Categories Reveal About the Mind.* Chicago and London: University of Chicago Press.

———, and Mark Johnson. 1980. *Metaphors We Live By.* Chicago and London: University of Chicago Press.

Lane, Anthony. 2002. "The Current Cinema: Out of the Past." *The New Yorker,* 2 September.

———. 2008. "Beautiful Friendships." *New Yorker,* 26 May.

Lang, Peter J., Margaret M. Bradley, and Bruce N. Cuthbert. 1998. "Emotion, Motivation, and Anxiety: Brain Mechanisms and Psychophysiology." *Biological Psychiatry* 44: 1248-63.

———, Mark K. Greenwald, Margaret M. Bradley, and Alfons O. Hamm. 1993. "Looking at Pictures: Affective, Facial, Visceral, and Behavioral Reactions." *Psychophysiology* 30 (3): 261-73.

Laughlin, H. P. 1979. *The Ego and its Defenses.* 2d ed. New York: Jason Aronson.

Ledoux, Joseph. 1998. *The Emotional Brain: The Mysterious Underpinnings of Emotional Life.* New York: Simon & Schuster/Touchstone.

Leone, Sergio. 1966. *Buono, Il Brutto, Il Cattivo, Il.* DVD version. 171 min. Clint Eastwood, Lee van Cleef, and Eli Wallach. Metro-Goldwyn-Mayer.

Leslie, Alan M. 1995. "A Theory of Agency." In *Causal Cognition: A Multidisciplinary Debate.* A Fyssen Foundation symposium. Ed. Dan Sperber, David Premack, and Ann James Premack. Oxford: Clarendon Press. 121–41.

———, and Stephanie Keeble. 1987. "Do Six-Month-Old Infants Perceive Causality?" *Cognition* 25 (3, April): 265-88.

Leslie, Charles Robert. 1843. *Memoirs of the Life of John Constable, Esq. R.A. Composed Chiefly of His Letters.* 2nd ed. London: Longmans, Brown, Green, and Longmans.

Lesser, Simon O. 1957. *Fiction and the Unconscious.* Boston: Beacon Press.

Lewis, Robert T. 1979. "Organic Signs, Creativity, and Personality Characteristics of Patients Following Cerebral Commissurotomy." *Clinical Neuropsychology* 1 (4): 29-33.

Lichtenstein, Heinz. 1961. "Identity and Sexuality: A Study of Their Interrelationship in Man." *Journal of the American Psychoanalytic Association* 9: 179-260.

———. 1970. "Changing Implications of the Concept of Psychosexual Development: An Inquiry Concerning the Validity of Classical Psychoanalytic Assumptions Concerning Sexuality." *Journal of the American Psychoanalytic Association* 18 (2): 300-18.

———. 1977. *The Dilemma of Human Identity.* New York: Jason Aronson.

Lightman, Alan. 2003. "Essay: Spellbound by the Eternal Riddle, Scientists Revel in Their Captivity." *The New York Times*, 11 November.

Liotti, Mario, and Helen S. Mayberg. 2001. "The Role of Functional Neuroimaging in the Neuropsychology of Depression." *Journal of Clinical and Experimental Neuropsychology* 23 (1, February): 121-36.

Livingstone, Margaret. 2002. *Vision and Art: The Biology of Seeing*. New York: Harry N. Abrams.

Llinás, Rodolfo R. 2001. *The I of the Vortex: From Neurons to Self*. Cambridge MA: MIT Press.

Luria, Aleksandr Romanovich. 1973. *The Working Brain: An Introduction to Neuropsychology*. Trans. Basil Haigh. New York: Basic Books.

Maher, Brendan. 2003. "Schizophrenia, Aberrant Utterance and Delusions of Control: The Disconnection of Speech and Thought, and the Connection of Experience and Belief." *Mind & Language* 18 (1, February): 1-22.

———, Theo C. Manschreck, Toni M. Hoover, and C. Cecily Weisstein. 1987. "Thought Disorder and Measured Features of Language Production in Schizophrenia." In *Positive and Negative Symptoms in Psychosis: Description, Research, and Future Directions*. Ed. Philip D. Harvey and Elaine F. Walker. Hillsdale NJ: Erlbaum. 195-215.

Malkiel, Burton. 2000. *A Random Walk Down Wall Street*. 7th ed. New York: Norton.

Markowitsch, Hans J. 2000. "Memory and Amnesia." In *Principles of Behavioral and Cognitive Neurology*. 2nd ed.. Ed. M-Marsel Mesulam. New York: Oxford University Press. 257-293.

Marks, Gary, and Norman Miller. 1987. "Ten Years of Research on the False-Consensus Effect: An Empirical and Theoretical Review." *Psychological Bulletin* 102 (1, July): 72-90.

Martindale, Colin. 1990. *The Clockwork Muse: The Predictability of Artistic Change*. New York: Basic Books.

———. 1999. "Biological Bases of Creativity." In *Handbook of Creativity*. Ed. Robert J. Sternberg. New York: Cambridge University Press. 257-293.

———, and Nancy Hasenfus. 1978. "EEG Differences as a Function of Creativity, Stage of the Creative Process, and Effort to be Original." *Biological Psychology* 6 (3, April): 157-67.

———, ed. 1988. *Psychological Approaches to the Study of Literary Narratives*. Hamburg, Mainz: Helmut Busche Verlag.

Matisse, Henri. 1939. "Notes d'un Peintre sur Son Dessin." *Le Point IV* 21:14.

Maturana, Humberto R., and Francisco J. Varela. 1980. *Autopoiesis and Cognition: The Realization of the Living.* Dordrecht, Boston, and London: D. Reidel.

McCarley, Robert W. 1982. "REM Sleep and Depression: Common Neurobiological Control Mechanisms." *American Journal of Psychiatry* 139 (5, May): 565-70.

McKeon, Richard, ed. 1947. *Introduction to Aristotle.* New York: Modern Library.

Menand, Louis. 2003. "True Story: The Art of Short Fiction." *The New Yorker*, 1 December.

———. 2004. "Bad Comma." Review of Lynne Truss, *Eats, Shoots and Leaves. The New Yorker*, 28 June.

Mesulam, M-Marsel. 1998. "From Sensation to Cognition." *Brain* 121 (6): 1013-52.

———, ed. 2000. *Principles of Behavioral and Cognitive Neurology.* Oxford New York: Oxford University Press.

Miall, David S. 1989. "Beyond the Schema Given: Affective Comprehension of Literary Narratives." *Cognition and Emotion* 3 (1): 55-78.

———. 1995. "Anticipation and Feeling in Literary Response: A Neuropsychological Perspective." *Poetics* 23:275-98.

———. 2001. "An Evolutionary Framework for Literary Reading." In *The Psychology and Sociology of Literature: in Honor of Elrud Ibsch.* Ed. Dick Schram and Gerald Steen. Amsterdam / Philadelphia: John Benjamins. 407-19.

———, and Don Kuiken. 1994. "Beyond Text Theory: Understanding Literary Response." *Discourse Processes* 17:337-52.

Miller, Bruce L., and Craig E. Hou. 2004. "Portraits of Artists: Emergence of Visual Creativity in Dementia." *Archives of Neurology.* 61: 842-44.

———, et al. 1998. "Emergence of Artistic Talent in Frontotemporal Dementia." *Neurology* 51 (4, October): 978-82.

———, et al. 2000. "Functional Correlates of Musical and Visual Ability in Frontotemporal Dementia." *British Journal of Psychiatry* 176 (May): 458-63.

Miller, Geoffrey. 2000. *The Mating Mind.* New York: Anchor Books.

Miller, J. Hillis. 2002. *On Literature.* London and New York: Routledge.

Mishkin, Mortimer, and Leslie G. Ungerleider. 1982. "Contribution of Striate Inputs to the Visuospatial Functions of Parieto-Occipital Cortex in Monkeys." *Behavioural Brain Research* 6:57-77.

———, Leslie G. Ungerleider, and Kathleen A. Macko. 1983. "Object Vision and Spatial Vision: Two Cortical Pathways." *Trends in Neuroscience* 6:414-17.

Mithen, Steven. 2001. "The Evolution of Imagination: An Archaeological Perspective." *SubStance* 94/95:28-54. Special issue, H. Porter Abbot <ed>.

Modell, Arnold H. 1993. *The Private Self.* Cambridge MA: Harvard University Press.

Moore, Allen, Rob Tranchin, and Rob Eustis, directors. 2003. *Albert Alcalay: Self Portraits.* Documentary biography.

Morasso, Pietro, and Vittorio Sanguinetti. 1997. *Self-Organization, Computational Maps, and Motor Control.* Amsterdam; New York: Elsevier.

Morgann, Maurice. 1777. *An Essay on the Dramatic Character of Sir John Falstaff . . .* London: T. Davis.

Morrison, J. H., and S. L. Foote. 1986. "Noradrenergic and Serotoninergic Innervation of Cortical, Thalamic, and Tectal Visual Structures in Old and New World Monkeys." *Journal of Comparative Neurology* 243 (1, 1 January): 117-38.

Moscovitch, Morris. 1989. "Confabulation and the Frontal Systems: Strategic Versus Associative Retrieval in Neuropsychological Theories of Memory." In *Varieties of Memory and Consciousness: Essays in Honour of Endel Tulving.* Ed. H. L. Roediger, III. and F. I. M. Craik. Hillsdale NJ: Erlbaum. 133-60.

———, and Brenda Melo. 1997. "Strategic Retrieval and the Frontal Lobes: Evidence from Confabulation and Amnesia." *Neuropsychologia* 35 (7, July): 1017-34.

Nashe, Thomas. 1592. "The Defence of Playes." In *Pierce Penilesse His Supplication to the Diuell . . .* London: Richard Ihones [etc.]. Retrieved January 29, 2009. http://www.luminarium.org/renlit/penniles.htm.

Nell, Victor. 1988. *Lost in a Book: The Psychology of Reading for Pleasure.* New Haven and London: Yale University Press.

Niedowski, Erika. 2004. "Cruel Disease Bestows Rare Gift." *Baltimore Sun*, 20 June.

Niesz, Anthony J., and Norman N. Holland. 1984. "Interactive Fiction." *Critical Inquiry* 11:110-29.

"No Words to Describe Monkeys' Play." *BBC News*. 9 May 2003. Retrieved January 29, 2009. http://news.bbc.co.uk/1/3013959.stm.

Oatley, Keith. 1999. "Why Fiction May be Twice as True as Fact: Fiction as Cognitive and Emotional Simulation." *Review of General Psychology* 3 (2, June): 101-17.

———, and Philip N. Johnson-Laird. 1996. "The Communicative Theory of Emotions: Empirical Tests, Mental Models, and Implications for Social Interaction." In *Striving and Feeling: Interactions Among Goals, Affect, and Self-Regulation*. Ed. L. L. Martin and A. Tesser. Mahwah NJ: Erlbaum. 363-80.

———, ed. 1992. *Best Laid Schemes: The Psychology of Emotions*. Studies in Emotion and Social Interaction. Cambridge UK: Cambridge University Press.

Oz, Amos. 1999. "Leisurely Pleasure." In *The Story Begins: Essays on Literature*, trans. Maggie Bar-Tura. Retrieved January 29, 2009. http://www.thenation. com/doc.mhtml?i=19990614&s=oz.

Pally, Regina. 2000. *The Mind-Brain Relationship*. London and New York: Karnac Books.

Panksepp, Jaak. 1998. *Affective Neuroscience: The Foundations of Human and Animal Emotions*. New York and Oxford: Oxford Univerisity Press.

———. 2000. "Affective Consciousness and the Instinctual Motor System: The Neural Sources of Sadness and Joy." In *The Caldron of Consciousness: Motivation, Affect and Self-Organization—an Anthology*. Ed. Raph D. Ellis and Natika Newton. Amsterdam: John Benjamins. 27-54.

———. 2003. "At the Interface of the Affective, Behavioral, and Cognitive Neurosciences: Decoding the Emotional Feelings of the Brain." *Brain and Cognition* 52:4-14.

———. 2006. "The Core Emotional Systems of the Mammalian Brain: The Fundamental Substrates of Human Emotions." In *About a Body: Working with the Embodied Mind in Psychotherapy*. Ed. J. Corrigall, H. Payne, and H. Wiilkinson. Hove UK and New York: Routledge. 14–32.

———. 2007. "Neuroevolutionary Sources of Laughter and Social Joy: Modeling Primal Human Laughter in Laboratory Rats." *Behvioural Brain Research* 182 (2, 4 September): 231-44.
———. 2008. "The Power of the Word May Reside in the Power of Affect." *Integrative Psychological and Behavioral Science* 42 (1, March): 47-55.
———, and Douglas Watt. 2003. "Review of Antonio Damasio, *Looking for Spinoza*." *Neuropsychoanalysis* 5 (2): 201-15.
Paris, Bernard J. 2008. *Bargains with Fate: Psychological Crises and Conflicts in Shakespeare and His Plays* [Rpt]. Piscataway NJ: Transaction Publishers.
Passingham, Richard. 1993. *The Frontal Lobes and Voluntary Action.* Oxford Psychology Series 21. New York and London: Oxford University Press.
Pessoa, Luiz. 2004. "Seeing the World in the Same Way." *Science* 303 (12 March):1617-18.
Petsche, Hellmuth. 1996. "Approaches to Verbal, Visual and Musical Creativity by EEG Coherence Analysis." *International Journal of Psychophysiology* 24 (1-2, November): 145-59.
Phillips, Mary L. 2002. "Functional Neuroanatomy of Emotion Processing in Normal and Psychiatric Populations." Grand Rounds, May 28. University of Florida Department of Psychiatry. Gainesville FL, 28 May.
Pinker, Steven. 1999. *How the Mind Works.* New York: Norton.
———. 2002. *The Blank Slate: The Modern Denial of Human Nature.* New York: Viking.
Plath, Sylvia. 2000. *The Unabridged Journals of Sylvia Plath.* Ed. Karen V. Kukil. New York: Anchor Books.
Poe, Edgar Allan. 1902 [1845]. "Review of William Hazlitt, *The Characters of Shakespeare*." In *The Complete Works of Edgar Allan Poe.* 12 vols. Ed. James A. Harrison. 12: 225.
Pope, Alexander. 1961 [1709]1. "An Essay on Criticism." In *Pastoral Poetry and An Essay on Criticism.* Ed. Emile Audra and Aubrey Williams. Twickenham Edition, v. 1. New Haven: Yale University Press.
Posner, Michael I., and Marcus E. Raichle. 1994. *Images of Mind.* New York: Scientific American Library.
Premack, David, and Ann James Premack. 1995. "Origins of Human Social Competence." In *The Cognitive Neurosciences.* Ed. Michael S. Gazzaniga. Cambridge MA: MIT Press. 205–18.

Prentice, Deborah A., and Richard J. Gerrig. 1999. "Exploring the Boundary Between Fiction and Reality." In *Dual-Process Theories in Social Psychology*. Ed. Shelly Chaiken and Yaacov Trope. New York: Guilford Press. 529-46.

Proust, Marcel. 1971 [1905]. *On Reading*. Trans. and ed. Jean Autret and William Burford. New York: Macmillan.

———. 1981 [1921/22]. "Cities of the Plain." In *Remembrance of Things Past*. 3 vol., trans. C. K. Scott Moncrieff and Terence Kilmartin. New York: Random House.

Provine, Robert R. 2000. *Laughter: A Scientific Investigation*. New York: Viking.

Purves, Dale, and Jeff W. Lichtman. 1985. *Principles of Neural Development*. Sunderland MA: Sinauer Associates.

Purves, Dale, and Robert D. Hadley. 1985. "Changes in the Dendritic Branching of Adult Mammalian Neurones Revealed by Repeated Imaging *in Situ*." *Nature* 315 (30 May):404-06.

Ramachandran, Vilayanur S. 1995. "Mirror Neurons and Imitation Learning as the Driving Force Behind 'the Great Leap Forward' in Human Evolution." Decade of the Brain Lecture. Society for Neuroscience. San Diego CA. Retrieved January 29, 2009. http://www.edge.org/3rd_culture/ramachandran/ramachandran_index.html.

———. 1998. "The Neurology and Evolution of Humor, Laughter, and Smiling: The False Alarm Theory." *Medical Hypotheses* 51:351-54.

———, and Sandra Blakeslee. 1998. *Phantoms in the Brain*. New York: William Morrow.

Reddy, Michael. 1979. "The Conduit Metaphor." In *Metaphor and Thought*. Ed. Andrew Ortony. Cambridge: Cambridge University Press. 284-324.

Restak, Richard M. 1986. *The Infant Mind*. Garden City NY: Doubleday.

Riestra, Alonso, Gregory Crucian, Kyle Womack, and Kenneth M. Heilman. 2002. "It is Horrible! Role of Valence and Arousal in Initial Visual Exploration." *Journal of the International Neuroscience Society* 8 (2): 226.

Rizzolatti, Giacomo, Luciano Fadiga, Vittorio Gallese, and Leonardo Fogassi. 1996. "Preactivity Cortex and the Recognition of Motor Actions." *Cognitive Brain Research* 3:131-41.

———, et al. 2006. "The Inferior Parietal Lobule: Where Action Becomes Perception." In *Percept, Decision, Action: Bridging the Gaps*, Novartis Foundation Symposium 270. Chichester: Wiley. 129-45.

Robeck, Mildred C., and Randall R. Wallace. 1990. *The Psychology of Reading: An Interdisciplinary Approach.* 2d ed. Hillsdale NJ: Lawrence Erlbaum.

Robinson, T. E., and K. C. Berridge. 1993. "The Neural Basis of Drug Craving: An Incentive-Sensitization Theory of Addiction." *Brain Research: Brain Research Reviews* 18 (3, September-December): 247-91.

Rolls, Edmund T. 1995. "A Theory of Emotion and Consciousness, and its Application to Understanding the Neural Basis of Emotion." In *The Cognitive Neurosciences.* Ed. Michael S. Gazzaniga. Cambridge MA: MIT Press. 1091-1106.

———. 1999. *The Brain and Emotion.* New York: Oxford University Press.

Ross, Lee, David Greene, and Pamela House. 1977. "The 'False Consensus Effect': An Egocentric Bias in Social Perception and Attribution Processes." *Journal of Experimental Social Psychology* 13 (3, May): 279-301.

Rothenberg, Albert. 1979. *The Emerging Goddess: The Creative Process in Art, Science, and Other Fields.* Chicago: University of Chicago Press.

Ruder, Debra Bradley. 2008. "A Work in Progress: The Teen Brain." *Harvard Magazine*, October. 8-10.

Rumelhart, D. E. 1980. "Schemata: The Building Blocks of Cognition." In *Theoretical Issues in Reading Comprehension: Perspectives from Cognitive Psychology, Linguistics, Artificial Intelligence, and Education*, eds Rand J. Spiro, Bertram C. Bruce, and William F. Brewer. Hillsdale NJ: Lawrence Erlbaum. 33-58.

Rushdie, Salman. 2007. "Humanism and the Territory of Novelists." *The Humanist* 67 (4, August): 19-21.

Rycroft, Charles. 1979. *The Innocence of Dreams.* New York: Pantheon.

Sacks, Oliver. 1974. *Awakenings.* New York: Vintage Books.

———. 1984. *A Leg to Stand On.* New York: Summit Books /Simon and Schuster.

———. 1990. "Letters: Alzheimer's and Creativity." *Art and Antiques*, January.

Sargolini, Francesca, et al. 2006. "Conjunctive Representation of Position, Direction, and Velocity in Entorhinal Cortex." *Science* 312 (5774, 5 May): 758-62.

Schafer, Roy. 1968. *Aspects of Internalization.* New York: International Universities Press.

Schank, Roger, and Robert P. Abelson. 1977. *Scripts, Plans, Goals, and Understanding: An Inquiry into Human Knowledge Structures.* Hillsdale NJ: Lawrence Erlbaum.

Schnider, Armin, C. von Daniken, and K. Gutbrod. 1996. "The Mechanisms of Spontaneous and Provoked Confabulations." *Brain* 119 (4, August): 1365-75.

———, and Radek Ptak. 1999. "Spontaneous Confabulators Fail to Suppress Currently Irrelevant Memory Traces." *Nature: Neuroscience* 2 (7, July): 677-81.

Schore, Allan N. 1994. *Affect Regulation and the Origin of the Self: The Neurobiology of Emotional Development.* Hillsdale NJ: Lawrence Erlbaum.

———. 1999. "Commentary on Jaak Panksepp's 'Emotions as Viewed by Psychoanalysis and Neuroscience'." *Neuropsychoanalysis* 1 (1): 49-55.

———. 2003. *Affect Regulation & the Repair of the Self.* New York: W. W. Norton.

———. 2003. "The Right Brain, the Right Mind, and Psychoanalysis." In *Affect Regulation and the Repair of the Self.* New York: Guilford. 206-49.

Scott, A. O. 2002. "Forever Obsessing About Obsession." Review of Jonze, *Adaptation. The New York Times*, 6 December.

Servan-Schreiber, D., H. Printz, and J. D. Cohen. 1990. "A Network Model of Catecholamine Effects: Gain, Signal-to-Noise Ratio, and Behavior." *Science* 249 (4971, August): 892-95.

Shermer, Michael. 2006. "The Political Brain." *Scientific American*, July. 30.

———. 2008. "Five Ways Brain Scans Mislead Us." *Scientific American Mind.* Retrieved January 29, 2009. http://www.sciam.com/article.cfm?id=five-ways-brain-scans-mislead-us. (November).

Shiffrin, Richard M. 1997. "Attention, Automatism, and Consciousness." In *Scientific Approaches to Consciousness*, eds Jonathan D. Cohen and Jonathan W. Schooler. Hillsdale NJ: Erlbaum. 49-64.

Shklovskii, Victor. 1988 [1917]. "Art as Technique." In *Modern Criticism and Theory: A Reader.* Ed. David Lodge. London: Longmans. 16-30.

Skolnick, Deena, and Paul Bloom. 2006. "What Does Batman Think About SpongeBob? Children's Understanding of the Fantasy/Fantasy Distinction." *Cognition* 101 (1, August): B9-B18.

Small, Dana M., et al. 2001. "Changes in Brain activity Related to Eating Chocolate: From Pleasure to Aversion." *Brain* 124 (9, September): 1720-33.

Smith, Adam. 1976 [1759]. *The Theory of Moral Sentiments.* 6th edn. 1790. Ed. D. D. Raphael and A. L. Macfie. Oxford: Clarendon.

Solms, Mark. 2002. "An Example of Neuro-Psychoanalytic Research: Korsakoff's Syndrome." *Journal of European Psychoanalysis* 14 (Winter-Spring):133-45.

———. 2003. "The Man Who Lived in a Dream." Keynote address. 20th International Conference in Literature and Psychology, University of Greenwich, July 3.

———, and Oliver Turnbull. 2002. *The Brain and the Inner World: An Introduction to the Neuroscience of Subjective Experience.* New York: Other Press.

———, and Yoram Yovell. 2003. "Korsakoff Syndrome and Psychoanalysis as Analogue of the System Unconscious." 4th International Neuropsychoanalysis Congress. New York University School of Medicine, 2003, 26 July.

Spelke, Elizabeth S., Ann Phillips, and Amanda L. Woodward. 1995. "Infants' Knowledge of Object Motion and Human Action." In *Causal Cognition: A Multidisciplinary Debate.* A Fyssen Foundation Symposium, Dan Sperber, David Premack, and Ann James Premack. Oxford: Clarendon Press. 44–78.

Sperber, Dan, ed. 2000. *Metarepresentations: A Multidisciplinary Perspective.* Vancouver Studies in Cognitive Science. New York: Oxford University Press.

Spolsky, Ellen. 2001a. "Why and How to Take the Fruit and Leave the Chaff." *SubStance* 94/95: 178-98. Special issue, H. Porter Abbot <ed>.

———. 2001b. "Response to John Tooby and Leda Cosmides." *SubStance* 94/95: 201-02. Special issue, H. Porter Abbot <ed>.

Springer, Sally P., and Georg Deutsch. 1998. *Left Brain, Right Brain: Perspectives from Cognitive Neuroscience.* 5th edn. New York: W. H. Freeman.

Spurgeon, Caroline Frances Eleanor. 1935. *Shakespeare's Imagery, and What It Tells Us.* Cambridge UK: Cambridge University Press.

Stanley, Alessandra. 2004. "No Inhibitions, or Excuses, for a Hollywood Madam." *The New York Times*, 29 March.

Stanovich, Keith E. 2004. *The Robot's Rebellion: Finding Meaning in the Age of Darwin.* Chicago: University of Chicago Press.

Steig, Michael. 1989. *Stories of Reading: Subjectivity and Literary Understanding.* Baltimore and London: Johns Hopkins University Press.

Stein, Barry E., Mark T. Wallace, and M. Alex Meredith. 1995. "Neural Mechanisms Mediating Attention and Orientation to Multisensory Cues." In *The Cognitive Neurosciences.* Ed. Michael S. Gazzaniga. Cambridge MA: MIT Press / A Bradford Book. 683-702.

———, Mark T. Wallace, and Terrence R. Stanford. 1999. "Merging Sensory Signals in the Brain: The Development of Multisensory Integration in the Superior Colliculus." In *The New Cognitive Neurosciences.* Ed. Michael S. Gazzaniga. Cambridge MA: MIT Press. 55-71.

Steiner, George. 1967. *Language and Silence: Essays on Language, Literature, and the Inhuman.* New Haven: Yale University Press.

Storey, Robert. 1996. *Mimesis and the Human Animal: On the Biogenetic Foundations of Literary Representation.* Evanston IL: Northwestern University Press.

Strachey, James. 1959. "Editor's Introduction." In *The Standard Edition of the Complete Psychological Works of Sigmund Freud, Vol. XX.* London: Hogarth Press. 77-86.

Suzuki, Wendy A., and Howard Eichenbaum. 2000. "The Neurophysiology of Memory." In *The Parahippocampal Region: Implications for Neurological and Psychiatric Diseases.* Ed. Helen E. Scharfman, Menno P. Witter, and Robert Schwarcz. New York: New York Academy of Sciences. 175-191.

Swift, Jonathan. 1742. *A New Miscellany in Prose and Verse. Containing, Several Pieces Never Before Made Public.* London: T. Read.

Tan, Ed S. 1996. *Emotion and the Structure of Narrative Film: Film as an Emotion Machine.* Mahwah NJ: Lawrence Erlbaum.

Taylor, Insup. 1990. "Language and Brain." Ch. 12. In *Psycholinguistics: Learning and Using Language.* In collaboration with M. Martin Taylor. Englewood Cliffs NJ: Prentice Hall. Ch. 12.

Tettamanti, Marco, et al. 2005. "Listening to Action-Related Sentences Activates Fronto-Parietal Motor Circuits." *Journal of Cognitive Neuroscience* 17 (2): 273-81.

Tomasello, Michael, Josep Call, and Brian Hare. 2003. "Chimpanzees Understand Psychological States—the Question is Which Ones and to What Extent." *Trends in Cognitive Sciences* 7 (4, April): 153-56.

Tooby, John, and Leda Cosmides. 2001. "Does Beauty Build Adapted Minds? Toward an Evolutionary Theory of Aesthetics, Fiction, and the Arts." *SubStance* 94/95:6-27. Special issue, H. Porter Abbot, ed.

Trevarthen, Colwyn. 1979. "Communication and Cooperation in Early Infancy: A Description of Primary Intersubjectivity." In *Before Speech: The Beginning of Interpersonal Communication.* Ed. M. M. Bullowa. New York: Cambridge University Press. 321-348.

———. 1993. "The Self Born in Intersubjectivity: The Psychology of an Infant Communicating." In *The Perceived Self: Ecological and Interpersonal Sources of Self-Knowledge.* Ed. Ulric Neisser. New York: Cambridge University Press. 121-73.

Turner, Mark. 1991. *Reading Minds: The Study of English in the Age of Cognitive Science.* Princeton: Princeton University Press.

Ungerleider, Leslie G., and Mortimer Mishkin. 1982. "Two Cortical Visual Systems." In *Analysis of Visual Behavior.* Ed. D. J. Ingle, M. A. Goodale, and R. J. W. Mansfield. Cambridge MA: MIT Press. 549–86.

van Oostendorp, Herre, and Susan R. Goldman, eds. 1999. *The Construction of Mental Representations During Reading*. Mahwah NJ: Lawrence Erlbaum.

Varela, Francisco J. 1979. *Principles of Biological Autonomy*. New York and Oxford: North Holland.

Wallas, Graham. 1926. *The Art of Thought*. New York: Harcourt Brace.

Waterhouse, B. D., and D. J. Woodward. 1980. "Interaction of Norepinephrine with Cerebrocortical activity Evoked by Stimulation of Somatosensory Afferent Pathways in the Rat." *Experimental Neurology* 67 (1, January): 11-34.

Watt, Douglas F. 2001. "Review of *Cognitive Neuroscience of Emotion*. Ed. Richard D. Lane, Lynn Nadel, and Geoffrey Ahern." *Neuropsychoanalysis* 3 (1): 126-28.

Weaver, Charles A., III, Suzanne Mannes, and Charles R. Fletcher, eds. 1995. *Discourse Comprehension: Essays in Honor of Walter Kintsch*. Hillsdale NJ: Erlbaum.

Weeks, Robert A., et al. 1999. "A PET Study of Human Auditory Spatial Processing." *Neuroscience Letters* 262:155-58.

Weinstein, Sara, and Roger E. Graves. 2002. "Are Creativity and Schizotypy Products of a Right Hemisphere Bias?" *Brain and Cognition* 49 (1, June): 138-51.

Weisberg, Robert W. 2006. *Creativity: Understanding Innovation in Problem Solving, Science, Invention, and the Arts*. Hoboken NJ: John Wiley.

Westen, Drew. 1997. "Towards a Clinically and Empirically Sound Theory of Motivation." *International Journal of Psycho-Analysis* 78:521-48.

———. 2007. *The Political Brain: The Role of Emotion in Deciding the Fate of the Nation*. Cambridge MA and New York: Public Affairs Press.

———, et al. 2006. "Neural Bases of Motivated Reasoning: An FMRI Study of Emotional Constraints on Partisan Political Judgment in the 2004 U.S. Presidential Election." *Journal of Cognitive Neuroscience* 18 (11, November): 1947-58.

Whiter, Walter. 1794. *A Specimen of a Commentary on Shakespeare . . . Derived from Mr. Locke's Doctrine of the Association of Ideas*. Rpt. Menston, Yorks.: Scolar Press, 1972; London: T. Cadell.

———. 1967. *A Specimen of a Commentary on Shakspeare*. Ed. Alan Over. Completed by Mary Bell. London: Methuen.

Wilford, John Noble. 2002. "When Humans Became Human." *The New York Times*, 26 Feburary.

Winner, Ellen. 1982. *Invented Worlds: The Psychology of the Arts.* Cambridge MA: Harvard University Press.

———. 2000. "The Origins and Ends of Giftedness." *American Psychologist* 55 (1, January): 159-69.

Winokur, Jon, comp. 1986. *Writers on Writing.* Philadelphia PA: Running Press.

Wolff, Ulrika, and Ingvar Lundberg. 2002. "The Prevalence of Dyslexia Among Art Students." *Dyslexia* 8 (1, January-March): 34-42.

Woolf, Virginia. 1932. "How Should One Read a Book?" In *The Common Reader, Second Series.* London: Hogarth Press. Ch. 22. Retrieved January 29, 2009. http://ebooks.adelaide.edu.au/w/woolf/virginia/w91c2/chapter22.html.

Wordsworth, William. 1951 [1800]. "Observations Prefixed to 'Lyrical Ballads'." In *The Great Critics.* Ed. Harry Smith James and Winfield Parks. New York: W. W. Norton. 495-519.

Wynne, Clive D. L. 2004. *Do Animals Think?* Princeton NJ: Princeton University Press.

Yarkoni, Tal, Nicole K. Speer, and Jeffrey M. Zacks. 2008. "Neural Substrates of Narrative Comprehension and Memory." *NeuroImage* 41:1408-25.

Zeki, Semir. 1999. *Inner Vision: An Exploration of Art and the Brain.* New York: Oxford University Press.

Zeman, Adam. 2002. *Consciousness: A User's Guide.* New Haven and London: Yale University Press.

Zillmer, Eric A., and Mary V. Spiers. 2001. *Principles of Neuropsychology.* Belmont CA: Wadsworth.

Zunshine, Lisa. 2006. *Why we Read Fiction: Theory of Mind and the Novel.* Columbus OH: Ohio University Press.

Index

CPSIA information can be obtained at www.ICGtesting.com
Printed in the USA
BVOW02s1602100414

350170BV00002B/306/P

9 780578 025124